PrepPros Presents

The Complete Guide to

SAT Math

By Matthew Stroup and Michael Stroup

1ST Edition

Introduction

The SAT Math is an incredibly repetitive and predictable standardized test. You do not need to be a gifted math student to achieve a top score. If you are willing to put in the time and effort to learn everything in this book, you can improve your SAT Math score by up to 250 points. In this book, we will teach you all of the content, strategies, tips, and techniques that have helped drastically improve the SAT math scores for over 1,000 of our students, many of whom have achieved a perfect 800.

How to Best Use this Book

Great, you purchased *PrepPros The Complete Guide to SAT Math*. Now what? To maximize your improvement, make sure to follow these tips:

1. **Work front to back.** This book is designed to be completed from front to back. To maximize your improvement, we recommend working through all of the chapters. That being said, each chapter is written to be independent of the other chapters. If you are already proficient in certain topics, you can skip around and focus on the chapters that you need to learn to improve your score.

2. **Diagnose your weaknesses.** Take a practice SAT and use the glossary on our website to identify your areas of weakness. Based on the questions you answer incorrectly, the glossary will tell you exactly which chapters to study. Details about this are in the "What Else to Do?" section on the next page.

3. **Repetition is key.** We recommend completing every question, especially in your areas of weakness.

4. **Learn from your mistakes.** The students who improve most are the ones who learn the most from their mistakes.

5. **Do not be afraid to struggle.** This book includes very thorough answer explanations, but do not look at these before attempting to solve the question. The struggle is one of the best ways to learn. If you are stuck, look back at the teaching pages in the chapter first. Only use the answer explanations when you are truly stumped.

Difficulty of Practice Questions

In each chapter, the difficulty of the practice questions increases as you work through the problem sets. Just like on the SAT Math Tests, the earlier questions will be easier while the later questions will be much more difficult. Practice questions are divided into non-calculator and calculator portions. We have done this to reflect the nature of how the questions appear on test day.

When practicing, be sure to follow the no-calculator or calculator instructions. Do not use your calculator for no-calculator questions.

What Else to Do?

Take practice tests…lots of them! In addition to this book, you should take at least 4 full practice SATs. **We strongly recommend only using official SAT Practice tests**, which can be found for free on the College Board website (https://collegereadiness.collegeboard.org/sat/practice/full-length-practice-tests). Any practice tests that are not written by the College Board are not an accurate representation of the SAT.

For the free practice SATs at the College Board website, we have a glossary on our website at www.preppros.io/math-book that tells you which chapter in this book applies to each question on the practice SATs. By using the glossary, you can easily find which chapters you need to study based on the questions you are answering incorrectly.

About the Authors

Matthew Stroup and Michael Stroup are both master tutors, brothers, and the founders of PrepPros. Together, they have over 10,000 hours of private tutoring experience and have both achieved perfect scores on the SAT. Their students have improved their SAT scores up to 400 points. Matthew Stroup graduated from Johns Hopkins University, where he studied biology, economics, and was pre-med, and Georgetown University, where he obtained a master's degree in biotechnology. Michael graduated from Georgetown University with a degree in Marketing and Entrepreneurship.

Matthew and Michael both work as full-time tutors. If you want to work directly with Matthew and Michael in private tutoring or group classes, check out the PrepPros website at www.preppros.io.

Introduction to the SAT Math

Before we dive into all of the details, let's start by understanding the basic format of the test and general strategies you will need for success.

Format of the Test

The SAT Math Test consists of two sections: a 25-minute no-calculator section with 20 questions and a 55-minute calculator section with 38 questions. In the no-calculator section, there are 15 questions multiple-choice questions and 5 grid-in questions. In the calculator section, there are 30 multiple-choice questions and 8 grid-in questions. On the multiple-choice questions, there are 4 possible answer choices. On the grid-in questions, you will need to calculate the exact answer yourself.

Difficulty of the Questions

As you progress through the no-calculator and calculator sections, the questions will increase in difficulty as you work through the multiple-choice questions. When you get to the grid-in questions, the difficulty will reset and again increase from easy to hard. The table below breaks down where you will generally see the easy, medium, and hard questions.

Question Type	Difficulty	No-Calculator	Calculator
Multiple-Choice	Easy	1 – 5	1 – 10
	Medium	6 – 10	11 – 22
	Hard	11 – 15	23 – 30
Grid-In	Medium	16 – 18	31 – 34
	Hard	19 – 20	35 – 38

In this book, the practice questions at the end of each chapter will increase in difficulty just as they do on the SAT.

Time Management

On average, you have 80 seconds (1 minute and 20 seconds) to answer each question. Some questions can be solved very quickly while others can take much longer to solve. In general, you should be solving the earlier questions in less than 80 seconds, as the later, more difficult questions will require more time. Make sure that you save enough time to answer the grid-in questions. A common mistake we see students make is getting stuck on the most difficult multiple-choice questions and running out of time on the grid-in questions.

If you get to a question that you do not know how to do, circle the number, bubble in an answer, and move on. You can always come back to the questions that your circled at the end if you have time left.

Guessing

There is no penalty for guessing. Make sure that you bubble in an answer for every single question. On a multiple-choice questions, there is no best method for guessing, so look at the answer choices and pick the answer that looks best to you.

For grid-in questions, still make a guess. Integers, particularly from 1 to 9, are the common answers on grid-in questions. The odds that you will guess correctly are, of course, quite low, but you might get lucky so do not leave any answer blank.

Tips to Maximize Your Score

The test-taking tips below will help you maximize your scores on test day.

1. **Keep Moving.** Do not get stuck on any one question for too long. We often see students make this mistake and run out of time on the last few questions of a section. If you get stuck on a question, mark it, bubble in your best guess, and move on. You can come back to the question at the end if you have time left over. Remember, there is no penalty for guessing.

2. **Look for Shortcuts.** Often, solving SAT math questions algebraically is not the easiest or fastest method. In this book, we will refer to solving questions algebraically as the "math teacher way." Look for shortcuts to get to the answer more quickly and easily. We will teach you a variety of different strategies to help you learn to spot shortcuts and avoid doing questions the "math teacher way."

3. **Memorize the Equations.** In this book, all of the equations, formulas, and rules that you need to memorize are in bold lettering. Having all of equations, formulas, and rules memorized for test day will help you solve questions more quickly and will help maximize your score.

4. **Use the Calculator (when you have it).** In the calculator section, use the calculator as much as possible. Even for simple calculations, avoid mental math as much as possible, as mental math often leads to avoidable errors.

5. **Practice Like Its Test Day.** When working on practice SAT tests, set a timer and strictly follow the timer. The best way to get ready for test day is to treat your practice SATs like it is the real thing.

Table of Contents

Chapter 1: Backsolving

In these first two chapters, you will learn two important test taking techniques: backsolving and substitution. **As you work through the rest of the book, use these techniques whenever you can to solve questions.**

Backsolving is plugging the answer choices back into the question. On the SAT, you are given 4 answer choices for multiple choice questions, and one of those 4 choices must be correct. Rather than solving the question algebraically and determining whether your answer matches one of the answer choices, you can guess-and-check with the answer choices to find which one is correct. Backsolving is often the fastest and easiest way to solve SAT questions, especially if you get stuck and cannot solve a question algebraically, so use it to your advantage.

Backsolving can be done using five steps:

1. **Start with B or C.** Plug the value back into the question. The answer choices are always in order of smallest to largest or largest to smallest so starting in the middle will save you time.

2. **Solve the question using this value.** Find any other unknowns if necessary.

3. **If this answer choice works correctly, you're done!** Bubble it in and move on.

4. **If this answer choice does not work, cross it off.** If you know the correct answer needs to be smaller or larger than the value you just tried, cross off any other incorrect answers.

5. **Pick one of the remaining answer choices and plug it back into the question.** Repeat this until you find the correct answer. Remember, one of the 4 answer choices must work!

Example 1: If $\sqrt{x + 10} - 2\sqrt{x - 2} = 0$ what is the value of x?

    A) 2   B) 6   C) 14   D) 18

Solution: The quickest and easiest way to solve this question is backsolving. Finding the right answer is just a process of guess-and-check. Below, you can see how the correct answer, when $x = 6$, makes the equation be true.

$$\sqrt{6 + 10} - 2\sqrt{6 - 2} = 0$$
$$\sqrt{16} - 2\sqrt{4} = 0$$
$$4 - 2(2) = 0$$
$$4 - 4 = 0$$
$$0 = 0$$

The answer is B. If we plug in any of the other answer choices, we will get an equation that is not equal on both sides and is incorrect.

Example 2: If $\frac{3}{x+1} = \frac{2}{x}$, what is the value of x?

    A) -2 B) 0   C) 1   D) 2

Solution: As in the last example, the quickest way to solve this question is backsolving. Plug the answer choices back into the question. Below, you can see how the correct answer $x = 2$ makes the equation true.

$$\frac{3}{2+1} = \frac{2}{2}$$
$$\frac{3}{3} = \frac{2}{2}$$
$$1 = 1$$

The answer is D.

$\frac{13}{4}$

Backsolving Practice: A calculator may be used on the following questions. Answers on page 232.

1. For what value of x is the equation $3.25x + 6 = 5x - 8$ true?

    A) 4
    B) 6
    C) 8
    D) 12

2. The length of a rectangle is 8 inches longer than the width. If the perimeter of the rectangle is 52 inches, what is the width of the rectangle?

    A) 4
    B) 9
    C) 11
    D) 18

3. If the area of a rectangle is 16 and one side has a length of 20, what is the width of the rectangle?

    A) $\frac{2}{5}$

    B) $\frac{1}{2}$

    C) $\frac{4}{5}$

    D) 1

4. If $\sqrt{3x} = 9$, what is the value of x?

    A) 3
    B) 9
    C) 27
    D) 81

5. In the triangle below, the value of y is twice the value x and the value of z is three times the value of x. What is the value of x?

    Note: Figure not drawn to scale.

    A) 20
    B) 30
    C) 45
    D) 60

    $x + 2x + 3x = 180$
    $6x = 180$
    $x = 30$

6. James withdrew one fifth of his savings last week. This week, James withdrew one quarter of the remaining amount. He is left with $150. How much did he originally have?

    A) $195
    B) $220
    C) $250
    D) $280

7. Which of the following values of x satisfies the equation below?

    $$\left|\frac{1}{2}x + 6\right| = 8$$

    I. -28
    II. -4
    III. 4

    A) I only
    B) II only
    C) III only
    D) I and III only

8. $$\sqrt{x} = x - 2$$

    For the equation above, what value(s) of x make the equation true?

    A) 4
    B) -1
    C) 0
    D) $-1, 4$

Chapter 2: Substitution

Do you prefer working with numbers or variables? We would guess your answer is numbers! On the SAT, some questions have many unknown variables and few or no numbers at all. Most students hate these questions. If you prefer to work with numbers, let's work with numbers. With substitution, we substitute simple numbers in for variables and solve the question using numbers instead of relying on more complex algebra with variables.

Substitution can be done with these four steps:

1. **Pick a number for the variable(s) in the question.**

   a. **Pick easy numbers…avoid using 0 but instead pick 1 or 2.** Use 10 for percent problems, 10 or 20 for group size, etc.

   b. **Select different numbers for each variable.** For example, if a question has an x and a y, pick $x = 1$ and $y = 2$.

   c. **Follow any rules in the question.** For example, if a question says x is a number that is negative and even, pick $x = -2$.

2. **Write down the number(s) that you have picked.**

3. **Use your numbers to work your way through the question and find your answer.**

4. **Plug your numbers into the answer choices. The correct answer will be the one that matches your answer.**

Substitution may seem a bit confusing just reading the steps, so let's take a look at some example questions to see how useful this technique can be.

Example 1: If $\cos(2x) = a$, which of the following must be true for all values of x?

   A) $\sin(2x) = a$ B) $\cos(x) = a$ C) $\sin(90 - 2x) = a$ D) $\cos(90 - 2x) = a$

Solution: For this example, let's assume you can use your calculator. The easiest way to solve this question is to pick a value for x. Let's pick $x = 10$. First, we need to find out what a equals if $x = 10$.

$$\cos(20) = 0.9397$$

Now that we know what a equals, we can plug in $x = 10$ for the x-values in the answer choices to see which is equal to 0.9397. Here, we can see how the correct answer choice of C works.

$$\sin(90 - 20) = \sin(70) = 0.9397$$

This trick will work for any value of x that we pick. **The answer is C.**

Example 2: If the length of a rectangle is tripled and the width is halved, how many times larger is the area of the new rectangle than the area of the original rectangle?

   A) 1.5   B) 2   C) 3   D) 6

Solution: To make this question easier, we can pick values for the length and width of the rectangle. Let's make the length 3 and the width 2. Now, we just follow the steps in the questions.

Original

The length is tripled: $3(3) = 9$ The new length is 9.

The width is halved: $2(\frac{1}{2}) = 1$ The new width is 1.

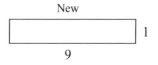

New

Next, we find the areas of the rectangles and compare. The new rectangle has an area of 9. The original rectangle has an area of 6, so we find that the new rectangle is 1.5 times as large. **The answer is A.**

Substitution Practice: A calculator may be used on the following questions. Answers on page 232.

1. For variables a, b and c, the expression $0 < a < b < c$ is true. Which of the following expressions has the smallest value?

   A) $\frac{b}{c}$

   B) $\frac{c}{b}$

   C) $\frac{a}{c}$

   D) $\frac{c}{a}$

2. When each side length of a square with sides s is increased by 4 inches, which of the following expresses the new area of the square?

   A) $s^2 + 4$
   B) $s^2 + 16$
   C) $(s^2 + 4)^2$
   D) $(s + 4)^2$

3. If x and y are positive integers such that $x + y = 11$, what is the value of $\frac{x-11}{3y}$?

   A) $-\frac{1}{3}$

   B) $\frac{1}{3}$

   C) $\frac{4}{5}$

   D) 1

4. If $\frac{x}{5} = \frac{y}{2}$, which of the following is equal to $\frac{y}{3}$?

   A) $\frac{4x}{15}$

   B) $\frac{2x}{15}$

   C) x

   D) $\frac{2x}{3}$

5. Money raised by m school clubs will be divided equally among the clubs. Based on school records, n people each gave p dollars? Which of the following describes how much money, in dollars, will each club receive?

   A) mpn

   B) $\frac{mp}{n}$

   C) $\frac{np}{m}$

   D) $pn + m$

6. If x is an odd integer and y is an even integer, which of the following must be an odd integer?

   A) $2x^2 + y$
   B) $3x + y$
   C) $2x + 6$
   D) $x - \frac{y}{2}$

7. For all real numbers x and z such that the product of x and 5 is z, which of the following represents the sum of z and 3 in terms of x?

   A) $5x + 3$

   B) $5(x + 3)$

   C) $\frac{x+3}{5}$

   D) $\frac{x}{5} + 3$

8. If $3x = 4y = 6z$, which of the following expresses the average of x and y in terms of z?

   A) $\frac{7z}{4}$

   B) $\frac{5z}{3}$

   C) $\frac{10}{4z}$

   D) $\frac{13z}{9}$

9. If the sides of a triangle are all quadrupled, how many times greater if the area of the new triangle than the area of the original triangle?

    A) 4
    B) 8
    C) 10
    D) 16

10. The distance between Albert's front door and the end of his driveway is d miles. If he can run at c miles per hour, how long, in minutes, will it take him to run from his front door to the end of the driveway?

    A) $\frac{d}{c}$

    B) $60c$

    C) $\frac{60d}{c}$

    D) $\frac{60c}{d}$

Chapter 3: Equivalent Questions in the No-Calculator Section

In the no-calculator section, some questions ask you to identify which of the answer choices is equivalent to a given expression. These questions often look difficult, but they are easy as long as you use this technique:

1. **Plug in $x = 1$ to the original expression and solve.**

2. **Plug in $x = 1$ to the answer choices and solve.**

3. **Find which answer choice gives you the same value as the original expression. This is the correct answer.**

4. **If you cannot tell which answer choice is correct after plugging in $x = 1$ because multiple answers equal the same value, plug in $x = 2$ or another simple value for x.**

If you do the math correctly, you can identify the correct answer without doing any fancy algebra!

Example 1:
$$\frac{x^2 - 5x + 1}{x - 2}$$

Which of the following expressions is equivalent to the one above for $x \neq 2$?

 A) $x - 3 + \frac{13}{x-2}$

 B) $x - 3 - \frac{5}{x-2}$

 C) $x + 1 + \frac{4}{x-2}$

 D) $x + 1 - \frac{17}{x-2}$

Solution: Plug in $x = 1$ to the original expression and solve.

$$\frac{(1)^2 - 5(1) + 1}{1 - 2} = \frac{1 - 5 + 1}{-1} = \frac{-3}{-1} = 3$$

We know that if $x = 1$, the expression equals 3. The equivalent answer choice must also equal 3. To find which answer choice is correct, plug in $x = 1$ to the answer choices and find which one equals 3.

 A) $1 - 3 + \frac{13}{1-2} = 1 - 3 + \frac{13}{-1} = 1 - 3 - 13 = -15$ ✖

 B) $1 - 3 - \frac{5}{1-2} = 1 - 3 - \frac{5}{-1} = 1 - 3 - (-5) = 3$ ✓

 C) $1 + 1 + \frac{4}{1-2} = 1 + 1 + \frac{4}{-1} = 1 + 1 + (-4) = -2$ ✖

 D) $1 + 1 - \frac{17}{1-2} = 1 + 1 - \frac{17}{-1} = 1 + 1 - (-17) = 19$ ✖

The answer is B.

Even if you do not know how to solve this question algebraically, you can still use the $x = 1$ trick to get equivalent questions like this one correct.

> *** Test Day Tip** – For those of you who are comfortable solving equivalent questions algebraically, you should do that first to save time. Only use the equivalent trick when you get stumped and cannot otherwise solve the question.

Equivalent Questions Practice: **A calculator may NOT be used on the following questions.** Answers on page 233.

1. Which of the following expressions is equivalent to $x^2 - 5x - 18$?

   A) $(x + 3)(x - 6) - 2x$
   B) $(x + 3)(x - 6) + 5x$
   C) $(x + 2)(x - 9) - 2x$
   D) $(x + 2)(x - 9) + 5x$

2. Which of the following expressions is an equivalent form of the expression $(2x + 2)^2 + (2x + 2)$?

   A) $2x^2 + 10x + 6$
   B) $4x^2 + 16x + 10$
   C) $(2x + 2)(2x + 3)$
   D) $(4x + 8)(x + 1)$

3. $$\frac{2}{x+7} + \frac{1}{2}$$

   Which of the following expressions is equivalent to the one above where $x \neq -7$?

   A) $\frac{x+11}{2x+14}$
   B) $\frac{x+7}{2x+14}$
   C) $\frac{5}{x+7}$
   D) $\frac{3}{x+9}$

4. Which of the following is equivalent to $(-3x + 4)^2 - 9x^2$?

   A) $-16\,(x + 1)$
   B) $4\,(-2x + 4)$
   C) $-8\,(3x - 2)$
   D) $8\,(x + 2)$

5. For $a > 0$, which of the following is equivalent to $\frac{6a^2 - 3a}{2a+1}$?

   A) $3a$
   B) $3a - 3$
   C) $3a - 3 + \frac{3}{2a+1}$
   D) $3a - \frac{a}{2a+1}$

6. Which of the following expressions is equivalent to $x + 2 + \frac{3}{x+1}$ where $x \neq -1$?

   A) $\frac{x+5}{x+1}$
   B) $\frac{x^2+3x+5}{x+1}$
   C) $\frac{x^2+5x}{x+1}$
   D) $x + 3$

7. Which of the following is equivalent to the expression below?

   $$16x^4 + 8x^3 - 24x^2 - 12x$$

   A) $(2x + 1)(2x^2 - 3)$
   B) $x(4x + 2)(4x^2 - 6)$
   C) $4x(2x - 1)(2x^2 - 3)$
   D) $4x(2x + 3)(2x^2 + 1)$

8. Which of the following expressions is an equivalent form of $x^2 + 10x + 20$?

   A) $(x + 4)(x + 6) - 4$
   B) $(x + 4)(x + 6) + 4x$
   C) $(x + 12)(x - 2) + 4$
   D) $(x + 12)(x - 2) + 24$

Chapter 4: Algebra Skills

Many SAT questions test your core algebra skills. To answer these questions correctly, you need to be able to isolate the unknown variable, such as x or y, or solve for a more complex term, such as $a + b$. **For any algebra question, take your time, write out each step of your analysis and calculation, and use the calculator when you have it to avoid silly mistakes like making a mental math error or forgetting a negative sign.**

In this section, we will cover the algebra skills that you need in your toolbox for test day.

1. Combining Like Terms

Whenever we have the chance, we should combine like terms. Doing so will help us simplify the equation and get to the correct answer more quickly.

> **Example 1:** If $2(3x - 6) + 3y = 6x - y + 8$, what is the value of y?

Solution: First, distribute the 2 on the left side of the equation.

$$6x - 12 + 3y = 6x - y + 8$$

We have x and y terms on both sides of the equation, so we need to combine like terms. Here, the $6x$ terms on both sides cancel, so we get

$$-12 + 3y = -y + 8$$

Now, combine the y-terms and the numbers and solve.

$$4y = 20$$
$$y = 5$$

The answer is 5.

2. Cross Multiply Fractions

Whenever we have two fractions equal to one another, we can cross multiply to get rid of the fractions.

$$\frac{x}{z} = \frac{y}{w}$$

Cross multiplying, we get

$$xw = yz$$

> **Example 2:** If $\frac{3x}{4} = \frac{6}{7}$, what is the value of x?

Solution:
$$\frac{3x}{4} = \frac{6}{7}$$
$$21x = 24$$
$$x = \frac{24}{21} = \frac{8}{7}$$

The answer is $\frac{8}{7}$.

3. Square Both Sides of an Equation Correctly

In algebra questions with square roots, we often need to square both sides to get rid of the square root. It is important to remember that we need to square both sides and not just each individual term. Students will often make a mistake on a question like the example below.

Example 3:	$\sqrt{x} = x - 2$
What value(s) of x solve the equation above?	
A) 1 B) 4 C) 1, 4 D) 1, 2	

Solution: When we see the square root in this question, we should start by squaring both sides of the equation. Most students will properly get rid of the square root on the left side of the equation, but they make a mistake on the right side by doing this:

$$x = x^2 - 4$$

WRONG! We cannot just square each individual term. We must square the entire equation on each side, so it should look like this:

$$(\sqrt{x})^2 = (x - 2)^2$$

If you prefer, you can also write out the right side of the equation to help make sure you remember to properly expand the term.

$$(\sqrt{x})^2 = (x - 2)(x - 2)$$

If we properly square both sides of the equation, we get

$$x = x^2 - 4x + 4$$

From here, we combine like terms, set the equation equal to zero, and factor. Moving all of the terms to the right side, we get

$$0 = x^2 - 5x + 4$$
$$0 = (x - 4)(x - 1)$$
$$x = 1, 4$$

It looks like there are two answers to this question, but that is not the case! **Anytime you square both sides of an equation, you NEED to plug the answers back into the original equation to look for extraneous solutions** (we will learn more on extraneous solutions in Chapter 6). Sometimes when we square both sides of an equation, we get answers that look correct but do not actually work in the original equation. Let's start by checking $x = 1$.

$$\sqrt{1} = 1 - 2$$
$$1 \neq -1$$

We see that $x = 1$ does not work in the original equation, so it is an extraneous solution. Now, we can check $x = 4$.

$$\sqrt{4} = 4 - 2$$
$$2 = 2$$

We find that $x = 4$ works in the original equation, so **the answer is B.**

Shortcut solution: We can backsolve this question using the answer choices. By plugging the answer choices in of 1, 2, and 4 in for x, we can test each answer choice. Only 4 works, so the answer is B.

Whenever you see a multiple-choice question like this, backsolve by plugging the answer choices back in. It is much faster than solving out algebraically! However, you might see a grid-in question like this, so make sure you know how to properly square both sides as well.

4. Factoring to Isolate A Variable

Variables in some equations can be more difficult to isolate. If the variable we are trying to isolate is in multiple terms, we need to be able to factor to isolate the variable.

Example 4:
$$z = \frac{x}{x-3y}$$

Which of the following equations expresses x in terms of y and z?

A) $\frac{y}{z+3}$ B) $\frac{3y}{1-z}$ C) $\frac{3yz}{z-1}$ D) $\frac{1+z}{3yz}$

Solution: To start, multiply both sides by $x - 3y$ to get rid of the fraction.

$$z(x - 3y) = x$$
$$zx - 3yz = x$$

We want to isolate x, so we need to put all terms containing x on the left side and all other terms on the right side.

$$zx - x = 3yz$$

To isolate x, factor x out of the terms on the left side and solve.

$$x(z - 1) = 3yz$$
$$x = \frac{3yz}{z-1}$$

The answer is C.

5. Factoring by Grouping for Cubic Functions

If you ever see an equation with an x^3 term that you need to factor, you should always try to factor by grouping. This is rarely tested on the SAT, but you should know it just in case!

Example 5: For the equation $x^3 - 5x^2 + 4x - 20 = 0$, x is an integer that solves the equation. What is the value of x?

Solution: To factor by grouping, we want to look at the terms in pairs to see what we can factor out. Here, we can factor out x^2 from the first two terms and 4 from the last two terms.

$$x^2(x - 5) + 4(x - 5) = 0$$

Notice that the terms inside the parentheses are the same. **To factor by grouping, the terms in parentheses must match!** We can rewrite the equation as

$$(x^2 + 4)(x - 5) = 0$$

To solve, set each term equal to 0 and solve for x.

$$x^2 + 4 = 0 \qquad\qquad x - 5 = 0$$
$$x^2 = -4 \qquad\qquad x = 5$$

Since x^2 is always positive, no real solution can come from the $(x^2 + 4)$ term. **The answer is $x = 5$.**

6. Solving Directly for the Answer

Some questions ask us to solve for an expression like $2x + y$. Anytime we see a question like this, we should first see if we can solve directly for the answer before solving for any specific variable.

Example 6:
$$\sqrt{x - 3} = \frac{5 - \sqrt{2}}{\sqrt{x-3}}$$

For the equation above, what is the value of $x - 3$?

    A) $8 - \sqrt{2}$ B) 23   C) $5\sqrt{2} - 4$ D) $5 - \sqrt{2}$

Solution: Here, we should first determine if we can solve directly for $x - 3$. There is no need to even bother solving for x if we can solve for $x - 3$. Can we solve directly for $x - 3$?

Yes, we can! If we multiply both sides by $\sqrt{x - 3}$, we get

$$x - 3 = 5 - \sqrt{2}$$

It's that simple. **The answer is D.**

Anytime you see a question similar to this one, always see if you can solve directly for the term the question is asking you to find first. If you cannot solve for the term directly, then solve the unknown(s) and plug them back in to find the answer.

Algebra Skills Practice: A calculator may NOT be used on the following questions. Answers on page 234.

1. $(x^4 + x) + (x^3 - x)$

   Which of the following is equivalent to the expression above?

   A) x^7
   B) $x^4 + x^3 - x^2$
   C) $x^4 + x^3$
   D) x^{12}

2. If $3(x + 5) = 16$, what does x equal?

   A) $\frac{1}{3}$

   B) 1

   C) 3

   D) $5\frac{1}{3}$

3. If $4x - 18 = 14$, what is the value of x?

   A) -1
   B) 4
   C) 8
   D) 12

4. If $x^2 + 4 = 40$, what does $x^2 - 8$ equal?

   A) 24
   B) 28
   C) 30
   D) 36

5. Which expression is equivalent to $(3x^2 - 2x + 5) - (-2x^2 + 3x - 2)$?

   A) $x^2 + x + 3$
   B) $x^2 - 5x + 7$
   C) $5x^2 + x + 3$
   D) $5x^2 - 5x + 7$

6. If $3x + 4 = 4x - 1$, what is the value of $2x + 3$?

   A) 5
   B) 8
   C) 13
   D) 17

7. If $3x = 36$, what is the value of $4x - 6$?

A) 6
B) 12
C) 30
D) 42

8. Which expression is equivalent to $(x^2 + 5) - (-2x^2 - 2)$?

A) $-x^2 + 3$
B) $-x^2 + 7$
C) $3x^2 + 3$
D) $3x^2 + 7$

9. What is the value of x in the equation below?

$$\frac{2x}{3} = \frac{5}{6}$$

A) $\frac{5}{4}$

B) $\frac{9}{5}$

C) $\frac{5}{9}$

D) $\frac{4}{5}$

10. If $\frac{x+4}{4} = k$ and $k = 2$, what is the value of x?

A) 2
B) 4
C) 6
D) 8

11. Which of the following is equivalent to the expression below?

$(x^2y^2 - 4x^3 + 2xy^2) - (2x^2y^2 + 2x^3 - 3xy^2)$

A) $3xy^2 + 6x^3 - xy^2$
B) $-x^2y^2 + 2x^3 - 5xy^2$
C) $-x^2y^2 - 6x^3 + 5xy^2$
D) $x^2y^2 + 6x^3 - 3xy^2$

12. Which of the following values of x is the solution to the equation below?

$$x - 3 = \sqrt{x + 17}$$

A. -1
B. 1
C. 5
D. 8

13. If $5(3x - 3) - 2(2x - 4) = 5(2x + 2)$, what is the value of x?

A) -13
B) 3
C) 17
D) 33

14. If $\sqrt{x - 3} = x - 3$, what value(s) of x solve the equation?

A) 1
B) 3
C) 4
D) 3, 4

15. If $ab = 24$ and $\frac{b}{4} = 2$, what is the value of $a - b$?

A) -5
B) 3
C) 5
D) 8

16. What value(s) of x satisfy the equation below?

$$x - 4 = \sqrt{x + 2}$$

A) -2
B) 2
C) 7
D) 2, 7

17. If $\sqrt{4x} = 8$, what is the value of x?

22. For the equation below, which of the following expresses x in terms of y, and z?

$$y = \frac{xz - z^2}{x - 1}$$

A) $\frac{z^2 - y}{z - y}$

B) $\frac{1 + y}{z^2 + y}$

C) $\frac{y - z^2}{z + 1}$

D) $\frac{z^2 + y}{1 - y}$

18. Based on the equation below, what is the value of $ax - b$?

$$5ax - 5b - 7 = 28$$

A) 5

B) $\frac{28}{5}$

C) 7

D) 14

23. For the equation $x^3 - 4x^2 + 3x - 12 = 0$, x is an integer that solves the equation. What is the value of x?

19. What is the solution to the equation below?

$$\frac{8x + 24}{x + 3} = x$$

24. In the equation below, what is the value of $x - 2$?

$$x - 2 = \frac{3^2}{x - 2}$$

A) 1

B) 3

C) 5

D) 9

20. Which of the following is equivalent to $\left(x + \frac{y}{4}\right)^2$?

A) $x^2 + \frac{y}{16}$

B) $x^2 + \frac{xy}{2} + \frac{y^2}{16}$

C) $x^2 + \frac{xy}{4} + \frac{y^2}{16}$

D) $x^2 + \frac{y^2}{4}$

21. Which of the following is equivalent to the expression below?

$$x^2 + 8x + 11$$

A) $(x + 4)^2 - 5$
B) $(x + 4)^2 + 3$
C) $(x + 4)^2 + 11$
D) $(x + 4)^2$

Algebra Skills Practice: A calculator may be used on the following questions.

25. Given that $\frac{2}{x} = 10$ and $\frac{x}{y} = 8$, what is the value of y?

    A) $\frac{1}{40}$

    B) $\frac{1}{8}$

    C) 8

    D) 40

26. If $x = -2$, what is the value of b in the equation below?

    $$x + \frac{1}{4}b = 2$$

27. Which of the following is equivalent to the expression below?

    $$2(3x + 1)(2x + 2)$$

    A) $8x + 3$

    B) $12x^2 + 4$

    C) $6x^2 + 8x + 2$

    D) $12x^2 + 16x + 4$

28. If $x = 3$ in the equation below, what is the value of b?

    $$x - \frac{15}{b} = 0$$

29. If $x - y = 14$ and $\frac{y}{3} = 12$, what is the value of x?

    A) 12

    B) 24

    C) 36

    D) 50

30. Which value of x satisfies the equation below?

    $$3(5x - 20) - (5x - 60) = 80$$

31. What value(s) of x satisfy the equation $12x^3 + 4x^2 - 3x - 1 = 0$?

    A) $-\frac{1}{3}$

    B) $\frac{1}{2}$

    C) $-\frac{1}{2}, \frac{1}{2}$

    D) $-\frac{1}{2}, -\frac{1}{3}, \frac{1}{2}$

32. For the equation below, which of the following expresses a in terms of b, and c?

    $$ab = \frac{a + bc + 6c}{3}$$

    A) $\frac{bc + 6c}{3b}$

    B) $\frac{bc + 6c}{3b - 1}$

    C) $\frac{a + bc + 6c}{3b}$

    D) $3 + bc + 6c$

33. What is the solution to the equation below?

    $$\frac{11x - 22}{x - 2} = x + 5$$

Chapter 5: Fractions

For success on the SAT, you need to be comfortable with fractions. Fractions are a topic that many students struggle with. If you are one of those students, fear not! In this chapter, we cover all of the fundamental techniques that will allow you to answer any question involving fractions quickly and efficiently.

1. Combining Fractions

To add or subtract fractions, we must make the denominators the same by finding the least common multiple of the numbers or expressions in the denominators. Let's start with a simple example:

$$\frac{1}{2} + \frac{2}{5}$$

Here, the least common denominator is 10. An easy trick to find the least common denominator is to multiply the numbers in the denominator together. For the fractions above, $2 \times 5 = 10$. Once we find the least common denominator, we convert all fractions to have the same common denominator and then combine.

$$\frac{1}{2} \times \frac{5}{5} + \frac{2}{5} \times \frac{2}{2} = \frac{5}{10} + \frac{4}{10} = \frac{9}{10}$$

On the SAT, you will often see questions with expressions in the denominators instead of just numbers. These are more difficult, but the concept and approach are the exact same.

Example 1:
$$\frac{1}{x} + \frac{3}{x-4}$$

Which of the following is equivalent to the equation above for $x \neq 0$ and $x \neq 4$?

A) $\frac{4x-4}{x(x-4)}$ B) $\frac{4}{2x-4}$ C) $\frac{4x-12}{x-4}$ D) $\frac{x-1}{x(x-4)}$

Solution: To start, we need to find the common denominator. Here, the common denominator is the product of the two denominators: $x(x-4)$. To make both terms have the same denominator, we need to multiply the top and bottom of each fraction by the term they are missing in the denominator.

$$\frac{1}{x} \times \frac{x-4}{x-4} + \frac{3}{x-4} \times \frac{x}{x} = \frac{x-4}{x(x-4)} + \frac{3x}{x(x-4)} = \frac{x-4+3x}{x(x-4)} = \frac{4x-4}{x(x-4)}$$

The answer is A.

Shortcut Solution: For any "equivalent" questions like this one, we can also use the method we discussed in Chapter 3 and just plug in $x = 1$.

2. Dividing Fractions

Let's say that we are solving an equation and get to

$$\frac{2}{3}x = \frac{1}{5}$$

To solve for x, we divide both sides by $\frac{2}{3}$. How do we divide a fraction by a fraction? **Take the fraction on the bottom, flip it to get the reciprocal, and then multiply the top fraction by the reciprocal of the bottom fraction.** It's as easy as that! For this example, the reciprocal of the bottom fraction is $\frac{3}{2}$, so we multiply the top fraction by $\frac{3}{2}$.

$$x = \frac{\frac{1}{5}}{\frac{2}{3}} = \frac{1}{5} \times \frac{3}{2} = \frac{3}{10}$$

You can use this method anytime you are dividing by a fraction, even if the right side is a whole number. For example,

$$\frac{2}{7}x = 3$$

To solve for x, we need to divide both sides by $\frac{2}{7}$, so we use the same trick of flipping the fraction and multiplying by the reciprocal, which here is $\frac{7}{2}$.

$$x = \frac{3}{\frac{2}{7}} = 3 \times \frac{7}{2} = \frac{21}{2}$$

Example 2:	$\frac{3}{4}x + \frac{1}{5} = \frac{1}{3}$
For the equation above, what is the value of x?	

Solution: First, we need to combine like terms by subtracting $\frac{1}{5}$ from both sides.

$$\frac{3}{4}x = \frac{1}{3} - \frac{1}{5}$$

Next, we need to combine the fractions on the right side by finding the common denominator. For 3 and 5, the least common denominator is 15.

$$\frac{1}{3} \times \frac{5}{5} - \frac{1}{5} \times \frac{3}{3} = \frac{5}{15} - \frac{3}{15} = \frac{2}{15}$$

Now, substitute this back into the equation.

$$\frac{3}{4}x = \frac{2}{15}$$

To isolate x, we divide both sides by $\frac{3}{4}$, so we flip the fraction and multiply by the reciprocal of $\frac{4}{3}$.

$$x = \frac{2}{15} \times \frac{4}{3} = \frac{8}{45}$$

The answer is $\frac{8}{45}$.

3. Simplifying Fractions

When simplifying fractions, you must be able to divide all terms in the numerator and denominator by the same number. Simplifying fractions with only numbers is easy.

$$\frac{6}{15} \div \frac{3}{3} = \frac{2}{5}$$

Many students struggle when there are multiple terms in the numerator or denominator. Let's start with a variable in the numerator.

$$\frac{2x+10}{4}$$

Can we simplify this fraction? Yes, but only if we can divide all terms by the same number. Here, we can divide every term by 2, so we can simplify the fraction.

$$\frac{2x+10}{4} \div \frac{2}{2} = \frac{x+5}{2}$$

Many students will make the mistake and will only divide the first term and not the 10 like this:

$$\frac{2x+10}{4} \neq \frac{x+10}{2}$$

WRONG! You must divide all terms by the same number to simplify. If you cannot divide all terms by the same number, you cannot simplify the fraction. For example, if we instead had

$$\frac{8x+3}{4}$$

We can no longer simplify this fraction, but we can split this fraction into two:

$$\frac{8x+3}{4} = \frac{8x}{4} + \frac{3}{4} = 2x + \frac{3}{4}$$

If you cannot simplify a fraction by dividing all terms by the same number, you should look to split and simplify the fraction this way.

The same concept applies for simplifying fractions when we have a variable in the denominator.

$$\frac{3}{6x+30}$$

Can we simplify this fraction? Yes, all terms can be divided by 3, so we can simplify the fraction.

$$\frac{3}{6x+30} \div \frac{3}{3} = \frac{1}{2x+10}$$

Again, make sure that you divide all terms by the same number. If you cannot divide all terms by the same number, the fraction cannot be simplified. For example, if we had

$$\frac{3}{6x+10}$$

we cannot simplify the fraction. While we just saw that you can split up the numerators of a fraction, you cannot split up the denominators.

$$\frac{3}{6x+10} \neq \frac{3}{6x} + \frac{3}{10}$$

We cannot simplify a fraction like this one at all.

Example 3:
$$\frac{12x+2}{6} + \frac{1}{3}$$

Which of the following is equivalent to the equation above?

A) $2x + \frac{1}{2}$ B) $2x + \frac{2}{3}$ C) $\frac{7}{3}x + \frac{1}{3}$ D) $4x + \frac{7}{3}$

Solution: First, we need to make the denominators the same, so we can combine the fractions. The least common denominator of 3 and 6 is 6.

$$\frac{12x+2}{6} + \frac{1}{3} \times \frac{2}{2} = \frac{12x+2}{6} + \frac{2}{6} = \frac{12x+4}{6}$$

Next, we simplify the fraction. All of the terms can be divided by 2.

$$\frac{12x+4}{6} \div \frac{2}{2} = \frac{6x+2}{3}$$

Finally, we can split the numerator and simplify to solve.

$$\frac{6x+2}{3} = \frac{6x}{3} + \frac{2}{3} = 2x + \frac{2}{3}$$

The answer is B.

Shortcut Solution: Since this is an "equivalent" question, we can also use the method we discussed earlier in Chapter 3 and just plug in $x = 1$.

4. Getting Rid of Fractions

For questions with only numbers in the denominator, it is usually easiest to get rid of the fractions. We can get rid of the fractions by multiplying both sides by the least common denominator.

$$\frac{1}{4}x + \frac{1}{2} = \frac{3}{8}x$$

The least common denominator of 4, 2, and 8 is 8, so we can multiply all terms by 8 to eliminate all of the fractions.

$$\frac{1}{4}x \times 8 + \frac{1}{2} \times 8 = \frac{3}{8}x \times 8$$

The equation becomes

$$2x + 4 = 3x$$

Now, solving is easy!

$$x = 4$$

If you struggle with fractions, always use this method to convert fractions to whole numbers whenever there are only numbers in the denominator.

Example 4: If $\frac{3x}{5} - \frac{2x}{6} - \frac{1}{2} = \frac{x}{10}$, what is the value of x?

Solution: Since all the terms in denominator are numbers, we can get rid of the fractions. The least common denominator of 5, 6, 2, and 10 is 30, so we can multiply all of the terms by 30.

$$\frac{3x}{5} \times 30 - \frac{2x}{6} \times 30 - \frac{1}{2} \times 30 = \frac{x}{10} \times 30$$

$$18x - 10x - 15 = 3x$$

$$8x - 15 = 3x$$

$$8x = 3x + 15$$

$$5x = 15$$

$$x = 3$$

The answer is 3.

5. Turn Fractions into Decimals

If you really dislike fractions, another trick is to turn fractions into decimals. In the calculator section, we can always convert fractions to decimals using the calculator. In the no-calculator section, we can still convert simple fractions into decimals, such as converting $\frac{1}{4}$ to 0.25.

Example 5:

$$\frac{3}{4}x - \frac{4}{10} = \frac{1}{2}x$$

For the equation above, what is the value of x?

Solution: With simple fractions like these, we can change the fractions to decimals without a calculator.

$$0.75x - 0.4 = 0.5x$$

Now, we solve for x algebraically.

$$0.75x = 0.5x + 0.4$$

$$0.25x = 0.4$$

$$x = \frac{0.4}{0.25}$$

Many students get stuck here, but we need to finish simplifying this. The easiest trick here is to convert the decimals into whole numbers by multiplying the top and bottom by 100.

$$\frac{0.4}{0.25} \times \frac{100}{100} = \frac{40}{25}$$

Now, we can simplify and find the answer.

$$x = \frac{40}{25} = \frac{8}{5}$$

The answer is $\frac{8}{5}$.

Fractions Practice: A calculator may NOT be used on the following questions. Answers on page 235.

1. $\frac{4}{3} + \frac{3}{2} =$

2. $\frac{3}{5} - \frac{1}{4} =$

3. $\frac{7}{8} + \frac{1}{2} =$

4. $\frac{2}{3} - \frac{5}{2} =$

5. $\frac{6}{7} - \frac{1}{3} =$

6. $\frac{21}{5} + \frac{3}{2} =$

7. $\frac{16}{3} - \frac{7}{2} =$

8. $\dfrac{\frac{3}{5}}{\frac{4}{3}} =$

9. $\dfrac{\frac{1}{2}}{\frac{1}{3}} =$

10. $\dfrac{\frac{2}{5}}{\frac{3}{2}} =$

11. $\dfrac{\frac{4}{3}}{\frac{1}{3}} =$

12. If $x = 3$ in the equation below, what is the value of b?

$$x - \frac{2}{3}b = 0$$

13. If $x > 0$, which of the following is equivalent to $\frac{2}{x} + \frac{1}{3}$?

A) $\frac{6x+3}{3x}$

B) $\frac{3}{x+3}$

C) $\frac{6+x}{3x}$

D) $\frac{6+x}{x}$

14. Which of the following is equivalent to $\frac{3+9x}{15}$?

A) $\frac{3+3x}{5}$

B) $\frac{1+9x}{5}$

C) $\frac{1+3x}{5}$

D) $\frac{1}{5} + 3x$

15. If $x = \frac{2}{5}y$ and $y = 10$, what is the value of $3x + 3$?

    A) 4
    B) 9
    C) 12
    D) 15

16. Which of the following is equivalent to $\frac{2}{x-1} + \frac{3}{x}$ where $x \neq 0$ and $x \neq 1$?

    A) $\frac{5x-3}{x^2-x}$
    B) $\frac{3x-3}{x^2-x}$
    C) $\frac{5x+3}{x^2-x}$
    D) $\frac{-1}{x-1}$

17. If $\frac{x}{y} = 3$, what is the value of $\frac{3y}{x}$?

    A) 0
    B) 1
    C) 3
    D) 9

18. If $x > 1$, which of the following is equivalent to $\frac{x}{x+1} - \frac{3}{x-1}$?

    A) $\frac{x^2-4x-3}{x^2-1}$
    B) $\frac{x^2+2x-3}{x^2-1}$
    C) $\frac{x^2+4x+3}{x^2-1}$
    D) $\frac{x-3}{x^2-1}$

19. Which of the following is equivalent to $\frac{x^2+5x}{x}$ where $x \neq 0$?

    A) $\frac{x+5}{x}$
    B) $\frac{x^2+5}{x}$
    C) $x + 5$
    D) 6

20. Which of the following is equivalent to the equation below where $x \neq 2$?

    $$\frac{4}{x-2} + \frac{6}{3(x-2)}$$

    A) $\frac{6}{x-2}$
    B) $\frac{22}{3x-2}$
    C) $\frac{16}{3x-6}$
    D) $\frac{28}{3x-6}$

21. What is the solution to $\frac{1}{3}x + \frac{2}{7} = \frac{4}{7}x$?

22. What is the solution to $\frac{4}{3}x - \frac{1}{2} = \frac{3}{6}x$?

23. If $\frac{m+3}{m+5} = 8$, what is the value of m ?

    A) $-\frac{3}{5}$
    B) $-\frac{5}{3}$
    C) $-\frac{37}{7}$
    D) $-\frac{40}{7}$

24. What is the solution to $x - \frac{4}{5} = 2 + \frac{1}{3}x$?

25. What value of x is the solution to the equation below?

$$\frac{8}{3}x = \frac{2}{3}$$

26. What value of x is the solution to the equation below?

$$\frac{2x+8}{3} = \frac{10}{3}$$

27. If $\frac{2a}{3} = \frac{4}{3}$, what is the value of a ?

A) $\frac{1}{4}$

B) $\frac{1}{2}$

C) 2

D) 4

28. For the equation below, which of the following gives y in terms of x?

$$y\left(\frac{2}{x+3}\right) = \left(\frac{x+1}{x}\right)$$

A) $y = \frac{x^2+4x+3}{2x}$

B) $y = \frac{x^2+3x+3}{2x}$

C) $y = \frac{2x+2}{x^2+3x}$

D) $y = \frac{2x+4}{2x}$

29. For the equation below, which of the following gives y in terms of x?

$$y\left(\frac{x-2}{x+3}\right) = \left(\frac{x+2}{x+1}\right)$$

A) $y = \frac{x^2-4}{x^2+4x+3}$

B) $y = \frac{x^2-x-2}{x^2+5x+6}$

C) $y = \frac{x^2+x-6}{x^2+3x+2}$

D) $y = \frac{x^2+5x+6}{x^2-x-2}$

30. If $\frac{8k}{4b} = \frac{1}{3}$, what is the value of $\frac{b}{k}$?

A) $\frac{1}{6}$

B) $\frac{1}{2}$

C) 2

D) 6

31. In the equation below, what is the value of a?

$$\frac{x}{x-3} + \frac{2}{3} = \frac{ax-6}{3x-9}$$

32. In the equation below, what is the value of $a + b$?

$$\frac{x}{x-3} + \frac{4}{x+2} = \frac{ax^2+bx-12}{x^2-x-6}$$

33. In the equation below, what is the value of $a + b$?

$$\frac{x+2}{x-3} + \frac{5}{x+3} = \frac{ax^2+bx-9}{x^2-9}$$

35. If $\frac{7}{5}x = \frac{9}{8}$, what is the value of x?

A) $\frac{8}{9}$

B) $\frac{9}{7}$

C) $\frac{45}{56}$

D) $\frac{56}{45}$

34. What value of x satisfies the equation below?

$$\frac{5x^2+2x}{x^2-4} - \frac{3x}{x-2} = \frac{3}{x+2}$$

A) -2

B) $-\frac{3}{2}$

C) $\frac{3}{2}$

D) 2

36. If $\frac{4x+y}{2x+y} = \frac{8}{5}$, what is the value of $\frac{y}{x}$?

A) $\frac{3}{4}$

B) $\frac{4}{3}$

C) $\frac{5}{8}$

D) $\frac{13}{36}$

Chapter 6: Extraneous Solutions

The SAT includes algebra questions that have extraneous solutions. Extraneous solutions are "fake" answers that look correct when solving algebraically but do not work when plugged back into the original equation. **Anytime you see variables in the denominator of a fraction or underneath a square root, you need to check for extraneous solutions**. To see how this works, take a look at the example questions below:

> **Example 1:** What value(s) of x satisfy the equation $\sqrt{2x+7} = x + 2$?
> A) -3 B) 1 C) $0, 1$ D) $-3, 1$

Solution: Method #1 – Math Teacher Way: To solve this equation, we need to solve for x.

$$\sqrt{2x+7} = x + 2$$

$$(\sqrt{2x+7})^2 = (x+2)^2$$

$$2x + 7 = x^2 + 4x + 4$$

$$0 = x^2 + 2x - 3$$

$$0 = (x-1)(x+3)$$

$$x = 1, -3$$

It looks like the answer here is D, but that is incorrect. We need to plug $x = 1$ and $x - -3$ back into the original equation to test for extraneous solutions.

To test $x = 1$	To test $x = -3$
$\sqrt{2(1)+7} = 1 + 2$	$\sqrt{2(-3)+7} = -3 + 2$
$\sqrt{2+7} = 3$	$\sqrt{-6+7} = -1$
$\sqrt{9} = 3$	$\sqrt{1} = -1$
$3 = 3$	$1 \neq -1$

We find that $x = 1$ works but $x = -3$ does not. This means that $x = -3$ is an extraneous solution, so the only value of x that works is $x = 1$. **The correct answer is B.**

That is a lot of work to solve, so if you ever see one of these questions on the SAT, use the shortcut method below. **Never use the math teacher way**, as it will lead you to the incorrect answer if you forget to check for extraneous solutions.

Method #2 – Backsolve: To find the correct answer, plug the answer choices back into the question and solve.

To test answer choice A, plug in $x = -3$ to the equation:

$$\sqrt{2(-3)+7} = -3 + 2$$

$$\sqrt{-6+7} = -1$$

$$\sqrt{1} = -1$$

$$1 \neq -1$$

Since $x = -3$ does not work, we know that answer choices A and D are both incorrect.

To test answer choice B, plug in $x = 1$ to the equation:

$$\sqrt{2(1) + 7} = 1 + 2$$
$$\sqrt{2 + 7} = 3$$
$$\sqrt{9} = 3$$
$$3 = 3$$

so $x = 1$ works. Now, we need to test $x = 0$ to see if the correct answer is B or C.

To test answer choice C, plug in $x = 0$ to the equation:

$$\sqrt{2(0) + 7} = 0 + 2$$
$$\sqrt{0 + 7} = 2$$
$$\sqrt{7} \neq 2$$

We find that $x = 0$ does not satisfy the equation. The only value of x that did satisfy the equation was $x = 1$, so **the answer is B.**

TIP – How to Spot and Quickly Solve Extraneous Solutions Questions

On the SAT, algebra questions with extraneous solutions are easy to spot. The questions will always have square roots or fractions. The answer choices will almost always look like the answer choices in the question we just solved: two answer choices (usually A and B) will just have one number and the other two answer choices (usually C and D) will have multiple numbers. The answer choices usually look like this:

    A) 0
    B) 2
    C) 0, 2
    D) 2, 5

Rather than solving these questions algebraically and having to deal with extraneous solutions, you should always backsolve and see which answer choice is correct!

This trick will work with any type of algebra question, but it is especially helpful for these types of extraneous solutions questions.

Example 2: What value(s) of x satisfy the equation $\frac{x}{x-2} = \frac{1}{2x-4}$?

    A) 0.5   B) 2   C) 2, 4   D) 0.5, 4

Solution: The fastest and easiest way to solve is to plug the answer choices into the given equation.

To test answer choice A, plug in $x = 0.5$ to the equation:

$$\frac{0.5}{0.5 - 2} = \frac{1}{2(0.5) - 4}$$
$$\frac{0.5}{-1.5} = \frac{1}{-3}$$
$$-\frac{1}{3} = -\frac{1}{3}$$

so $x = 0.5$ works. So far, we know that A or D could be the correct answer.

To check answer choice D, plug in $x = 4$ to the equation:

$$\frac{4}{4-2} = \frac{1}{2(4)-4}$$

$$\frac{4}{2} = \frac{1}{4}$$

$$2 \neq \frac{1}{4}$$

Since $x = 4$ does not satisfy the equation, we know that D in incorrect. The only value of x that satisfied the equation was $x = 0.5$, so **the answer is A.**

Here, we will also check answer choice B to walk you through the process. As seen above, we would not need to check this if we first checked answer choice A.

To check answer choice B, we plug in $x = 2$ to the equation:

$$\frac{2}{2-2} = \frac{1}{2(2)-4}$$

$$\frac{2}{0} = \frac{1}{0}$$

Since any fraction divided by 0 is undefined, $x = 2$ does not work. We know that answer choices B and C are incorrect.

Extraneous Solutions Practice: **A calculator may NOT be used on the following questions.** Answers on page 237.

1. What value(s) of x are solutions to the equation below?

$$x - 6 = \sqrt{3x}$$

   A) 3
   B) 12
   C) 6
   D) 3, 6

2. What value(s) of x satisfy the equation below?

$$-x = \sqrt{6x}$$

   A) 0
   B) 1
   C) 6
   D) 0, 6

3. What value(s) of x are solutions to the equation below?

$$x - 10 = \sqrt{5x}$$

   I.   5
   II. 20

   A) I only
   B) II only
   C) I and II
   D) Neither I nor II

4. What value(s) of x that solutions to the equation below?

$$\frac{5}{x+2} = \frac{x-3}{2x+4}$$

   A) 2
   B) 8
   C) 13
   D) 2, 13

5. What value(s) of x satisfy the equation below?

$$-x = \sqrt{x + 6}$$

   A) -2
   B) 0
   C) 3
   D) $-2, 3$

6. Which of the following value(s) of x are solutions to the equation below?

$$x - 4 = \sqrt{3x - 2}$$

   A) 1
   B) 2
   C) 9
   D) 2, 9

7. What are the value(s) of x that satisfy the equation below?

$$\sqrt{2x} = x - 4$$

   A) 2
   B) 8
   C) 4
   D) 2, 8

8. What value(s) of x are solutions to the equation below?

$$\frac{2x}{x+1} - 3 = \frac{2}{x^2+x}$$

   A) -2
   B) -1
   C) $0, -1$
   D) $-2, -1$

Chapter 7: "In Terms of"

"In Terms of" questions ask you to express a certain variable "in terms of" the other variables. If a question says, "solve for x in terms of y and z," you need to isolate x and determine what it is equal to. If you have done this correctly, the x will be on the left side of the equals sign and the y and z values, along with any numbers, will be on the right side of the equation.

The expressions in these questions can be very complex and intimidating at times, but as long as you use the algebra skills that we learned in Chapter 4, you should be able to solve these questions without any issue. The answer choices usually make it obvious which variable you are being asked to isolate.

Example 1: The equation below describes how a water pump displaces w gallons of water from a well every h minutes when the water is at a depth of x feet. Which of the following equations expresses x in terms of h and w?

$$2000 + xh^2 = 4wh$$

A) $x = \sqrt{4wh - 2000}$

B) $x = 4wh - 2000 + h^2$

C) $x = \frac{4wh - 2000}{h^2}$

D) $x = \frac{4w}{h} - 2000$

Solution: We need to isolate x. To start, we want to get all terms with x on the left side and all other terms on the right side:

$$2000 + xh^2 = 4wh$$

$$xh^2 = 4wh - 2000$$

Now, we can divide both sides by h^2 to solve for x.

$$x = \frac{4wh - 2000}{h^2}$$

The answer is C.

Example 2: For the equation below, which of the following expresses m in terms of p and q?

$$15p - 2m = 2mq + 300$$

A) $m = 15p + 2q + 300$

B) $m = \frac{15p + 300 + 2q}{2}$

C) $m = \frac{300 - 15p}{2q}$

D) $m = \frac{15p - 300}{2q + 2}$

Solution: We need to isolate m. To do so, we need to move all of the terms with m to the left side and move all other terms to the right side. We do this by subtracting $15p$ and $2mq$ from both sides to get

$$-2mq - 2m = -15p + 300$$

Now, we need to factor out m from the terms on the left side.

$$m(-2q - 2) = -15p + 300$$

To isolate m, we divide both sides by $-2q - 2$.

$$m = \frac{-15p + 300}{-2q - 2}$$

This does not match any of the answer choices yet, but we are close. If we multiply the right side by $\frac{-1}{-1}$, the equation instead will look like

$$m = \frac{15p - 300}{2q + 2}$$

The answer is D.

If the variable that you are trying to isolate appears in multiple terms, as with m in Example 2 above, you will always need to move all terms including that variable to one side and then factor that term out. Once the term is factored out, you can then use division to isolate the term and find the correct answer. If you need to review this, go to page 10.

"In Terms of" Practice: A calculator may NOT be used on the following questions. Answers on page 238.

1. A painter uses the formula $z = 20hw$ to estimate that z liters of paint are needed to paint a wall that is h feet high and w feet wide. Which of the following expresses w in terms of h and z?

   A) $w = 20z - h$

   B) $w = \frac{z}{h-20}$

   C) $w = \frac{z}{20h}$

   D) $w = \frac{h}{20z}$

2. The velocity v of an object is found by taking the change in position m of an object and dividing it by the time s. Which of the following gives time s in terms of m and v?

   A) $s = mv$

   B) $s = \frac{v}{m}$

   C) $s = \frac{m}{v}$

   D) $s = m - v$

3. A helium machine blows up balloons such that after starting with an empty balloon, the machine will fill the balloon with c cubic inches of air every t seconds, where $c = 6t\sqrt{t}$. Which of the following gives the average rate at which the balloon is filled in terms of t?

   A) $\sqrt{t}$

   B) $6\sqrt{t}$

   C) $\frac{6}{\sqrt{t}}$

   D) $6t$

4. For the expression below, which of the following expresses p in terms of g, m, and q?

   $$g = \frac{m+3p+5}{q}$$

   A) $p = \frac{gq+5}{m}$

   B) $p = \frac{gq-m-5}{3}$

   C) $p = \frac{gq-5}{3+m}$

   D) $p = \frac{gq+m+5}{3}$

5. The line $y = kx - 3$, where k is a constant, is graphed in the xy-plane. If the point (a, b) is on the line, where a and b are not equal to zero, what is the slope of the line in terms of a and b?

A) $\dfrac{a+3}{b}$

B) $\dfrac{a-3}{b}$

C) $\dfrac{b+3}{a}$

D) $\dfrac{b-3}{a}$

6. If $3\sqrt{5x} = b$, what is $5x$ in terms of b?

A) $\dfrac{b}{3}$

B) $\dfrac{b^2}{3}$

C) $\dfrac{b^2}{9}$

D) $15b^2$

7. Due to a new tax, steel prices have recently increased. The original pre-tax price of a steel bar is p dollars. The new price of steel bar after the increase is represented by n dollars. The equation below shows this relationship. What is p in terms of n?

$$1.18p + 40 = n$$

A) $p = 40n - 1.18$

B) $p = 1.18n - 40$

C) $p = \dfrac{n-40}{1.18}$

D) $p = \dfrac{1.18}{n-40}$

8. If $5x = \sqrt{a}$, what is a in terms of x?

A) $\sqrt{5x}$
B) $5x^2$
C) $25x$
D) $25x^2$

9. Which of the following gives e in terms of $a, b, c,$ and d?

$$abd - bcd = ed - cd$$

A) $abd - bcd - cd$
B) $abd - bcd + cd$
C) $ab - bc + c$
D) $ab - bc - c$

10. If $2\sqrt[3]{5x} = b$, what is x in terms of b?

A) $\dfrac{b^3}{\frac{2}{5}}$

B) $\dfrac{b^3}{10}$

C) $\dfrac{b^3}{20}$

D) $\dfrac{b^3}{40}$

11. If $a^2 = 16b^4$, what is b in terms of a?

A) $\dfrac{a}{4}$

B) $\dfrac{\sqrt{a}}{4}$

C) $\dfrac{\sqrt{a}}{2}$

D) $\dfrac{\sqrt{a}}{16}$

12. The formula below is used to show E, the expected time to complete a marathon, where f is the fastest time to finish the race, A is the average time to finish, and s is the slowest time to finish. Which of the following correctly gives s in terms of $E, f,$ and A?

$$E = \sqrt{\dfrac{s^2 + 2f}{A}}$$

A) $s = \sqrt{E^2A - 2f}$

B) $s = E\sqrt{A - 2f}$

C) $s = \sqrt{\dfrac{E^2A}{2f}}$

D) $s = EA - 2$

Chapter 8: Inequalities

In math, two values are not always equal. Sometimes, we just know that one value is bigger or smaller when compared to another value. In these situations, we use inequalities.

Algebra with Inequalities

To solve inequalities on the SAT, treat the inequality signs ($<,>,\le,\ge$) like an = sign and solve using algebra. Inequalities can be solved as normal algebraic expressions with the exception of one very important rule:

> **When multiplying or dividing by a negative number, switch the direction of the inequality sign.**

This rule is the most important thing to remember from this section. Students most commonly make mistakes on inequalities questions involving multiplication and division with negative numbers. As a quick example, let's see how to solve the equation below.

$$-2x + 5 \le 11$$

Subtract 5 from both sides to get

$$-2x \le 6$$

When dividing by -2 to isolate x, we switch the direction of the inequality sign, so we get

$$x \ge -3$$

Let's see a second example:

$$3x + 6 > x - 4$$

The first step is combining like terms. We subtract x from both sides to get the x-terms on the left side. We then subtract 6 from both sides to get the numbers on the right side.

$$3x - x > -4 - 6$$

$$2x > -10$$

$$x > -5$$

In this example, **we never multiply or divide by a negative number, so the inequality sign stays the same**. Just because we are working with a negative number does not mean we need to flip the inequality sign. Some students flip the sign whenever they divide and see a negative sign. Don't make that mistake! **Only flip the inequality when you multiply or divide both sides by a negative number.**

Example 1: Which of the following shows the solution for $6x + 12 \le 9x + 17$?

    A) $x \ge \dfrac{29}{3}$ B) $x \ge \dfrac{29}{3}$ C) $x \le -\dfrac{5}{3}$ D) $x \ge -\dfrac{5}{3}$

Solution: To solve, we need to isolate x. Here, let's move all the x-terms to the left side and all the numbers to the right side. To do this, we subtract $9x$ from both sides and 12 from both sides to get

$$-3x \le 5$$

Now we divide both sides by -3. Since we are dividing by a negative number, we switch the direction of the inequality sign.

$$x \ge -\frac{5}{3}$$

The answer is D.

Systems of Inequalities

A system of inequalities is a set of multiple inequalities with multiple variables. On the SAT, systems of inequalities questions usually include two inequalities with two variables.

Example 2:
$$2x > 15$$
$$3y - 2x > 21$$

Which of the following consists of the y-coordinates of all the points that satisfy the system of inequalities below?

    A) $y > 36$ B) $y > 12$ C) $y > 7$ D) $y > 3$

Solution: To solve a system of inequalities, we need to solve each inequality. We can solve using normal algebra. In addition, we use the substitution method that we will learn in Chapter 12 to combine the inequalities.

To start, we solve the first inequality by dividing both sides by 2 to get

$$x > \frac{15}{2}$$

Now for the tricky part: solving the second inequality for y. To solve for y, we want to get rid of the x using substitution, so that equation is expressed wholly in terms of y. From solving the first equation, we know that $x > \frac{15}{2}$. The trick here is to think of the first inequality as $x = \frac{15}{2}$ and substitute the $\frac{15}{2}$ for the x. Now, we have

$$3y - 2(\tfrac{15}{2}) > 21$$

$$3y - 15 > 21$$

This looks like an equation we can solve.

$$3y > 36$$

$$y > 12$$

The solution to this system of inequalities is $x > \frac{15}{2}$ and $y > 12$. **The answer is B.**

Shortcut Method: We could have taken a shortcut if you just noticed that the $2x$ in the second equation matches the $2x$ in the first equation. Rather than solving the first equation, we could have jumped straight to plugging in 15 for $2x$ and then solved for y. The math is pretty much the same, but the shortcut is a bit faster.

Example 3:
$$y > 3x + 1$$
$$2y + x < 13$$

In the xy-plane, point A is contained in the graph of the solution set of the system of inequalities above. Which of the following could be the coordinates of point A?

    A) $(-2, -8)$ B) $(1, 5)$ C) $(1, 7)$ D) $(3, 3)$

Solution: If you see a question with two inequalities with both x-terms and y-terms, the easiest way to solve is to plug the answer choices back into the inequalities. Whichever answer works for both inequalities will be the correct answer. Solving this question algebraically is more difficult and time consuming, so we will not go over how to do it here.

Let's plug the correct answer of $(1, 5)$ into both inequalities. Let's start with the first inequality

$$5 > 3(1) + 1$$
$$5 > 4$$

The first inequality works, so let's move on to the second one.

$$2(5) + 1 < 13$$
$$11 < 13$$

The second inequality works as well. Since both inequalities work with the point $(1, 5)$, we find **the answer is B.** All of the other answer choices are not true for one or both inequalities.

Graphing Inequalities

When graphing inequalities in the coordinate plane, you just need to remember three simple steps:

1) **Rearrange the equation into $y = mx + b$ form.**

2) **Plot the line. For greater than and less than ($>$ and $<$), draw a dashed line. For greater than or equal to and less than or equal to ($\geq$ and $\leq$), draw a solid line.**

3) **For greater than and greater than or equal to ($>$ and $\geq$), shade above the line. For less than and less than or equal to ($<$ and $\leq$), shade below the line.**

Let's start by graphing the inequality $2x + 3y \geq 6$.

First, we need to rearrange this into slope-intercept form to isolate y. If we do this correctly, we will get

$$y \geq -\frac{2}{3}x + 2$$

Since this is greater than or equal to, we draw a solid line and shade above the line, so the graph looks like

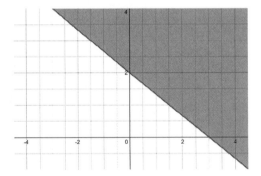

The solution set is the shaded area of the graph.

For a system of inequalities in the coordinate plane, the solution is where the shaded regions overlap. For example, let's consider the inequalities $4x - 2y > 8$ and $x + 3y > -2$

To graph these inequalities, we need to rearrange them into slope-intercept form to isolate y. If we do this correctly, we get

$$y < 2x - 4 \quad \text{and} \quad y > -\frac{1}{3}x - \frac{2}{3}$$

For the $y < 2x - 4$ line, we draw a dashed line and shade below the line. For the $y > -\frac{1}{3}x - \frac{2}{3}$ line, we draw a dashed line and shade above the line.

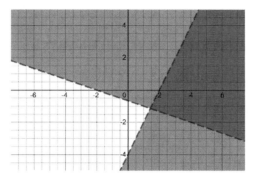

The solution set to this system of inequalities is the area in the top right where the shaded regions overlap.

Inequalities and Word Problems

The SAT also includes word problems with inequalities and asks you to select the answer choice that properly models the situation described. As always with word problems, read the question very carefully and try to convert the words into equations. If you have trouble writing the equations yourself, use the answer choices to help.

Example 4: Trevor is ordering lunch for the office. He has to spend less than $500 and buy lunch for 35 people. The options for lunch today are a salmon salad for $18 and a roast beef sandwich for $11. If s represents salmon salads and r represents roast beef sandwiches, which of the following inequalities correctly represents this situation?

A) $r + s > 35$
   $11r + 18s > 500$
B) $r + s = 35$
   $18r + 11 = 500$
C) $r + s = 35$
   $18s + 11r < 500$
D) $18r + 11s < 500$
   $r - s < 35$

Solution: We are told that Trevor has to buy lunch for 35 people, so the total number of meals needs to be 35. The first equation needs to be $r + s = 35$. Trevor also needs to spend less than $500. To find the total dollars spent on salmon salad, we need to multiply the number of salads, s, by the price, $18. To find the total dollars spent on roast beef sandwiches, we need to multiply the number of sandwiches, r, by the price, $11. Putting all of this together, the second equation needs to be $18s + 11r < 500$. **The answer is C.**

Inequalities Practice: A calculator may be used on the following questions. Answers on page 239.

1. John plants trees at a constant rate of 40 trees per hour. John planted 200 trees so far today and plans to spend h hours planting trees for the rest of the day. If John wants to plant at least 440 trees by the end of the day, which of the following inequalities best represents this situation?

   A) $40h \geq 440$
   B) $40h - 200 \geq 440$
   C) $40h + 200 \geq 440$
   D) $200h + 40 \geq 440$

2. Which of the following inequalities includes the y-coordinates of all points that satisfy the system of inequalities below?

   $$y > 3x - 3$$
   $$3x > 12$$

   A) $y > 1$
   B) $y > 4$
   C) $y > 9$
   D) $y > 15$

3. Which of the following inequalities is equivalent to the inequality below?

   $$18x - 12y > 24$$

   A) $6x - 4y > 8$
   B) $6x - 9y > 12$
   C) $9x - 4y > 12$
   D) $6x - 4y < 8$

4. At the beginning of the day, John had 15 pieces of candy. John gave away x pieces of candy to his friend Tom, and Dave gave John y pieces of candy. At the end of the day John had at least 23 pieces of candy. Which of the following inequalities can be used to correctly represent this situation?

   A) $15 - x + y \geq 23$
   B) $15 + x - y \geq 23$
   C) $-x + 15 + y \leq 23$
   D) $23 - x + y \geq 15$

5. James has 3,000 square feet of wood. He wants to make at least ten dressers and 5 bed frames. Each dresser requires 150 square feet of wood, and each bed frame requires 120 square feet of wood. If d represents dressers and b represents bed frames, which of the following systems of inequalities correctly represents this situation?

   A) $d + b \leq 3,000$
   $d \geq 10$
   $b \geq 5$
   B) $120d + 150b \leq 3,000$
   $d \geq 10$
   $b \geq 5$
   C) $150d + 120b \leq 3,000$
   $d \geq 10$
   $b \geq 5$
   D) $10d + 5b \leq 3,000$
   $d \geq 150$
   $b \geq 120$

6. Shawn has two jobs. He works as a barista, which pays \$13 per hour, and as a surf instructor, which pays \$15 per hour. He can work no more than 25 hours per week, and he wants to earn at least \$340 per week. Which of the following systems of inequalities represents this situation in terms of x and y, where x is the number of hours he works as a barista and y is the number of hours he works as a surf instructor?

   A) $13x + 15y \geq 340$
   $x + y \geq 25$
   B) $13x + 15y \geq 340$
   $x + y \leq 25$
   C) $13x + 15y \leq 340$
   $x + y \geq 25$
   D) $13x + 15y \leq 340$
   $x + y \leq 25$

7. One of the following graphs in the standard (x, y) coordinate plane is the graph of $y \le x + 1$. Which graph is correct?

A)

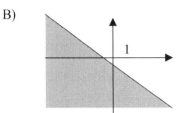

B)

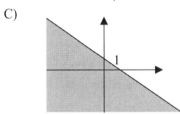

C)

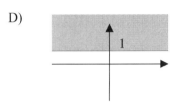

D)

8. A taco stand is buying pork for carnitas and flank steak for carne asada from its distributer. The distributer will deliver no more than 400 pounds of meat in a shipment. Pork comes in 9-pound packages, and flank steak comes in 6-pound packages. The taco stand wants to order at least three times as many packages of pork as packages of flank steak. Let p represent the number of packages of pork and let f represent the number of packages of flank steak. Which of the following systems of inequalities best represents this situation?

A) $9p + 6f \le 400$
$3p \ge f$
B) $9p + 6f \le 400$
$p \ge 3f$
C) $27p + 6f \le 400$
$3p \ge f$
D) $27p + 6f \le 400$
$p \ge 3f$

9. A workshop class is split into groups that are building large and small coffee tables. A large coffee table requires 6 legs and 4 segments of plywood. A small coffee table requires 3 legs and 2 segments of plywood. There are 85 legs and 79 segments of plywood. Each group must construct at least 2 small coffee tables and 1 large coffee table. What is the maximum number of groups that the workshop class can be split into?

10. A car manufacturer is shipping two types of cars across the Atlantic Ocean on a car ferry. Car A is 3 tons and Car B is 6 tons. The car manufacturer wants to transfer at least 50% more of Car A than Car B. The ferry can transport up to 230 tons of cars and hold no more than 50 cars. What is the maximum number of Car B cars that can be transported on the ferry?

11. A heat wave is defined as 5 or more days where the daily temperature is at least 9 °F higher than the average temperature during that month. If the month of June in San Diego has an average temperature of A °F and the daily temperature each of the last five 5 days is defined by x °F, which of the following would give the inequality for a heat wave occurring in the last 5 days in San Diego in June?

A) $A = x + 9$
B) $A \le x - 9$
C) $A \ge x + 9$
D) $A \ge x - 9$

Chapter 9: Percentages

On the SAT, you need to know how to solve questions with simple percentages and with percentage increase and decrease. While percentages may seem simple, they can often stump students who do not know how to set them up correctly. This chapter provides you all of the skills that you need to know in order to handle percentage questions quickly and easily on test day.

Simple Percentages

Simple percentage questions can be solved by properly setting up a proportion:

$$\frac{is}{of} = \frac{\%}{100}$$

You can think of the "of" as the starting value (the 100%) and the "is" as the percentage of the starting value. If you are given a percentage value, always put it where the % is.

> **Example 1:** Joey buys a new set of golf clubs for $720 when the clubs are on sale for 80% of the original price. What was the original price, in dollars, of the set of golf clubs?

Solution: Method #1 – Proportion: To solve, we can set up a proportion:

$$\frac{720}{x} = \frac{80}{100}$$

$$80x = 72,000$$

$$x = \frac{72,000}{80} = 900$$

The answer is 900.

Method #2 – Decimal Shortcut:

You can also turn percentages into decimals by dividing the percentage value by 100. 120% is the same as 1.2. 85% is the same as 0.85. For this question, we can turn 80% in 0.8 and solve:

$$0.8x = 720$$

$$x = \frac{720}{0.8} = 900$$

The answer is 900.

> **Example 2:** Isaiah purchased a new watch for 72% of the original price. Isaiah paid no sales tax. If the original price was $160, how much did Isaiah pay for the watch?

Solution: Here, we can turn the 72% into 0.72. Let the price Isaiah paid for the watch be p. We know that Isaiah paid 72% of the original price of $160 so

$$p = 0.72(160)$$

$$p = 115.2$$

Isaiah paid $115.20 for the watch.

The SAT also asks questions with multiple percentage changes. To solve these questions the fastest, you should do all of the percentage changes together in one step.

> **Example 3:** Fred is trying to sell his bicycle, but he is having a hard time finding someone interested in ... To sell the bicycle quickly, Fred decides to sell the bicycle for 95% of the original price to ... e sells the bicycle 6 months later for 80% of the price that he purchased the bicycle for from ... e that Dave sells the bicycle for is what percent of the original price of the bicycle?

"Math Teacher Way": Let the original price of the bicycle be p. When Fred sells the bi... ...f the original price, you multiply by 0.95. When Dave later sells the bicycle for 80% of the ... ultiply by 0.8. The final price that Dave sold the bicycle for is then:

$$p(0.95)(0.8) = 0.76p$$

The final pri... ...ne original price. **The answer is 76.**

Method 2 – Plug in Numbers: The most confusing part of this question is that we are never given any actual price for the bicycle. To make this question easier, pick an original price for the bicycle and use that price to solve. Let's say the original price of Fred's bicycle $100. 100 is always a good number to pick for percentage problems because it is easy to calculate percent changes from 100. Since Dave buys the bicycle for 95% of the original price, Dave pays $95 for the bicycle. Dave then sells the bicycle for 80% of the $95, so you can solve for the final price:

$$Final\ Price = 0.8(95) = 76$$

The final price is $76. Since the original price was $100, the final price is 76% of the original price. **The answer is 76.**

Simple Percentages Practice: A calculator may be used on the following questions. Answers on page 239.

1. What is 80% of 50?

   A) 20
   B) 40
   C) 42
   D) 45

2. On his English test, Justin missed 8 of the 50 questions. What percentage of the questions did Justin answer correctly?

   A) 40%
   B) 60%
   C) 75%
   D) 84%

3. Jim is a farmer. Last year, Jim planted 280 acres of corn and 420 acres of soybeans. What percentage of the acres that Jim planted was corn?

   A) 28%
   B) 40%
   C) 66%
   D) 75%

4. 48 is 150% of what number?

   A) 30
   B) 32
   C) 40
   D) 72

5. If $y = 200$ and x is 40% of y, what is 125% of x?

   A) 80
   B) 100
   C) 120
   D) 150

6. When a black bear hibernates, its heart rate drops by 15 beats per minute. This drop is 25% of its normal heart rate. What is the black bear's normal heart rate?

   A) 30
   B) 45
   C) 60
   D) 75

7. Christina has 10 hours of free time each week. If she spends 18% of her free time reading, how many <u>minutes</u> per week will she spend reading?

   A) 1.8
   B) 18
   C) 64
   D) 108

8. Cardiff Market is selling their famous tri-tip steak sandwiches at a local music and arts festival. As a special promotion, they promise to donate 27% of the sandwich sales to charity. If they sold $870 dollars in sandwiches, how much will they be donating to charity?

   A) $234.90
   B) $247.00
   C) $469.80
   D) $722.10

9. Last month, Amanda spent a total of $800. She spent $240 on food, $90 on gas, $400 on rent, and $70 on clothing. The category in which that Amanda spent the second largest sum of money on is closest to what percentage of her total spending?

   A) 20%
   B) 30%
   C) 50%
   D) 60%

10. A survey at the local high school of 25 students from the senior class revealed that only 20% of the students liked the school's lunches. If the other 275 seniors have the same percentage of students who like the school's lunch as those surveyed, how many students in the entire senior class like the school's lunches?

    A) 55
    B) 60
    C) 80
    D) 240

11. How Did Attendees First Hear About Coachella?

Source	Percent of those surveyed
Social Media	35%
Friend Attended	12%
TV	5%
Internet	38%
Other	10%

The table above shows a summary of 1,500 responses from attendees at Coachella when asked how they first learned about the festival. Based on the table, how many people learned from a friend who attended or from social media?

    A) 525
    B) 675
    C) 705
    D) 720

12. At the Palm Coast Country Club, approximately 12 percent of junior members and 26 percent of premium members have golfing memberships. If there are 252 junior members and 780 premium members, which of the following is closest to the total number of junior and premium members who have golfing memberships?

    A) 467
    B) 233
    C) 203
    D) 30

13. Rebecca sells her pickup truck to Jeremy for 76% of the original price. Jeremy does some work on the car and then sells it for 110% of the price at which he purchased the car. Which of the following is closest to percent of the original price that Jeremy sold the pickup truck for?

    A) 84
    B) 86
    C) 93
    D) 110

14. How many gallons of a 40% chlorine solution must be added to 10 gallons of a 5% chlorine solution to make a 20% chlorine solution?

15. The groups of students who are graduating with honors from a university have a variety of different majors. 30% are science majors, 15% are history majors, 25% are humanities majors, and the remaining 24 students are all business majors. Of the students graduating with honors, how many more science majors are there than history majors?

    A) 6
    B) 12
    C) 15
    D) 25

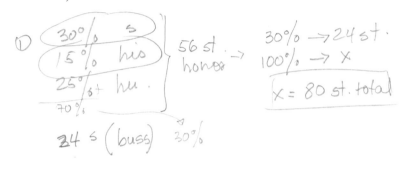

① 30% s
15% his
25% t hu. } 56 st. → honor

30% → 24 st.
100% → X
x = 80 st. total

70%

24 s (buss) 30%

② 70% → 56
30% → X

$\dfrac{30 \cdot 56}{70} = 24$

70% → 56
15% → X

$\dfrac{15 \cdot 56}{70} = 12$

12

Percentage Increase and Decrease

Percentage questions are more difficult when there is an increase or a decrease to the percentage, but you can still set them up as a proportion.

Percentage increase: $\frac{New}{Original} = \frac{100 + \%}{100}$ **Percentage decrease:** $\frac{New}{Original} = \frac{100 - \%}{100}$

The "original" is the starting value (the 100%), and the "new" is the percentage increase or decrease from the starting value. **If you are given a percentage value, always insert it into the equation where the % sign is.**

> **Example 1:** Jarvis construction company is building a new exit ramp for the local highway. The company initially said that the project would take 250 days, but a forecast for bad winter weather led the company to estimate that the project would take 12% longer to finish. How many days does Jarvis now estimate that the new exit ramp will take to complete?

Solution:
$$\frac{x}{250} = \frac{100+12}{100}$$

$$100x = (250)(112)$$
$$x = \frac{(250)(112)}{100} = 280$$

The answer is 280.

It is also important to know the shortcut for solving percentage increase and decrease questions. Let's say you want to increase x by 30%. Normally if we want to increase x by 30%, you will find 30% of the value and then add it to x:
$$x + 0.3x$$

This is the same as
$$x + 0.3x = x(1 + 0.3) = 1.3x$$

Instead of finding 30% of x and adding it to the original value, you can simply multiply x by 1.3. This shortcut will work for any percent value. To increase a value by 4%, multiply by 1.04. To decrease a value by 10%, multiply by 0.9. This technique will help you solve percentage increase and decrease questions more quickly and effectively on the SAT.

Both this shortcut technique and the proportion technique work, so use the one that you are more comfortable with.

> **Example 2:** Tim grew 15% more tons of tomatoes in 2019 than in 2018. If Tim grew 23 tons of tomatoes in 2019, how many tons of tomatoes did Tim grow in 2018?

Solution:
$$(1.15)(tons\ in\ 2018) = tons\ 2019$$
$$(1.15)(tons\ in\ 2018) = 23$$
$$tons\ in\ 2018 = \frac{23}{1.15}$$
$$tons\ in\ 2018 = 20$$

The answer is 20.

Example 3: The price of a painting decreased by 8% in 2017, increased by 25% in 2018, and increased by 40% in 2019. What percentage greater is the price of the painting in 2019 than the original price at the beginning of 2017?

Solution: Let the original price of the painting be p. When the price is decreased by 8% in 2017, we multiply by $(1 - 0.08)$ because it is the original price minus 8%. When the price is increased by 25% in 2018, we multiply by $(1 + 0.25)$ because we are adding 25% onto the price from 2017. When the price is increased by 40% in 2019, we multiply by $(1 + 0.40)$ because you are adding 40% onto the price from 2018. The final price is then:

$$p(1 - 0.08)(1 + 0.25)(1 + 0.40) = p(0.92)(1.25)(1.40) = 1.61p$$

The $1.61p$ shows that the price in 2019 is 61% higher than the price in the beginning of 2017. **The answer is 61.**

For other percentage questions, you will need to know how to calculate the percent by which a value increases or decreases. To solve these questions, you just need to use the equation below:

$$Percent\ Change = \frac{Final\ Value - Initial\ Value}{Initial\ Value} \times 100$$

If the percent change is a positive number, it is a percent increase. If the percent change is a negative number, it is a percentage decrease.

Example 4: In 2017, the average price of an avocado in California was $1.43. In 2018, the average price of an avocado in California was $1.54. Which of the following is closest to the percentage increase of the price of an avocado from 2017 to 2018?

   A) 7.1%   B) 7.7%   C) 8.2%   D) 8.4%

Solution:

$$Percentage\ Change = \frac{1.54 - 1.43}{1.43} \times 100 = 7.7\%$$

The answer is B.

Percentage Increase and Decrease Practice: **A calculator may be used on the following questions.**
Answers on page 240.

1. What number is 60% greater than 50?

    A) 30
    B) 60
    C) 70
    D) 80

2. What number is 30% less than 30?

    A) 15
    B) 21
    C) 24
    D) 27

3. Bob bought a house at a 20% discount. If the house was initially priced at 600,000 dollars, what was the price, in dollars, Bob paid?

    A) 120,000
    B) 480,000
    C) 720,000
    D) 750,000

4. Last year, 700 students graduated from Eastlake High. This year, 8% fewer students graduated than last year. How many students graduated this year?

    A) 620
    B) 644
    C) 648
    D) 756

5. In 2017, Jimmy's Surfboard Shapers made 1,231 surfboards. In 2018, Jimmy's Surfboard Shapers made 1,391 surfboards. Which of the following is closest to the percentage increase in surfboards made from 2017 to 2018?

    A) 11%
    B) 13%
    C) 16%
    D) 18%

6. Julie drives an average of 50 miles per hour during her 30-mile commute to work. Today, Julie is in a rush, so she drives 20% faster. How many minutes does it take her to drive to work today?

7. James bought three shirts for $168 during a 30% off sale. How much would the three shirts have cost without the sale?

    A) $118
    B) $200
    C) $218
    D) $240

8. The price of two sandwiches was $20 before sales tax. If a sales tax of 8% is added, how much do the two sandwiches cost including the sales tax?

    A) $18.40
    B) $20.08
    C) $20.80
    D) $21.60

9. John's average weekly grocery bill for 2016 was $176.45. His average weekly grocery bill for 2017 was $190.56. Which of the following is the closest to the percent increase in John's average grocery bill from 2016 to 2017?

    A) 7.1%
    B) 7.4%
    C) 8.0%
    D) 8.6%

10. Amy paid $76.00 for dinner after an 8% tax was paid. What was the price of her dinner before tax was added to the bill?

    A) $69.92
    B) $70.37
    C) $71.44
    D) $75.40

11. Bob's Woodshop buys 2 tons of wood from The Wood Depot. Each ton of wood costs $2,500. Bob gets a 15% discount for being a frequent customer. After the discount is applied, Bob has to pay a 10% sales tax. How much did Bob pay for the 2 tons of wood?

    A) $2,125
    B) $2,750
    C) $4,250
    D) $4,675

12. The price of the new PowerBros external phone charger is 30% more than the price of the old version. If the old version costs $85.00, which of the following best approximates the cost, in dollars, of the new external phone charger?

    A) $25.50
    B) $59.50
    C) $110.50
    D) $283.35

13. Andrew and Cole both work on a farm picking apples. Andrew picks apples 30% faster than Cole. If Andrew picked 325 apples yesterday, how many apples did Cole pick?

    A) 200
    B) 250
    C) 290
    D) 425

14. Max bought a new pair of hiking shoes for $118.00 dollars after an 8% sales tax. What was the price of the hiking shoes before the sales tax was added?

    A) $108.56
    B) $109.26
    C) $110.92
    D) $112.00

15. Julie's bakery sold 1,200 cookies in September and 1,403 cookies in October. If the percent increase from September to October was the same as the percent increase from August to September, which of the following is closest to the number of cookies Julie's bakery sold in August?

    A) 997
    B) 1026
    C) 1061
    D) 1613

16. When dining out, Dave spends an additional 32% on top of the listed price of the items he purchases after tax and tip are included. If Dave spends a total of $386 on a dinner for his family, what was the total listed price of the items purchased at the dinner before tax and tip were added?

    A) $292.43
    B) $262.48
    C) $509.52
    D) $567.65

17. Holly started the semester with $600 on her meal plan. Each meal costs $8. After eating three meals, what percent of the total dollars remaining on her meal plan was her fourth meal?

    A) 1.33%
    B) 1.38%
    C) 13.33%
    D) 13.88%

18. A rectangle is changed by decreasing its length by 20% and increasing its width by q percent. If these changes increased the area of the rectangle by 8%, what is the value of q?

    A) 8
    B) 10
    C) 25
    D) 35

19. John negotiated a 13% decrease from the initial listed price for the SUV he purchased. If he purchased the car for $34,000, which of the following is closest to the initial listed price of the SUV?

    A) $4,420
    B) $29,580
    C) $38,500
    D) $39,000

20. This month, Stella decided to try to be more energy efficient by turning off the lights in her house when she was not in the rooms and by using her air conditioning less. If her energy bill last month was $85.95 and her energy bill this month is $76.24, to the nearest tenth of a percent, what percent did her energy bill decrease?

    A) 12.7%
    B) 12.4%
    C) 11.8%
    D) 11.3%

21. Thomas recently purchased a new computer for college. Thomas had a coupon for a 20% discount from the original price. All items sold from the computer store also include an 8% sales tax added at the register. If Thomas paid a final price of $850.76, which included the discount and sales tax, what was the original price of the computer?

    A) $1,148.52
    B) $1,063.45
    C) $984.68
    D) $898.45

22. If there are 275 cognitive science majors and cognitive science majors make up 2.5% of the entire student body, how many students are in the entire student body?

    A) 1,100
    B) 6,875
    C) 10,000
    D) 11,000

23. Julie spent 2 hours and 20 minutes per day studying for her SAT over the first three weeks of April. During the last week in April, she studied an extra 30% each day. How much time did Julie spend studying during the last week?

    A) 3 hours and 2 minutes
    B) 2 hours and 51 minutes
    C) 20 hours and 2 minutes
    D) 21 hours and 14 minutes

24. Dave is currently making 250 pies per week. His boss wants him to increase the number of pies he is making by 12% each week. In two weeks, approximately how many pies will Dave be making?

    A) 274
    B) 280
    C) 308
    D) 314

25. A pair of sneakers were originally purchased for p dollars. The first owner sold the sneakers and made a 130% profit. The second owner resold the sneakers and made a 65% profit. Which of the following correctly solves for the final price the sneakers were sold for?

    A) $(1.3)(0.65)p$
    B) $(1.3)(1.65)p$
    C) $(2.3)(0.65)p$
    D) $(2.3)(1.65)p$

26. John's business made $18,000 in profit in 2015. In 2016, he made 30% more in profit than in 2015. In 2017, he made 6% less in profit than in 2016. Which of the following correctly expresses the profit John's business made in 2017?

    A) $(1.30)(1.06)(18,000)$
    B) $(1.30)(0.94)(18,000)$
    C) $(0.70)(1.06)(18,000)$
    D) $(0.70)(0.94)(18,000)$

Chapter 10: Exponents and Roots

Exponents

Let's start by reviewing the common exponent rules that you need to know for the SAT.

Rule Name	Rule	Example
Product Rule	$a^x \times a^y = a^{x+y}$	$3^3 \times 3^4 = 3^7$
Quotient Rule	$\dfrac{a^x}{a^y} = a^{x-y}$	$\dfrac{5^9}{5^4} = 5^5$
Power Rule	$(a^x)^y = a^{xy}$	$(2^4)^3 = 2^{12}$
Fraction Power Rule	$a^{\frac{x}{y}} = \sqrt[y]{a^x}$	$6^{\frac{2}{3}} = \sqrt[3]{6^2}$
Negative Exponent Rule	$a^{-x} = \dfrac{1}{a^x}$	$11^{-4} = \dfrac{1}{11^4}$
One Power Rule	$a^1 = a$	$(-4)^1 = -4$
Zero Power Rule	$a^0 = 1$	$13^0 = 1$

Make sure that you memorize all of these rules for test day. The product, quotient, and power rules are tested most often, but you will also need to know the fraction power rule and negative exponent rule for more difficult questions. To successfully solve exponent questions, you will need to use several of these rules together.

Example 1:
$$\frac{2x^6y^7}{16x^2y^{14}}$$

Which of the following equations is equivalent to the one above?

A) $\frac{x^3y^7}{8}$ B) $\frac{x^4}{8y^7}$ C) $\frac{x^3y^2}{8}$ D) $\frac{y^7}{14x^4}$

Solution: To solve, we use the quotient rule for the exponents. For the numbers, we just follow our normal algebra rules to simplify, so $\frac{2}{16}$ simplifies to $\frac{1}{8}$.

$$\frac{x^{6-2}y^{7-14}}{8}$$
$$\frac{x^4y^{-7}}{8}$$

Using the negative exponent rule, we get

$$\frac{x^4}{8y^7}$$

The answer is B.

Example 2:
$$\frac{(-2xy^3)^2}{x}$$

Which of the following equations is equivalent to the equation above?

A) $-2xy^6$ B) $-2x^2y^5$ C) $4xy^6$ D) $4x^2y^5$

Solution: Here, it is easiest to start with the power rule and simplify the numerator. Make sure that you remember to distribute the power to all of the terms including the -2 at the front.

$$\frac{4x^2y^6}{x}$$

Now, we use the quotient rule to simplify the x-terms.

$$4xy^6$$

The answer is C.

Example 3: If $4^{3x+1} = 4^{-x+7}$, what is the value of x?

Solution: In this question, the bases are the same, so the exponents must be equal.

$$3x + 1 = -x + 7$$
$$4x = 6$$
$$x = \frac{3}{2}$$

The answer is $\frac{3}{2}$.

Example 4: If $2x - y = 3$, what is the value of $\frac{9^x}{3^y}$?

Solution: The trick to this question is to recognize that 9 is the same as 3^2. Plugging in 3^2 for 9, we get

$$\frac{(3^2)^x}{3^y} = \frac{3^{2x}}{3^y} = 3^{2x-y}$$

Since $2x - y = 3$, we can plug in 3 for $2x - y$ and get

$$3^3 = 27$$

The answer is 27.

Example 4 is a more difficult than the first three because the bases of the exponents are different. Anytime you see different bases, look to find a way to substitute as we did in this question to make the bases the same. Once the bases are the same, we can use the exponent rules to solve the question.

Exponents Exercise: For questions 1-12, simplify the expressions until you only have positive exponents. For questions 13-20, solve for x. Answers on page 242.

1. $(x^4y)(x^2y^2) =$

2. $(3x^3)(2x^4)\left(\frac{1}{2}x^{-2}\right) =$

3. $(8x^{-3}y^4)(3x^6y^3) =$

4. $(2xy^3)^2 =$

5. $3x^{-2}y^5 =$

6. $\frac{18x^8}{2x^4} =$

7. $9x^{-3}yz^{-2} =$

8. $(x^{-2}y^2)(xy^{-2}) =$

9. $\frac{x^{-3}yz^2}{xyz} =$

10. $(3x^5y^{-2}z)^2 =$

11. $\frac{(4xy^2)^2}{xy} =$

12. $\frac{(5x^4y^{-2})^2}{(2x^{-3}y)^3} =$

13. $12^{-3} \times 12^5 = 144^x$

14. $\frac{7^2 \times 7^x}{49} = 7^8$

15. $\frac{x^7}{x^5} = 25$

16. $7^{-2x+3} = 7^{2-x}$

17. $(2^x)^3 = 2^4 \times 2^{\frac{3}{2}}$

18. $9^{\frac{3}{2}} = 3^{\frac{x}{2}}$

19. $16^{\frac{3}{2}} = 2^x$

20. $\frac{8}{8^{-3}} = 2^{2x-4}$

Roots

On the SAT, you need to know how to simplify and solve equations with roots. Let's begin by reviewing the common root rules:

$$\sqrt{xy} = \sqrt{x} \times \sqrt{y} \qquad\qquad \sqrt{18} = \sqrt{9} \times \sqrt{2} = 3\sqrt{2}$$

$$\sqrt{\frac{x}{y}} = \frac{\sqrt{x}}{\sqrt{y}} \qquad\qquad \frac{\sqrt{24}}{\sqrt{6}} = \sqrt{\frac{24}{6}} = \sqrt{4} = 2$$

To simplify a square root, factor the number underneath the radical and take out any pairs of the same number.

$$\sqrt{50} = \sqrt{5 \times 5 \times 2} = 5\sqrt{2}$$

In the example above, there were a pair of 5's underneath the radical, so we can take the 5 out. The 2 is not part of a pair, so it stays underneath the radical. Here's one more example:

$$\sqrt{108} = \sqrt{2 \times 2 \times 3 \times 3 \times 3} = (2 \times 3)\sqrt{3} = 6\sqrt{3}$$

Here, we have a pair of 2's and a pair of 3's, so we take both out and move them to the front. The third 3 is not part of a pair, so it says underneath the radical.

For some questions, you might need to go backwards and put a number outside back underneath the radical. To do this, take the number outside and put it back under the radical as a pair.

$$6\sqrt{3} = \sqrt{6 \times 6 \times 3} = \sqrt{108}$$

Example 5: If $\sqrt{45} + \sqrt{20} = x\sqrt{5}$, what is the value of x?

Solution: We need to simplify the radicals on the left side of the equation.

$$\sqrt{45} = \sqrt{3 \times 3 \times 5} = 3\sqrt{5}$$
$$\sqrt{20} = \sqrt{2 \times 2 \times 5} = 2\sqrt{5}$$

Plugging these values into the left side of the equation, we get

$$3\sqrt{5} + 2\sqrt{5} = x\sqrt{5}$$
$$5\sqrt{5} = x\sqrt{5}$$
$$x = 5$$

The answer is 5.

Example 6: If $\sqrt{2x} = 5\sqrt{6}$, what is the value of x?

Solution – Method #1: To solve for x, move the 5 back underneath the radical.

$$\sqrt{2x} = \sqrt{6 \times 5 \times 5}$$
$$\sqrt{2x} = \sqrt{150}$$

For these to be equal, the terms under the radical must be equal, so

$$2x = 150$$
$$x = 75$$

The answer is 75.

Method #2: We can also solve this question by squaring both sides.

$$(\sqrt{2x})^2 = (5\sqrt{6})^2$$
$$2x = 25 \times 6$$
$$2x = 150$$
$$x = 75$$

The answer is 75.

Remember, these same rules still apply to roots other than just square roots.

$$\sqrt[3]{xy} = \sqrt[3]{x} \times \sqrt[3]{y} \qquad\qquad \sqrt[3]{16} = \sqrt[3]{8} \times \sqrt[3]{2} = 2\sqrt[3]{2}$$

$$\sqrt[5]{\frac{x}{y}} = \frac{\sqrt[5]{x}}{\sqrt[5]{y}} \qquad\qquad \sqrt[5]{\frac{5}{32}} = \frac{\sqrt[5]{5}}{\sqrt[5]{32}} = \frac{\sqrt[5]{5}}{2}$$

To simplify a cube root, factor underneath the radical and take out triples of the same number.

$$\sqrt[3]{24} = \sqrt[3]{2 \times 2 \times 2 \times 3} = 2\sqrt[3]{3}$$

To simplify a 4th root, factor underneath the radical and take out four of the same number.

$$\sqrt[4]{80} = \sqrt[4]{2 \times 2 \times 2 \times 2 \times 5} = 2\sqrt[4]{5}$$

Chapter 10: Exponents and Roots

You are unlikely to see any higher roots on the SAT, but if you do just follow this same pattern to simplify any root.

Example 7: If $a = \sqrt[3]{162}$ and $b = \sqrt[3]{40}$, which of the following is equal to $a + b$?

A) $3\sqrt[3]{18} + 2\sqrt[3]{10}$ B) $2\sqrt[3]{20} + 2\sqrt[3]{5}$ C) $6\sqrt[3]{2} + 5\sqrt[3]{2}$ D) $3\sqrt[3]{6} + 2\sqrt[3]{5}$

Solution: To start, let's simplify to find the value of a.

$$a = \sqrt[3]{162} = \sqrt[3]{3 \times 3 \times 3 \times 6} = 3\sqrt[3]{6}$$

Now, simplify b.

$$b = \sqrt[3]{40} = \sqrt[3]{2 \times 2 \times 2 \times 5} = 2\sqrt[3]{5}$$

We can solve

$$a + b = 3\sqrt[3]{6} + 2\sqrt[3]{5}$$

The answer is D.

Roots and Variables with Powers

When you have exponent questions with roots and variables with powers underneath the root, **it is easiest to convert the root to a power and then use the exponent rules to solve.** For example,

$$\sqrt[3]{x^5 y} = (x^5 y)^{\frac{1}{3}} = (x^5)^{\frac{1}{3}} y^{\frac{1}{3}} = x^{\frac{5}{3}} y^{\frac{1}{3}}$$

This could also be solved using our fraction power rule, but the trick we just used makes complicated roots questions much easier.

Example 8: Which of the following is equivalent to $\sqrt[3]{5x^6 y^{18}}$?

A) $\sqrt[3]{5}\, x^2 y^6$ B) $\sqrt[3]{5}x^3 y^{15}$ C) $\sqrt[3]{5x^3 y^{15}}$ D) $5x^2 y^6$

Solution: The first step is to convert the root to an exponent.

$$(5x^6 y^{18})^{\frac{1}{3}}$$

Next, distribute the exponent to all terms.

$$(5x^6 y^{18})^{\frac{1}{3}} = 5^{\frac{1}{3}} (x^6)^{\frac{1}{3}} (y^{18})^{\frac{1}{3}}$$

Use the exponent rules to solve.

$$5^{\frac{1}{3}} (x^6)^{\frac{1}{3}} (y^{18})^{\frac{1}{3}} = \sqrt[3]{5}\, x^2 y^6$$

The answer is A.

Roots Exercise: For questions 1-12, simplify the radical. For questions 13-20, solve for x. Answers on page 243.

1. $\sqrt{60} =$

2. $\sqrt{150} + \sqrt{24} =$

3. $6\sqrt{5} - \sqrt{80} =$

4. $\sqrt{32} - \sqrt{18} + \sqrt{72} =$

5. $\sqrt[3]{48} + \sqrt[3]{162} =$

6. $\frac{\sqrt{45}}{\sqrt{15}} =$

7. $\frac{5\sqrt{12}}{10\sqrt{3}} =$

8. $\sqrt{8ab^4} =$

9. $\sqrt{16x^2y} =$

10. $\sqrt[4]{a^{12}b^2} =$

11. $\sqrt[3]{24x^6y^4} =$

12. $\sqrt{16x^{10}} =$

13. $\sqrt{3x - 2} = \sqrt{18}$

14. $\sqrt{15} = \frac{\sqrt{x}}{\sqrt{3}}$

15. $\sqrt{18} \times \sqrt{3} = x\sqrt{6}$

16. $\sqrt{x} - \sqrt{40} = \sqrt{10}$

17. $\sqrt{3x} + \sqrt{8} = \sqrt{50}$

18. $(3\sqrt{5})^2 = 2x$

19. $\sqrt{6x} = 2\sqrt{6}$

20. $\sqrt[3]{54} + \sqrt[3]{16} = x\sqrt[3]{2}$

Exponents and Roots Practice: A calculator may NOT be used on the following questions. Answers on page 243.

1. Which of the following is equivalent to $(2x^4)(9x^9)$?

   A) $11x^{14}$
   B) $11x^{36}$
   C) $18x^{13}$
   D) $18x^{36}$

2. Joe's spaceship can travel 2.5×10^6 feet per second. How many seconds would it take his spaceship to travel 10×10^{13} feet?

   A) 7.5×10^{-7}
   B) 2.5×10^{20}
   C) 4.0×10^7
   D) 7.5×10^7

3. $\frac{12 \times 10^{14}}{3 \times 10^2} = x$. What is x?

   A) 4.0×10^{12}
   B) 4.0×10^7
   C) 9.0×10^7
   D) 9.0×10^{12}

4. Which of the following is equal to $x^{\frac{3}{4}}$, for all values of x?

   A) $\sqrt{x^{\frac{1}{4}}}$
   B) $\sqrt[3]{x^4}$
   C) $\sqrt[4]{x^3}$
   D) $\sqrt{x^3}$

5. If $x > 0$, which of the following is equivalent to the given expression below?

   $$\sqrt{16x^2}$$

   A) $4|x|$
   B) $4x^2$
   C) $36|x|$
   D) $36x^4$

6. For all positive real numbers x, which of the following expressions is equivalent to $\frac{\left(\frac{x^{17}}{x^6}\right)}{\left(\frac{1}{x^4}\right)}$?

   A) x^7
   B) x^{11}
   C) x^{15}
   D) x^{19}

7. Which of the following expressions is equivalent to $\sqrt[y]{x^z}$?

   A) $x^{\frac{z}{y}}$

   B) $x^{\frac{y}{z}}$

   C) x^{y+z}

   D) x^{z-y}

8. When $x \neq 0$, what is the value of the equation below?

$$\frac{(2x)^3}{(4x)^3}$$

9. In the equation below, what is the value of z?

$$(x^{\frac{1}{3}})^6 \, (x^{\frac{4}{3}})^5 = x^z$$

10. If x and y are positive rational numbers such that $x^{5y} = 10$, what does x^{10y} equal?

    A) 20
    B) 50
    C) 80
    D) 100

11. For $x \neq 0$, what is the value of $\frac{(4x^4)^2}{(2x^2)^4}$?

12. For a positive real number x, where $x^4 = 4$, what is the value of x^8?

    A) 2
    B) 8
    C) 16
    D) 64

13. Which of the following is an equivalent form of $\sqrt[4]{g^8 m^2}$?

    A) $\sqrt{g}\, m^{-2}$

    B) $g^2 \sqrt{m}$

    C) $g^{\frac{1}{2}} \, m^{\frac{1}{2}}$

    D) $g^{-\frac{1}{2}} m^{-2}$

14. The expression $\frac{x^{-3} y^{\frac{1}{3}}}{x^2 y^{-2}}$, where $x > 1$ and $y > 1$, is equivalent to which of the following?

    A) $\frac{y^{\frac{2}{3}}}{x^5}$

    B) $\frac{y^{\frac{7}{3}}}{x^5}$

    C) $\frac{y^{\frac{7}{3}}}{x^{-5}}$

    D) $\frac{\sqrt[3]{y}}{x^5}$

15. Which of the following is an equivalent form of $\sqrt[2]{16a^2 b^6 c}$?

    A) $16ab^4 \sqrt{c}$
    B) $16ab^3 \sqrt{c}$
    C) $4ab^4 \sqrt{c}$
    D) $4ab^3 \sqrt{c}$

16. For a positive real number y, where $y^{20} = 16$, what is the value of y^5?

   A) 2
   B) $2\sqrt{4}$
   C) 4
   D) $4\sqrt{2}$

21. An exponential function is defined by $f(x) = a^x$, where a is a constant greater than 1. If $f(9) = 25f(7)$, what is the value of a?

17. If $3x + 4y = 16$, what is the value of $(8^x)(16^y)$?

   A) $\frac{1}{2}$
   B) $\left(\frac{1}{2}\right)^2$
   C) 2^8
   D) 2^{16}

22. Which of the following is an equivalent form of $\sqrt[3]{16x^5y}$?

   A) $16x^2 \sqrt[3]{y}$
   B) $16x \sqrt[3]{xy}$
   C) $2x^2 \sqrt[3]{2y}$
   D) $2x \sqrt[3]{2x^2y}$

18. An exponential function g is defined by $g(x) = c^x$, where c is a constant greater than one. If $g(5) = 9g(4)$, what is the value of c?

23. Which of the following is an equivalent form of $\sqrt[3]{24x^4y^2z^3}$?

   A) $2xz \sqrt{3xy^2}$
   B) $8xz \sqrt[3]{3xy^2}$
   C) $2xz \sqrt[3]{3xy^2}$
   D) $8xz \sqrt{xy^2}$

19. Which of the following expressions is equivalent to $(27x^3)^{\frac{1}{3}}$?

   A) $3x$
   B) $9x$
   C) $27x$
   D) $\sqrt[3]{27x}$

24. An exponential function h is defined by $h(x) = b^x$, where b is a constant greater than one. If $h(5) = 9h(3)$, what is the value of b?

20. If $x - 2y = 9$, what is the value of $\frac{3^x}{9^y}$?

   A) $\sqrt{\frac{1}{3}}$
   B) $\left(\frac{1}{3}\right)^2$
   C) 3^3
   D) 3^9

25. If $2x - 3y = 7$, what is the value of $\frac{9^x}{27^y}$?

   A) $\frac{1}{3}$
   B) 3^7
   C) 9^7
   D) Cannot be determined

Chapter 11: Quadratics

Quadratics are mathematical expressions containing a term to the second degree with a standard form of

$$y = ax^2 + bx + c$$

For quadratics on the SAT, you need to be able to multiply binomials (FOIL), factor, interpret quadratics on a graph, and use the quadratic equation.

Multiplying Binomials

In order to multiply binomials, you will need to FOIL, which stands for First, Outer, Inner, Last. You are likely familiar with how to multiply binomials by now, but for a quick review, here is an example of how to FOIL:

To multiply $(2x + 3)(x + 6)$ ...

$$\text{First terms: } (2x)(x) = 2x^2$$

$$\text{Outer terms: } (2x)(6) = 12x$$

$$\text{Inner terms: } (3)(x) = 3x$$

$$\text{Last terms: } (3)(6) = 18$$

so we get: $(2x + 3)(x + 6) = 2x^2 + 12x + 3x + 18 = \mathbf{2x^2 + 15x + 18}$

Multiplying Perfect Squares – Don't Forget to FOIL

When multiplying perfect squares, make sure to avoid the common mistake of forgetting to FOIL.

$$(x + 5)^2 \neq x^2 + 25$$

To help avoid this mistake, you can write the perfect square as two terms and then FOIL.

$$(x + 5)^2 = (x + 5)(x + 5) = x^2 + 5x + 5x + 25$$

Combine like terms to get

$$(x + 5)^2 = x^2 + 10x + 25$$

Example 1: Which of the following is equivalent to $(2x + 3)^2 + 4x$?

    A) $4x^2 + 16x + 9$ B) $4x^2 + 4x + 9$ C) $2x^2 + 4x + 3$ D) $6x^2 + 9$

Solution: To solve, multiply out the squared term and then combine like terms.

$$(2x + 3)^2 + 4x$$

$$(2x + 3)(2x + 3) + 4x$$

$$4x^2 + 12x + 9 + 4x$$

$$4x^2 + 16x + 9$$

The answer is A.

Don't forget the shortcut! In Chapter 3, we discussed an easy way to solve any "Equivalent to" questions: plug in $x = 1$ and solve. Solving questions similar to Example 1 algebraically works but plugging in $x = 1$ can be faster and easier for more challenging questions.

Factoring Quadratics

You also need to know how to factor quadratics. Factoring can help you simplify expressions or identify the solution(s) to a quadratic equation.

The "Box" Method

We can use the "box" method to find the factors for a quadratic equation. The factors appear on the outside of the box and the quadratic appears in the box.

To see how this works, let's factor the quadratic below:

$$f(x) = 3x^2 - x - 2$$

1. Place the x^2 term in the top left of the box. Place the number in the bottom right.

2. Write down the two terms that must multiply to the top left term outside the box. In this example, $3x$ and x multiply to $3x^2$.

	x	
$3x$	$3x^2$	
		-2

3. Identify which number(s) can multiply to the number in the bottom right of the box. In this example, we need a pair of numbers that multiply to -2. The possibilities are 1 and -2, 2 and -1.

4. Place the pairs of terms outside the box. You have the correct setup when the two other boxes (the x-terms) add up to the middle term in the quadratic. In this example, $-3x + 2x = -x$, so we know the numbers are correctly set up. The factors appear on the outside of the box.

	x	-1
$3x$	$3x^2$	$-3x$
2	$2x$	-2

5. Write down the quadratic in factored form. $3x^2 - x - 2 = (3x + 2)(x - 1)$

There are other ways to factor quadratics. If you know a different method that works for you, use that method. We will not review factoring beyond this example in this book. If you need to review factoring, look up some lessons and practice problems online and in your textbooks.

Solutions, Roots, x-intercepts, and Zeros for Quadratic Equations

The SAT may ask you to find the "solutions," "roots," x-intercepts," or "zeros" of a quadratic equation. All of these terms refer to the values of x that make $f(x) = 0$. Remember, all of these terms mean the same thing. We will refer to these terms collectively as the "solutions" in the rest of this chapter.

To find the solutions, set the quadratic equation equal to zero and factor. Let's continue with the example we are currently working on.

$$3x^2 - x - 2 = 0$$

We just showed how we can factor this quadratic to get

$$(3x + 2)(x - 1) = 0$$

To find the solutions, set each factor equal to zero and solve.

$$3x + 2 = 0 \qquad\qquad x - 1 = 0$$

$$x = -\frac{2}{3} \qquad \text{and} \qquad x = 1$$

The solutions are $x = -\frac{2}{3}$ and $x = 1$.

The solutions are also the x-intercepts if the quadratic is graphed (more on this on the next page).

Example 2: What is the sum of the solutions of the polynomial $f(x) = x^2 - 11x + 18$?

Solution: To solve, we need to find the values of x that make $f(x) = 0$.

$$x^2 - 11x + 18 = 0$$

$$(x - 2)(x - 9) = 0$$

$$x = 2, 9$$

The solutions are 2 and 9. The sum of the solutions is $2 + 9 = 11$. **The answer is 11.**

Shortcut Method: For any sum of solutions question, we can use the rule below:

For any quadratic equation where $ax^2 + bx + c = 0$, the sum of the solutions to a quadratic is always equal to $-\frac{b}{a}$.

For the equation in Example 2, $a = 1$ and $b = -11$, so

$$-\frac{b}{a} = -\frac{-11}{1} = 11$$

The answer is 11. Make sure to memorize this rule, as it is very useful for any questions that asks for the sum of solutions to a quadratic equation.

Example 3: If (x, y) is a solution to the system of equations below, what is a possible value of y given that $x > 0$?

$$y = 2x - 3$$
$$y = x^2 + 12x - 27$$

    A) 1   B) 2   C) 8   D) 12

Solution: This system of equations question involves quadratics. We will more thoroughly cover how to solve systems of equations in Chapter 12. When solving a system of equations, the solution(s) are the intersection point(s) of the two functions. Here, we are given the equations

$$y = 2x - 3$$
$$y = x^2 + 12x - 27$$

The easiest way to solve this system of equations is to set the equations equal to each other and solve for x.

$$x^2 + 12x - 27 = 2x - 3$$

$$x^2 + 10x - 24 = 0$$

$$(x - 2)(x + 12) = 0$$

$$x = 2, -12$$

Since the question specifies that $x > 0$, we must use $x = 2$. To find the y, plug in $x = 2$ to either of the original equations. Here, we will use the easier first equation.

$$y = 2(2) - 3$$

$$y = 1$$

Therefore, a point of intersection is at $(2, 1)$. **The answer is A.**

Example 4: Tom's math teacher is offering to buy Tom's sandwich. The teacher writes the equation $x^2 - 11x + 14 = 26$ on the board and says he will pay Tom t dollars for the sandwich, where t is equal to the positive solution to the equation on the board. What is the value of t?

Solution:

$$x^2 - 11x + 14 = 26$$
$$x^2 - 11x - 12 = 0$$
$$(x - 12)(x + 1) = 0$$
$$x = 12, -1$$

The question tells us that t is positive, so **the answer is 12.** Notice how we had to subtract the 26 before factoring. **You cannot factor a quadratic until the equation is set equal to 0.** This is a very common mistake that students make, so make sure you remember this critical step.

How Solutions Appear on a Graph

Solutions appear as the x-intercepts when graphed in the xy-plane. When we have a quadratic or other polynomial in factored form, we can see where the x-intercepts are. We will review the rules for multiplicity (the power to which a factor is raised) and zeros for polynomial functions below:

$y = (x + 2)(x - 4)$	$y = (x - 1)^2$	$y = (x + 3)^3$
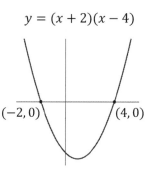	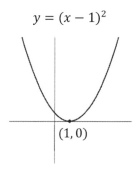	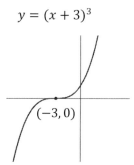
Multiplicity = 1	Multiplicity = 2	Multiplicity = 3
Zeros: The function has 2 solutions at $x = -2$ and $x = 4$. Behavior: The function passes straight through the x-axis at the solution.	Zeros: The function has 1 solution at $x = 1$. Behavior: The function bounces at the solution and does not cross the x-axis.	Zeros: The function has 1 solution at $x = -3$. Behavior: The function flattens and passes through the x-axis at the solution.

TIP – Functions with No Real Solution

If a function never crosses the x-axis, the function has no real solution. In other words, the function has no x-intercept.

As an example, the function $f(x)$ to the right has no real solution. This function cannot be factored to solve for x. If you use the quadratic formula to solve, the solutions are imaginary numbers.

$$f(x) = x^2 - 2x + 2$$

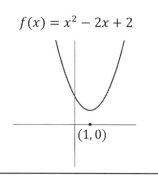

$(1, 0)$

Example 5: Which of the following equations correctly describes the function in the graph below?

A) $y = (x+2)^2(x-1)^2(x-3)$

B) $y = (x+2)(x-1)(x-3)$

C) $y = (x-2)^2(x+1)(x+3)$

D) $y = (x+2)(x-1)^2(x-3)^2$

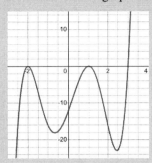

Solution: To solve this question, we need to look at the behavior of the function at each of the x-intercepts. There are x-intercepts at $x = -2$, $x = 1$, and $x = 3$, so we need to see the factors $(x+2)$, $(x-1)$, and $(x-3)$ in the correct answer. Now, we need to find out what power each term should be raised to. At $x = -2$ and $x = 1$, the function bounces, so the $(x+2)$ and $(x-1)$ terms are squared. At $x = 3$, the function goes straight through, so the $(x-3)$ should be to the first power. **The answer is A.**

The Quadratic Formula

If a quadratic is not easily factorable, you will need to use the quadratic formula to solve for the roots of a quadratic function. You will need to have the quadratic formula memorized.

$$\textbf{For } ax^2 + bx + c = 0\textbf{, the solution(s) are given by: } x = \frac{-b \pm \sqrt{b^2 - 4ac}}{2a}$$

Example 6: Which of the following is a solution for the function $f(x) = x^2 - 8x + 4$?

A) $8 + 4\sqrt{2}$ B) $4 - 2\sqrt{3}$ C) $-4 + 2\sqrt{3}$ D) $-8 + 4\sqrt{3}$

Solution: Since this quadratic cannot be factored, we must use the quadratic formula.

$x = \dfrac{-(-8) \pm \sqrt{(-8)^2 - 4(1)(4)}}{2(1)}$ 1. Plug in the values for a, b, and c.

$x = \dfrac{8 \pm \sqrt{64 - 16}}{2}$ 2. Begin to simplify terms.

$x = \dfrac{8 \pm \sqrt{48}}{2}$ 3. Combine terms under the radical.

$x = \dfrac{8 \pm 4\sqrt{3}}{2}$ 4. Simplify radical (if possible).

$x = 4 \pm 2\sqrt{3}$ 5. Simplify terms further (if possible).

$x = 4 + 2\sqrt{3}$ and $x = 4 - 2\sqrt{3}$ 6. Identify the value(s) of x.

The answer is B.

Example 7: The equations below intersect at the point (x, y). Which of the following is a value of x?

$$y = x^2 + 3x + 15$$

$$y = -3x + 11$$

A) 2   B) $6 + \sqrt{5}$ C) $-3 + \sqrt{13}$ D) $-3 - \sqrt{5}$

Solution: This is another system of equations question like the one we solved in Example 3. The solutions to the system of equations are where the functions intersect. The easiest way to solve this system of equations is to set the equations equal to each other and solve for x.

$$x^2 + 3x + 15 = -3x + 11$$

$$x^2 + 6x + 4 = 0$$

At this point, we cannot easily factor, so we need to use the quadratic formula.

$$x = \frac{-6 \pm \sqrt{6^2 - 4(1)(4)}}{2(1)}$$

$$x = \frac{-6 \pm \sqrt{20}}{2}$$

$$x = \frac{-6 \pm 2\sqrt{5}}{2}$$

$$x = -3 \pm \sqrt{5}$$

The x-values at the points of intersection for the system are at $x = -3 + \sqrt{5}$ and $x = -3 - \sqrt{5}$. **The answer is D.**

The Discriminant

In the quadratic formula, the discriminant is the $b^2 - 4ac$ term under the radical. This term is very important because it can quickly tell us how many real or complex solutions there will be for any quadratic equation. **The exact value of the discriminant is not important, but whether it is positive, negative, or zero is.**

Discriminant Value	Types of Solutions
$b^2 - 4ac > 0$	2 real solutions
$b^2 - 4ac = 0$	1 real solution
$b^2 - 4ac < 0$	0 real solutions, 2 complex solutions

Memorize these rules. **If you ever see a question about the number of solutions to a system of equations, use the discriminant to solve.**

Example 8: How many real solutions are there to the function below?

$$h(x) = 2x^2 - 7x + 9$$

A) 0   B) 1   C) 2   D) 3

Solution:
$$\text{Discriminant} = b^2 - 4ac = (-7)^2 - 4(2)(9)$$
$$\text{Discriminant} = -23$$

The discriminant is negative, so there are no real solutions. **The answer is A.**

Example 9: In the system of equations below, m is a constant. For which of the following values of m does the system of equations have exactly 1 real solution?

$$y = x^2 - 8x + 10$$
$$y = m - 2x$$

A) -1 B) 0 C) 1 D) 2

Solution: To start, we set the equations equal.
$$x^2 - 8x + 10 = m - 2x$$
$$x^2 - 6x + (10 - m) = 0$$

If the system of equations has one real solution, the equation above must have one real solution and the discriminant must be equal to 0.

$$\text{Discriminant} = b^2 - 4ac = (-6)^2 - 4(1)(10 - m) = 0$$

At this point, you can either test each of the answer choices to see which one makes the discriminant equal 0 or solve algebraically for m. The steps below show how to solve algebraically.

$$36 - 4(10 - m) = 0$$
$$36 - 40 + 4m = 0$$
$$-4 + 4m = 0$$
$$4m = 4$$
$$m = 1$$

The answer is C.

The Vertex

The vertex is the maximum or minimum of a parabola. For the parabola shown below, the vertex is at $(1, -4)$.

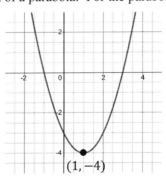

$(1, -4)$

You can think of the vertex as the midpoint of a parabola because the x-coordinate of the vertex is always the midpoint of the two solutions, or x-intercepts. More simply, the x-coordinate of the vertex is equal to the average of the solutions. Using the parabola above as an example, we can see how this works. Since the solutions (x-intercepts) for the parabola are located at $x = -1$ and $x = 3$, the x-coordinate of the vertex is at $x = \frac{-1+3}{2} = 1$, which matches the graph.

Remember, the vertex is always the maximum or minimum value of a quadratic. For the example above, the minimum is at $y = -4$.

Example 10: For the equation $f(x) = (x - 6)(x + 2)$, what is the value of x at the minimum value of the function?

Solution: The minimum value of a parabola is at the vertex, so we need to find the x-coordinate of the vertex. Since the function is already in factored form, we see the roots are at $x = 6$ and $x = -2$. The x-coordinate of the vertex is the average of the roots, so we can find

$$x = \frac{6 + (-2)}{2} = 2$$

The x-coordinate of the vertex is at $x = 2$, so **the answer is 2.**

The average method works perfectly if you are given a quadratic that is already factored. But what if you are not given a quadratic in factored form? Good news! There is a second way to quickly find the vertex.

For any quadratic in the form of $ax^2 + bx + c$, you can find the x-coordinate of the vertex using

$$x = -\frac{b}{2a}$$

Make sure you memorize this equation! It can really help you quickly and easily solve any questions where you need to find the vertex of a parabola.

Example 11: Andre runs a business that sells used cameras. To prepare the cameras for sale, Andre must spend x hours repairing and cleaning each camera. The equation $P(x) = -0.05x^2 + 0.4x + 0.9$ models the percentage of profit, P, that Andre gets from selling each camera he spent x hours repairing and cleaning. Which of the following shows the number of repair hours that maximizes Andre's percentage of profit for selling each camera?

 A) 3   B) 4   C) 6   D) 8

Solution: To determine the number of repair hours that maximize Andre's percentage of profit, we need to find the vertex of the equation. Since the leading value in the parabola is negative, the parabola is downward facing, so the vertex will be the maximum of the graph. The number of hours will be on the x-axis, so we need to find the x-coordinate of the vertex to solve.

To find the x-coordinate of the vertex, you can use the equation we just introduced above:

$$x = -\frac{b}{2a} = -\frac{0.4}{2(-0.05)} = 4$$

The answer is B.

Example 12: Claire's Big Top Circus has two high-flying acts: a man shot out of a cannon and a woman on a zip line. Claire wants to see if she can run the two high-flying acts at the same time without risking collision. The position of the man shot out of a cannon can be modeled by the equation $C(x) = -x^2 + 30x + 200$, where x represent seconds after launch. The zip line follows the equation $Z(x) = -5x + 150$, where x represents seconds after takeoff. Which of the following is the best advice to give Claire?

 A) The two high-flying acts cannot run at the same time because the performers will collide.
 B) The two high-flying acts can run at the same time because the performers will not collide.
 C) The two high-flying acts will be risky because the performers might sometimes collide.
 D) More information is needed to determine whether the high-flying acts can run at the same time.

Solution: We can solve this problem mathematically or by using a graphing calculator.

Method #1 – "Math Teacher Way": We are asked to determine whether the man shot out of a cannon and the woman will collide. In math terms, we are asked to determine if the equations $C(t)$ and $Z(t)$ will intersect and, if they do intersect, where the intersection will occur. Since we are given two equation, we need to solve the system of equations. We are given

$$C(t) = -x^2 + 30x + 200$$

$$Z(t) = -5x + 150$$

To solve, we can set the equations equal to each other.

$$-x^2 + 30x + 200 = -5x + 150$$

$$-x^2 + 35x + 50 = 0$$

At this point, we cannot easily factor, so we need to use the quadratic equation.

$$x = \frac{-35 \pm \sqrt{35^2 - 4(-1)(50)}}{2(-1)}$$

$$x = \frac{-35 \pm \sqrt{1425}}{-2}$$

$$x = \frac{-35 \pm 5\sqrt{57}}{-2}$$

$$x = -1.37, 36.37$$

We see the system will have solutions at $x = -1.37$ and $x = 36.37$. The solution at $x = -1.37$ will not be a point where the man and woman will collide because it is negative, and we cannot have a negative value for time. Now, we need to determine whether the intersection at $x = 36.37$ will or will not be a collision point. To do so, we can plug $x = 36.37$ into either of the initial equations.

$$Z(t) = -5(36.37) + 150 = -31.85$$

The functions will intersect at the point $(36.37, -31.85)$. Since y-value at this point is negative and the y-value represents the height, this will also not be a point of collision. By the point when $x = 36.37$, the man and woman will have already landed safely. As a result, the two high-flying acts can run at the same time without colliding. **The answer is B.**

Method #2 – Graphing the Equations: If you have a graphing calculator, we can skip this math and simply graph the equations. You can see on the graph below that the man and woman will not collide during the performance. You can also see the two points of intersection at $x = -1.37$ and $x = 36.37$ that we solved for above. **The answer is B.**

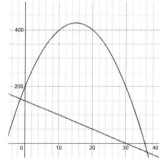

That is a very difficult question! Of course, graphing this equation is the easiest way to solve. If you have a graphing calculator, use it! But make sure you understand how we solved this mathematically in case a question similar to this come up on the no-calculator section (it would, of course, have easier numbers).

Quadratics Practice: A calculator may NOT be used on the following questions.   Answers on page 244.

1. What is the sum of the 4 binomials listed below?

$$x^2 + 3, 4x + 6, 3x^2 + 1, 3x - 1$$

[handwritten: $x^2 + 3x^2 = 4x^2$; $4x + 3x = 7x$; $3 + 6 + 1 - 1 = 9$]

A) $4x^2 + 7x + 9$
B) $4x^2 + 7x + 11$
C) $7x^2 + 4x + 9$
D) $4x^2 + 4x + 11$

2. Which of the following is equivalent to $(3x - 5)(-x + 7)$?

A. $(3x + 5)(x + 7)$
B. $(3x - 5)(x + 7)$
C. $(-3x + 5)(x - 7)$
D. $(-3x + 5)(x + 7)$

[handwritten: $3x - 5 = 0$; $0 = -3x + 5$; $-x + 7 = 0$; $0 = x - 7$]

3. What is the sum of the solutions of the polynomial $f(x) = x^2 - 7x + 12$?

A) -7
B) 3
C) 4
D) 7

[handwritten: $(x-4)(x-3)$; $x=4$, $x=3$, $)+ => 7$]

4. What are the solutions of the quadratic equation $3x^2 + 9x - 12 = 0$?

A) $x = 1$ and $x = 4$
B) $x = -1$ and $x = 4$
C) $x = -1$ and $x = -4$
D) $x = 1$ and $x = -4$

[handwritten: $x^2 + 3x - 4$; $(x+4)(x-1)$; $x=1$; $x=-4$]

5. If (x, y) is a solution to the system of equations below, what is a possible value of x?

$$y = x^2 + 6x + 6$$
$$y = 2x + 2$$

A) -2
B) 0
C) 2
D) 4

[handwritten: $x^2 + 6x + 6 = 2x + 2$; $x^2 + 4x + 4 = 0$; $(x+2)(x+2) = 0$; $x = -2$]

6. What is the sum of the solutions of the equation $x^2 - 4x - 21 = 0$?

[handwritten: $(x-7)(x+3) = 0$]

A) -10
B) -4
C) 3
D) 4

[handwritten: $x = 7$, $)+ 4$; $x = -3$]

7. The function $f(x)$ is graphed below. Which of the following could define the function $f(x)$?

A. $f(x) = x(x - 3)$
B. $f(x) = x(x + 3)$
C. $f(x) = x^2(x - 3)$
D. $f(x) = x^2(x + 3)$

8. In the xy-plane, the parabola with equation $y = (x + 3)(x + 4)$ intersects the equation $y = 20$ at two points. Which of the following is an x-value of a point of intersection?

A) -8
B) -1
C) 3
D) 4

[handwritten: $(x+3)(x+4) = 20$; $x^2 + 7x + 12 = 20$; $x^2 + 7x - 8 = 0$; $(x+8)(x-1) = 0$; $x = -8$; $x = 1$]

9. In the equation below, a and b are constants. Which of the following could be the value of a?

$$9x^2 - 16 = (ax - b)(ax + b)$$

A) 3
B) 4
C) 9
D) 16

10. Which of the following is equivalent to the expression below?

$$x^2 + 8x + 8$$

A) $(x + 4)^2 - 8$
B) $(x + 4)^2 + 8$
C) $(x - 4)^2 - 8$
D) $(x - 4)^2 + 8$

11. What is the sum of the solutions to $(x - 1.2)(x + 5) = 0$?

A) -6.2
B) -3.8
C) 3.8
D) 6.2

12.

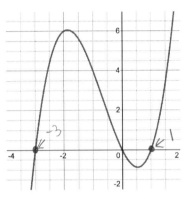

The function $f(x)$ is graphed above. Which of the following could define the function $f(x)$?

A) $f(x) = (x - 3)(x + 1)$
B) $f(x) = x(x - 3)(x + 1)$
C) $f(x) = (x + 3)(x - 1)$
D) $f(x) = x(x + 3)(x - 1)$

13. In the equation below, $j, l, k,$ and m are constants. If the equation has roots of $-4, 3,$ and -5. Which of the following could be a factor of the equation below?

$$jx^3 + lx^2 - kx - m = 0$$

A) $x - 4$
B) $x - 5$
C) $x - 3$
D) $x + 3$

14.

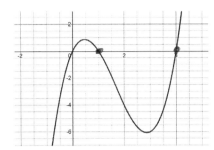

Which of the following correctly models the graph above?

A) $(x - 1)(x - 4)$
B) $x(x - 1)(x - 4)$
C) $(x + 1)(x + 4)$
D) $x(x + 1)(x + 4)$

15. Which of the following is a solution to the equation below?

$$x^2 + 6x + 3 = 0$$

A) $-3 + \sqrt{6}$
B) $-3 + \sqrt{13}$
C) $3 - \sqrt{6}$
D) $3 - \sqrt{13}$

$$\frac{36 - 12}{11}$$
$$x = \frac{-6 \pm \sqrt{6^2 - 4(3)}}{2} \quad x = \frac{-6 \pm \sqrt{24}}{2}$$
$$x = \frac{-6 \pm 2\sqrt{6}}{2} = -3 \pm \sqrt{6}$$

16. What is the sum of the solutions to the given equation?

$$x^2 - 13x + 40 = 6x - 8$$

A) -13
B) -19
C) 13
D) 19

17. The system of equations below is graphed in the xy-plane. Which of the following is the x-coordinate of an intersection point (x, y) of the system of equations?

$$y = x^2 + 8x + 9$$
$$y = 2x + 3$$

A) $-3 + \sqrt{3}$
B) $3 + 2\sqrt{3}$
C) $-5 - \sqrt{13}$
D) $3 - \sqrt{3}$

18.

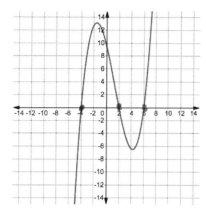

The function $g(x)$ is graphed above. Which of the following could define the function $g(x)$?

A) $g(x) = \frac{1}{5}(x-4)(x+2)(x+6)$

B) $g(x) = -\frac{1}{5}(x-4)(x+2)(x+6)$

C) $g(x) = \frac{1}{5}(x+4)(x-2)(x-6)$

D) $g(x) = -\frac{1}{5}(x+4)(x-2)(x-6)$

19.

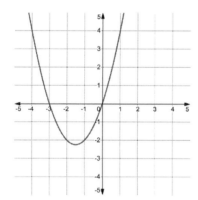

The function $f(x)$ is graphed above. Which of the following could define the function $f(x)$?

A) $f(x) = x^2 + 3x$

B) $f(x) = x^2 - 3x$

C) $f(x) = -x^2 + 3x$

D) $f(x) = -x^2 - 3x$

20. Given that $(2x + 3)$ and $(x - 4)$ are the factors of the quadratic below, what is the value of z?

$$2x^2 + (z-1)x + 2z - 4$$

A) -2

B) -4

C) 2

D) 8

21. $$x^3 + 8x^2 - 27x - 28 = 0$$

The polynomial above can be written as $(x + 1)(x + 7)(x^2 - 4) = 0$. What are all of the roots of the equation?

A) $-1, -7$

B) $-1, -7, \sqrt{2}$

C) $-2, -1, 2, 7$

D) $-7, -2, -1, 2$

22.

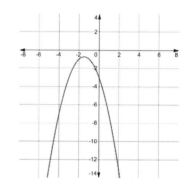

The function $f(x)$ is graphed above. Which of the following could define the function $f(x)$?

A) $f(x) = x^2 - 2x - 3$

B) $f(x) = x^2 - 3x - 3$

C) $f(x) = -x^2 - 3$

D) $f(x) = -x^2 - 3x - 3$

23. The system of equations below is graphed in the xy-plane. Which of the following is the sum of the values of the two x-coordinates of the intersection points (x, y)?

$$y = x^2 + 2x + 1$$
$$y = -3x - 3$$

A) -5

B) -3

C) 3

D) 5

24. Which of the following could be the graph of
$f(x) = x^2 - 2x + 3$?

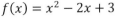

$y = \dfrac{-(-2)}{2}$

$y = 1$

A)

B)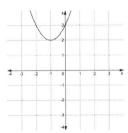

C)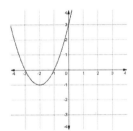

D)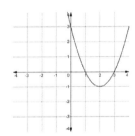

26. Which of the following could be the graph of
$f(x) = -x^2 + 4x - 1$?

$y = \dfrac{-4}{-2}$

$y = 2$

A)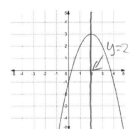

B)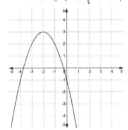

C)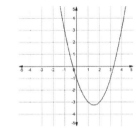

D)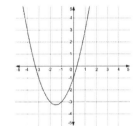

25. The system of equations below is graphed in the xy-plane. If x is not a negative number, what is a possible value of x?

$$y = x^2 + 5x + 8$$
$$y = 8 - 2x$$

27. Which of the following is a solution to the equation below?

$$x^2 - 4x + 1 = 0$$

A) $2 - \sqrt{6}$
B) $-2 + \sqrt{6}$
C) $2 + \sqrt{3}$
D) $-2 - \sqrt{3}$

28. The function $f(x)$ is graphed above. Which of the following could define the function $f(x)$?

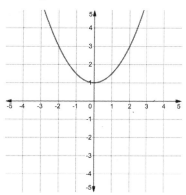

A) $f(x) = \frac{1}{2}(x-2)(x+2)$
B) $f(x) = (x-2)(x+2)$
C) $f(x) = \frac{1}{2}(x-2)(x+2)+1$
D) $f(x) = \frac{1}{2}(x-2)(x+2)+3$

$(0-2)(0+2) = 0$

$\frac{1}{2}(-2)(2) = \frac{1}{2} - 4$

-2

$\frac{1}{2}(-2)(2)+3$

$\frac{1}{2} \underbrace{\quad}_{-2} +3 = 1 = f(4)$

29. In the quadratic equation below, z is a constant. For what value of z, will the equation have one real solution?

$$zx^2 + 6x = 3$$

A) -3
B) 1
C) 3
D) 6

30. The equation below is graphed in the xy-plane. If a and b are positive constants and $a \neq b$, how many distinct x-intercepts does the graph have?

$$x^2 + ax + bx + ab = 0$$

A) 0
B) 1
C) 2
D) 3

Quadratics Practice: A calculator may be used on the following questions.

31. What is the solution set for $5x^2 + 6x = 8$?

A) $\{\frac{1}{5}, \frac{1}{2}\}$

B) $\{-\frac{1}{5}, -\frac{1}{2}\}$

C) $\{\frac{4}{5}, 2\}$

D) $\{\frac{4}{5}, -2\}$

32. If (x, y) is a solution to the system of equations below, what is a possible value of $y - x$?

$$y = x^2 + 9x + 8$$
$$y = 11x + 7$$

A) -1
B) 1
C) 17
D) 18

33. What is the sum of the solutions to the given equation?

$$x^2 - 12x + 26 = 2x + 2$$

A) 14
B) 11
C) -11
D) -14

34. How many solutions (x, y) are there to the system of equations below?

$$y = x^2 + 11x + 4$$
$$y = 5x - 5$$

A) 0
B) 1
C) 2
D) 4

35. $(80x - 42)(15x + 12) = ax^2 + bx + c$

    For the equation above, what is the value of $a + b + c$?

36. $(kx + 3)(4x^2 - mx - 3) = 20x^3 - 3x^2 - 24x - 9$

    For the equation above, what is the value of km?

    A) -15
    B) -5
    C) 3
    D) 15

37. $$ax^3 + bx^2 + cx + d = 0$$

    In the function above, a, b, c, and d are all constants. If the equation has roots at -3, 6, and 8, which of the following is a factor of $ax^3 + bx^2 + cx + d$?

    $X = -3 \Rightarrow X + 3 = 0$
    $X = 6 \Rightarrow X - 6 = 0$
    $X = 8 \Rightarrow X - 8 = 0$

    A) $x + 1$
    B) $x + 3$
    C) $x - 3$
    D) $x + 6$

38. $$h(x) = x^4 + 2x^3 - 8x^2 - 18x - 9$$

    The polynomial above can be written as $(x^2 - 9)(x + 1)^2$. What are all the real roots of the equation?

    $x^2 - 9 = 0 \quad (x+1)(x+1)$
    $x^2 = 9 \quad\quad x^2 + 2x + 1$
    $x = 3 \quad \dfrac{-2 \pm \sqrt{2^2 - 4}}{2}$
    $\dfrac{-2 \pm 0}{2}$

    A) $9, 1$
    B) $9, 1,$ and -1
    C) $3, -3,$ and -1
    D) $3, -3, 1,$ and -1

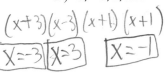

39. The equation below is graphed in the xy-plane. If a and b are positive constants and $a \neq b$, how many distinct x-intercepts does the graph have?

    $$y = (x + a)(x - a)(x + b)^2$$

    A) 1
    B) 2
    C) 3
    D) 4

40. Ben is throwing a ball from the top of his building. The ball's height is modeled by the function $H(x) = -x^2 + 10x + 56$, where x is the number of seconds after he throws the ball. How many seconds after throwing the ball does it hit the ground?

    A) 4
    B) 5
    C) 14
    D) 56

41. Which of the following is a solution to the equation below?

    $$2x^2 + 4x + 1 = 0$$

    A) $\dfrac{-2 + \sqrt{2}}{2}$
    B) $2\sqrt{2}$
    C) $-2 + \sqrt{2}$
    D) $\dfrac{2 - \sqrt{2}}{2}$

42. John is launching a rocket. The rocket's height in feet is modeled by the function $H(x) = -x^2 + 30x$, where x is the number of seconds after launch. What is the maximum height of the rocket?

    A) 10 feet
    B) 15 feet
    C) 200 feet
    D) 225 feet

    $-\dfrac{30}{-2} = 15$

43.

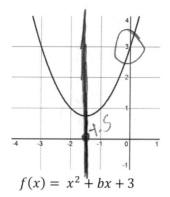

$$f(x) = x^2 + bx + 3$$

The graph and equation of the function $f(x)$ are shown above. Which of the following is the value of b?

$0^2 + .0b + 3 = 3$

A) 2
B) 3
C) 5
D) 8

44. Which of the following functions has a graph in the xy-plane with no x-intercepts?

A) $y = 6(x - 3)^3$
B) $y = 2x + 9$
C) $y = x^2 + 8x + 7$
D) $y = x^2 + 4x + 6$

45. Which of the following is a solution to the equation below?

$$5x^2 + 4x - 4 = 6x - 2$$

$5x^2 - 2x - 2 = 0$

A) $\frac{4}{5}$

B) $\frac{1 - \sqrt{11}}{5}$

C) $\frac{1}{5} - \sqrt{11}$

D) $\frac{\sqrt{11}}{5}$

$$\frac{2 \pm \sqrt{(2)^2 - 4(5)(-2)}}{10}$$

$$\frac{2 \pm \sqrt{4 + 40}}{10}$$

$$\frac{2 \pm \sqrt{44}}{10}$$

46. Dave and Charlie are trying to perform a trick shot. Dave will be on a zip line and his height is represented by the function $f(x) = -3x + 50$, where x represents seconds after starting the zipline. Charlie will be throwing a baseball and the baseball's height is represented by the function $g(x) = -x^2 + 6x + 30$, where x represents the number of seconds after Charlie releases the ball. In order to perform the trick shot, Dave and the baseball must intersect. If Dave starts the zipline at the same time as Charlie releases the ball, which of the following is the most appropriate conclusion about if the trick shot is possible?

A) The trick shot is not possible because the two functions do not intersect.
B) The trick shot is possible and there is only one point of intersection.
C) The trick shot is possible and there are two points of intersection.
D) More information is needed to figure out whether the trick shot is possible.

47.
$$y = x - 18$$
$$y^2 + (x - 14)^2 - 12 = 0$$

For the system of equations above, what is a possible value of y?

A) $-2 + \sqrt{2}$
B) $\sqrt{2}$
C) $2 + \sqrt{3}$
D) $-2 - \sqrt{6}$

$-x = -y - 18$
$x = y + 18$
$y^2 + (y + 18 - 14)^2 - 12 = 0$
$y^2 + y^2 + 8y + 16 - 12 = 0$
$2y^2 + 8y + 4 = 0$

48. In the system of equations below, a and b are constants. For which of the following values of a and b does the system of equations have exactly one real solution?

$$y = 6x + 2$$
$$y = ax^2 + b$$

A) $a = 3, b = 1$
B) $a = 3, b = 3$
C) $a = 9, b = 3$
D) $a = -3, b = 1$

Chapter 12: Systems of Equations

A system of equations is a set of two equations with the same set of variables. The SAT will give you two equations and ask you to solve for x, for y, or for some combination of the two. The easiest methods for solving a system of equations are elimination, substitution, and setting equal. You will need to be familiar with these methods and a few others that we will cover in this chapter to answer systems of equations questions correctly.

Elimination

We cannot solve an equation with two variables, so elimination is all eliminating one variable to get an equation with only one variable that can be solved. To do this, we make the coefficients of one variable have the same number and the opposite signs. With addition, one of the variables cancels out, leaving an equation with just one variable that can be solved.

Example 1: If $10x - 4y = 16$ and $2x + 4y = 8$, what is the value of y?

Solution: Whenever we have a system of equations question where none of the variables are already isolated, "elimination" is the fastest way to get to the answer. Since we are asked to solve for y, we want to cancel the x-terms. To do so, we multiply the second equation by -5.

$$10x - 4y = 16$$
$$-5\,(2x + 4y = 8)$$

$$10x - 4y = 16$$
$$-10x - 20y = -40$$

Next, add the equations together. Notice that the x-terms cancel out, so we get

$$-24y = -24$$
$$y = 1$$

The answer is 1.

Substitution

In substitution, we want to isolate one variable in the fastest and easiest way possible. Once we have an isolated variable in one equation, we can substitute that value into the second equation to get an equation with one variable that we can solve. This is not the same Substitution (plug in numbers) we learned in Chapter 2.

Example 2: If $12x + 8y = 8$ and $y = 6x - 14$, what does x equal?

Solution: If we are given a system of equations where one variable is isolated in an equation, use the "substitution" method. In this question, y is isolated in the second equations. Since $y = 6x - 14$, we can substitute $6x - 14$ for the y in the first equation.

$$12x + 8(6x - 14) = 8$$
$$12x + 48x - 112 = 8$$
$$60x - 112 = 8$$
$$60x = 120$$
$$x = 2$$

The answer is 2.

Set Equal

When we are given two equations that both isolate the same variable, it is fastest and easiest to set the equations equal and solve.

Example 3: If $y = 10x - 60$ and $y = -3x - 8$, what is the value of x at the point (x, y) where the lines intersect?

Solution: The point where the lines intersect is another way to ask for the solution to a system of equations. At the point where two lines intersect, the y-value must be the same for both equations, so we can set the equations equal to each other and solve for x.

$$10x - 60 = -3x - 8$$
$$13x - 60 = -8$$
$$13x = 52$$
$$x = 4$$

The answer is 4.

The Shortcut

If a question asks you for a value that is a combination of x and y-terms, such as $2x + 3y$, always look to see if you can add or subtract directly to the answer to save time. If you cannot get directly to the answer, use the elimination method to solve.

Example 4: If $8x + 17y = 90$ and $5x + 14y = 50$, what is the value of $3x + 3y$?

Solution: The fastest way to solve this question is to subtract the second equation from the first.

$$\begin{array}{r} 8x + 17y = 90 \\ -\quad \underline{5x + 14y = 50} \\ 3x + 3y = 40 \end{array}$$

The answer is 40.

Word Problems

Many word problems are systems of equations questions in disguise. For these questions, the greatest challenge is turning the words into equations. If you can do that successfully, then you only need to solve the system of equations. Usually, these questions on the test will be similar to the following example:

Example 5: For her garden, Mary buys 42 plants for a total of $108.00. Mary is only going to plant tomatoes and peppers. If a tomato plant costs $3.00 and pepper plant costs $2.00, how many pepper plants did Mary buy?

Solution: Let x be the number of tomato plants and y be the number of pepper plants. We can write two equations. The first equation comes from the fact that we know Mary bought a total of 42 plants.

$$x + y = 42$$

The second equation uses the prices of each plant to get to the total amount of money Mary spent buying plants.

$$3x + 2y = 108$$

Once we have these two equations, we can use elimination to solve. We are solving for the number of pepper plants, y, so we can eliminate the tomato plants, x, by multiplying the first equation by -3.

$$-3(x + y = 42)$$
$$3x + 2y = 108$$

$$-3x - 3y = -126$$
$$3x + 2y = 108$$

Next, add the equations together and solve for y.

$$-y = -18$$
$$y = 18$$

The answer is 18.

More Complex Systems of Equations

The SAT often includes more complex systems of equations with terms that are squared. For these questions, setting the equations equal is the quickest and easiest way to solve.

Example 6: The equations $y = x^2 - 11$ and $y = 10x + 13$ intersect at a point (x, y) where $x < 0$. What is the y-coordinate of this point of intersection?

    A) 12   B) 5   C) -2 D) -7

Solution: When given two equations, any point of intersection is where the x and y-values are equal. When we solve any system of equations question, we are solving for the point(s) of intersection.

In this question, y is already isolated in both equations, so we can set the equations equal and solve for x.

$$x^2 - 11 = 10x + 13$$

Since we have a quadratic, we need to move all of the terms to the left-hand side to make the equation equal to zero and factor.

$$x^2 - 10x - 24 = 0$$

$$(x - 12)(x + 2) = 0$$

$$x = -2, 12$$

The question tells us that $x < 0$, so we must use $x = -2$. To solve for the y-coordinate, plug $x = -2$ into either of one of our initial equations. We will use the first equation.

$$y = (-2)^2 - 11 = -7$$

The answer is D.

Example 7: The equations $y = x^2$ and $x^2 + (y - 3)^2 = 5$ intersect at the point (x, y). Which of the following is a value of x and y?

    A) -1 B) 1   C) 2   D) 4

Solution: In the first equation, we are given $y = x^2$, so we can plug this into the second equation. It is easiest here to replace x^2 with y.

$$y + (y - 3)^2 = 5$$

We have a quadratic, so we need to move all of the terms to the left side, set the equation equal to zero, and factor to solve.

$$y + y^2 - 6y + 9 = 5$$
$$y^2 - 5y + 4 = 0$$
$$(y - 1)(y - 4) = 0$$
$$y = 1, 4$$

To solve for the x-coordinate, we need to plug in $y = 4$ and $y = 1$ to one of the initial equations. Here, we will use the easier equation $y = x^2$. If $y = 4$, then $4 = x^2$ and $x = 2$. If $y = 1$, then $1 = x^2$ and $x = 1$. Since both $x = 1$ and $y = 1$, **the answer is B.**

Systems of Equations on Graphs

When systems of equations are graphed, the solution(s) are at the point(s) of intersection. To see how this works, let's consider the system of equations below:

Example 8:
$$y = \frac{3}{2}x + 3$$
$$y = -2x - 4$$

The system of equations above intersect at the point (a, b). What is the value of $a + b$?

A) -7 B) -2 C) 5   D) 9

Solution: We can solve this question in two ways: (1) graphing and finding where the graphs intersect and (2) solving algebraically.

Method #1 – Graph and Find Intersection: We can graph these equations to find the solution to this system of equations. For those of you with a graphing calculator, this can be an easy shortcut to solve systems of equations questions in the calculator section.

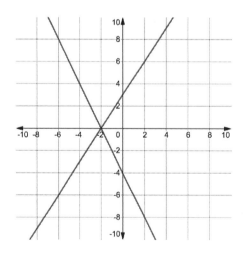

The solution to the system is at $(-2, 0)$, so we can now answer the question.

$$a + b = -2 + 0 = -2$$

The answer is B.

Method #2 – Solve Algebraically: The fastest way to solve this question algebraically is to set the equations equal and solve for x.

$$\frac{3}{2}x + 3 = -2x - 4$$

$$\frac{3}{2}x = -2x - 7$$

$$\frac{3}{2}x + 2x = -7$$

$$\frac{7}{2}x = -7$$

$$x = -2$$

Now that we have solved for x, plug $x = -2$ into one of the equations to solve for y. For this example, we will use the second equation because it is easier to solve.

$$y = -2x - 4$$

$$y = -2(-2) - 4$$

$$y = 0$$

We now know that the graphs intersect at the point $(-2, 0)$, so we can finish this question.

$$a + b = -2 + 0 = -2$$

The answer is B.

Note that graphing the equations and solving the system of equations both resulted in the same answer. Both methods work, so it is your job to identify which will be faster and easier for any given question.

System of Equations Practice: A calculator may NOT be used on the following questions. Answers on page 248.

1.
$$x - 3y = 3$$
$$x + y = 7$$

The solution to the system of equations above is (x, y). What is the value of x?

A) 2
B) 4
C) 5
D) 6

3.
$$0.25x - 2y = -4$$
$$x + y = 2$$

The solution to the system of equations above is the point (x, y). What is the value of y?

2.
$$x - y = 3$$
$$y = 3 - 2x$$

For the system of equations above, what is the value of x?

A) 6
B) 2
C) 0
D) -3

4.
$$2x - 3y = -6$$
$$3x + 2y = 4$$

For the system of equations above, what is the value of $x + y$?

A) -2
B) 0
C) 1
D) 2

5.
$$y = -1.5x - 1$$
$$2y = -8 + 3x$$

For the system of equations above, what is the value for $2y - x$?

A) 2
B) 0
C) −4
D) −6

6.
$$y = x^2 - 11x + 14$$
$$2y = 4 - 6x$$

The system of equations above is graphed in the xy-plane. Which of the following is the x-coordinate of an intersection point of the two equations?

A) 1
B) 4
C) 6
D) 10

7.
$$y = x^2$$
$$y = 7x + 8$$

The system of equations above is graphed in the xy-plane. The equations intersect at point (x, y) where $x < 0$ and $y > 0$. What is the y-coordinate at this point of intersection?

A) 1
B) 9
C) 49
D) 64

8.
$$y = (x - 5)(x + 2)$$
$$y = -6x - 12$$

The system of equations is graphed in the xy-plane. At which of the following points do the graphs intersect?

A) $(-1, -6)$
B) $(-1, -18)$
C) $(2, 0)$
D) $(2, -24)$

9. Max has $150 to spend on a picnic. He is going to buy cookies and brownies for the picnic. The table below gives the number of brownies and cookies in each box and the price per box.

Food Item	Number in each box	Price per box
Cookies	18	6
Brownies	12	8

Max will order a total of 20 boxes of cookies and brownies. Which system of equations gives a true relationship between the boxes of brownies, B, and boxes of cookies, C, that Max will order?

A) $C + B = 20$
   $6C + 8B = 150$
B) $C + B = 20$
   $18C + 12B = 150$
C) $C + B = 300$
   $6C + 8B = 150$
D) $6C + 8B = 20$
   $18C + 12B = 150$

10. According to the system of equations below, what is the value of x?
$$x - y = 21$$
$$x + 2y = -16$$

11. How many solutions are there to the system of equations below?
$$y = x^2 + 9x - 4$$
$$y - 5x + 8 = 0$$

A) There are no solutions.
B) There is one solution.
C) There are two solutions.
D) There are three solutions.

12.
$$x = y^2 + 8y$$
$$x + 2y = 24$$

The system of equations above is graphed in the xy-plane. Which of the following is the y-coordinate of an intersection point of the graphs of the two equations?

A) 8
B) 4
C) −2
D) −12

13.
$$(x - 1)^2 + (y - 2)^2 = 35$$
$$x = 2y + 2$$

Which of the following could be the x-coordinate of the solution to the system of equations above?

A) $\sqrt{6}$
B) $\frac{\sqrt{30}}{2}$
C) $2\sqrt{6} + 2$
D) $\sqrt{30} + 2$

System of Equations Practice: A calculator may be used on the following questions.

14.
$$3x + 5y = 26$$
$$x + y = 34$$

In the system of equations above, what is the value of x?

A) 18
B) 36
C) 72
D) 144

15.
$$6x = y + 8$$
$$y = 96 - 7x$$

In the system of equations above, what is the value of $x - y$?

A) −32
B) 32
C) 104
D) 736

16.
$$-4x - 15y = 78$$
$$3y + x = -30$$

The system of equations above is graphed in the xy-plane. At which point do the graphs intersect?

A) (14, −14)
B) (−72, 14)
C) (7, −52)
D) (228, 66)

17. If (x, y) is the solution to the system of equations below, what is the value of y?
$$4x + 3y = 10$$
$$6y + 2x = -4$$

A) −2
B) 2
C) 4
D) 8

18. If (x, y) is the solution to the systems of equations below, what is the value of x?
$$\frac{y}{x} = 3$$
$$2(y + 12) = 8x$$

A) 2
B) 4
C) 8
D) 12

19. If (x, y) is the solution to the system of equations below, what is the value of $y - x$?
$$2x - 3y = -9$$
$$3x + 2y = 19$$

A) −2
B) 2
C) 3
D) 8

20.
$$4x + 3y = 22$$
$$3x + 2y = 16$$

In the system of equations above, what is the value of $x + y$?

A) 4
B) 5
C) 6
D) 7

21. The linear function f is defined by $f(x) = ax + b$, where a and b are constants. If $f(15) = 850$ and $f(28) = 1,305$, what is the value of $a + b$?

22.
$$9x + y = 22$$
$$x^2 + y = 4$$

Which of the following is a y-coordinate of a solution to the system of equations above?

A) -32
B) -6
C) 3
D) 6

23. Jimmy's Deli sells Reuben sandwiches for $7.35 and brisket sandwiches for $8.10. Yesterday, the deli made $759.90 from selling a total of 99 Reuben and brisket sandwiches. How many Reuben sandwiches were sold yesterday?

A) 39
B) 43
C) 56
D) 74

24. Doug has 25 coins that add up to a total of $2.25. If Doug only has dimes and nickels, how many nickels does Doug have?

A) 1
B) 5
C) 10
D) 20

25. A group of 150 people went whitewater rafting. The group took 20 total rafts. The rafts could carry either 6 or 8 people. How many 8-person rafts did the group take?

A) 4
B) 6
C) 10
D) 15

26. If (x, y) satisfies the system of equations below, what is the value of x?
$$3x - 2y = -1$$
$$10x + 4y = 50$$

27. At the Pacific Beach boardwalk, there is a taco stand that sells carnitas tacos and fish tacos. Carnitas tacos have 50 more calories than fish tacos. If 3 carnitas tacos and 2 fish tacos have a total of 650 calories, how many calories does each fish taco have?

28.
$$x = y^2 \Rightarrow x = (-2)^2 = \boxed{4}$$
$$-14y + x = 32$$

The system of equations above is graphed in the xy-plane. The graphs of the equations intersect at point (x, y) where $y < 0$. What is the x-coordinate at this point of intersection?

A) -2
B) 4
C) 16
D) 256

$x = 32 + 14y \qquad y = 16$
$y^2 = 32 + 14y \qquad y = -2$
$y^2 - 14y - 32 = 0 \qquad \Uparrow$
$(y - 16)(y + 2) = 0 \qquad -2 < 0$

29. James took a trip from Maryland to Boston by car and train. When travelling by car, he averaged 40 miles per hour. When traveling by train, he averaged 60 miles per hour. The trip took him 7 hours and was 400 miles. How far did he travel by train?

A) 120
B) 200
C) 240
D) 360

$40x + 60y = 400 \qquad 20y = 120$
$\qquad y = 6$
$x + y = 7$
$\qquad 60x$
$x = 7 - y \qquad 40(7 - y) + 60y = 400 \qquad \frac{6}{360}$
$\qquad 280 - 40y + 60y = 400$

30. The system of equations below has a solution (x, y). What is the value of y?

$$\frac{1}{4}x = 4y - 4$$

$$\frac{-3}{4}x + 5y = -\frac{55}{10}$$

31. If (x, y) is a solution to the system of equations below where $x > 0$, what is the value of x?

$$y^2 + 4x^2 = 200$$
$$y = 2x$$

$(2x)^2 + 4x^2 = 200$
$8x^2 = 200$
$\boxed{x = 5}$

32. The quadratic function f is defined by $f(x) = ax^2 + bx + c$, where a, b, and c are constants. If $f(9) = 251$, $f(3) = 71$, and $c = 35$, what is the value of $f(7)$?

33. The number of chairs that a store will sell at different prices p is modeled by a quadratic function. When $p = 10$, 50 chairs are sold. When $p = 30$, 450 chairs are sold. When $p = 0$, 0 chairs are sold. When $p = 26$, how many chairs would the store sell?

34.
$$y^2 = 3x^2 - 6x - 72$$
$$y - 2x = 3 \qquad y = 2x + 3$$

Which of the following statements best describes the solutions to the system of equations above?

A) There are 0 real solutions.
B) There is 1 real solution.
C) There are 2 real solutions.
D) There are 3 real solutions.

$(2x + 3)^2 = 3x^2 - 6x - 72$
$4x^2 + 12x + 9 = 3x^2 - 6x - 72$
$x^2 + 18x + 81 = 0$
$(x + 9)(x + 9) = 0$
$\boxed{x = -9}$

Chapter 13: Systems of Equations with Infinite Solutions or No Solution

The SAT includes two special types of systems of equations questions: systems of equations with no solution and systems of equations with infinite solutions. While these questions may at first seem confusing, once you know the techniques needed to solve, they will be easy!

It is important to remember that the equations in most systems of equations questions are lines; they are just in standard form instead of $y = mx + b$. When solving a system of equations (as we learned in Chapter 12), we are finding the point (x, y) where the two function intersect. But what if the functions do not intersect? Or if the functions are identical? We will outline how to quickly and easily solve these questions below.

Parallel Lines with Systems of Equations

If two lines are parallel, they will never intersect. As a result, there is NO SOLUTION to a system of equations with parallel lines. This is the first type of unusual systems of equations question that you may see on test day.

> **Example 1:** For the equations below, for what value of k does the system of equations have no real solution?
> $$3x + 5y = 29$$
> $$9x + ky = 12$$

Solution: To solve this question, we want the lines to have the same slope so that they will never intersect. For two lines to have the same slope, the ratio of the coefficient for the x-term to the coefficient for the y-term must be the same in both equations. As a result, we can setup a simple ratio to find the answer.

$$\frac{3}{5} = \frac{9}{k}$$

$$3k = 45$$

$$k = 15$$

The answer is 15. This ratio method will always work for any type of no solution systems of equation question.

> **Example 2:** For the equations below, what value of k will give the system of equations no real solution?
> $$2x + 6y = -15$$
> $$6x + 2ky = 10$$

Solution: We can use the same ratio setup that we used as in Example 1 to solve for k.

$$\frac{2}{6} = \frac{6}{2k}$$

$$4k = 36$$

$$k = 9$$

The answer is 9.

Identical Lines with Systems of Equations

If two lines are identical, they have INFINITE solutions. Two identical lines must have the exact same equation for the line. When a systems of equations question asks for infinite solutions, we need to find a value for the variable in the question that makes the two equations identical.

Example 3: For the system of equations below, what value of m gives an infinite number of solutions?

$$8x + 4y = 52$$
$$4x + 2y = m$$

Solution: To solve this question, we need to find the value of m that makes the equations identical. To accomplish this, there are two methods:

Method #1 – Identical Equations: We can multiply by a coefficient to make the equations identical. For this question, we need to multiply the bottom equation by 2. Once the equations are identical, we can solve for the unknown.

$$8x + 4y = 52$$
$$2[4x + 2y = m]$$

$$8x + 4y = 52$$
$$8x + 4y = 2m$$

$$2m = 52$$
$$m = 26$$

The answer is 26.

Method #2 – Use Ratios: A similar ratio method to the one that we used to solve Example 1 also works. To set up the ratio correctly, we must choose one set of coefficients with no unknowns and a second set of coefficients with the unknown that we are solving for. For this question, let's use the x-coefficients, which have no unknowns, and the numbers, which have the unknown m, as our two pairs in the ratio.

$$\frac{8}{4} = \frac{52}{m}$$

Once the ratio is setup, we just solve the equation for m.

$$8m = 208$$
$$m = 26$$

The answer is 26.

Both methods work for any infinite solutions system of equations question, so you should just memorize whichever one you are more comfortable using.

Example 4: The system of equations below has an infinite number of solutions for what value of a?

$$\frac{1}{4}x + \frac{3}{4}y = \frac{11}{2}$$
$$x + ay = 22$$

Solution: For this question, we can use either of the methods. Here, we will use method #1 and make the equations identical by multiplying by a coefficient.

$$4\left(\frac{1}{4}x + \frac{3}{4}y = \frac{11}{2}\right)$$
$$x + ay = 22$$

$$x + 3y = 22$$
$$x + ay = 22$$

$$ay = 3y$$
$$a = 3$$

The answer is 3.

Example 5: The system of equations below has an infinite number of solutions. What is the value of $\frac{a}{b}$?

$$ax + by = 42$$
$$5x + 13y = 14$$

Solution: For this question, we can use method #2 to quickly solve for the answer using ratios. Since the system of equations has an infinite number of solutions, the equations must be identical. As a result, we can solve in one step:

$$\frac{a}{b} = \frac{5}{13}$$

The answer is $\frac{5}{13}$.

For infinite solutions, the ratio of the coefficients for the x and y terms must be the same. This is a great example of an SAT question that appears very difficult until you know the shortcut to solve.

Systems of Equations with Infinite Solutions or No Solution Practice: A calculator may NOT be used on the following questions. Answers on page 252.

1. In the system of equations below, b is a constant. If the system has no solution, what is the value of b?

$$5x - 4y = 12$$
$$bx - 12y = 12$$

A) -15
B) -5
C) 5
D) 15

2. In the system of equations below, a is a constant. If the system has no solution, what is the value of a?

$$3x + 4y = 7$$
$$5x + ay = 14$$

A) -4
B) 4
C) $\frac{20}{3}$
D) 8

3. Which of the following systems of equations has infinitely many solutions?

   A) $2x + 5y = 12$
      $2x - 5y = 12$
   B) $2x - 5y = 12$
      $4x + 10y = -24$
   C) $2x + 5y = 12$
      $-6x + 15y = 36$
   D) $2x + 5y = 12$
      $-4x - 10y = -24$

4. In the system of equations below, a and b are constants. If the system has no solution, what is the value of $\frac{a}{b}$?

   $$ax + by = 8$$
   $$6x + 3y = 12$$

   A) $\frac{1}{2}$
   B) 2
   C) 3
   D) 6

   $\frac{a}{b} = \frac{6}{3}^2 = 2$

5. In the system of equations below, a is a constant. If the system of equation has no solution, what is the value of a?

   $$4x + 8y = 15$$
   $$ax + 6y = 14$$

   A) 3
   B) 4
   C) $\frac{16}{3}$
   D) 8

   $\frac{b}{8} = \frac{a}{4}$ $a = 3$

6. In the system of equations below, b is a constant. If the system has infinite solutions, what is the value of b?

   $$3x - 6y = b$$
   $$5x - 10y = 50$$

   A) $\frac{5}{3}$
   B) 6
   C) 18
   D) 30

   $\frac{3}{5} = \frac{b}{50}$ $b = 30$

7. In the system of equations below, a and b are constants. If this system has infinitely many solutions, what is the value of $\frac{a}{b}$?

   $$4y = ax + 12$$
   $$cy = bx + 6$$

8. In the system of equations below, g and k are constants. If the system has no solution, which statement must be true?

   $$y = 4x + 5k$$
   $$gx + 5y = 20$$

   A) $g = -4, k = 4$
   B) $g = -4, k \neq 4$
   C) $g = -20, k = \frac{4}{5}$
   D) $g = -20, k \neq \frac{4}{5}$

9. In the systems of equations below a and b are constants. If the system of equations has infinite solutions, what is the value of $a + b$?

   $$4x - ay = 20$$
   $$-bx + 3y = 30$$

   A) -8
   B) -4
   C) 4
   D) 8

10. In the system of equations below, g, k, and z are constants. If the system has infinite solutions, which statement must be true?

    $$y = 2x + k$$
    $$gx + 9y = z$$

    A) $g = 18, \frac{z}{9} = k$
    B) $g = -18, \frac{z}{9} = k$
    C) $g = 2, \frac{k}{9} = z$
    D) $g = -2, \frac{k}{9} = 2$

    $y = 2x + k$ $y = -\frac{gx}{9} + \frac{z}{9}$

Chapter 14: Solving for Constants

On the SAT, you need to know how to solve for constants that appear in various forms of linear, quadratic, or other polynomial equations. There will be three forms of these questions: solving for constants in equivalent equations, solving for constants in equations with no solutions, and solving for constants in equations with infinite solutions.

Solving for Constants in Equivalent Equations

The SAT will ask you to find the value(s) of constant(s) in equivalent forms of the same equation. These questions are easy to spot because you will see an equal sign between the two forms of the equation.

Let's start with an easy example to understand the concept.

Example 1: $$2ax + 10 = 14x + 10$$

For the equation above, a is a constant. What is the value of a?

    A) 28   B) 14   C) 7   D) 2

Solution: For the equations to be equal, both sides must be identical. Since both sides already have numbers $(+10)$ that are the same, we need to make the x-terms equal.

$$2ax = 14x$$
$$ax = 7x$$

So we can see that

$$a = 7$$

The answer is C.

Example 2: $$(px - 5)(7x + 1) = 14x^2 - 33x - 5$$

For the equation above, p is a constant. What is the value of p?

    A) 1   B) 2   C) 3   D) 4

Solution: Using our rules for multiplying polynomials (FOIL), we know that we multiply the first 2 terms "px" and "$7x$" in the binomials to get first term $14x^2$, so

$$(px)(7x) = 14x^2$$

We can see that

$$p = 2$$

The answer is B.

Example 3: $$x^4 - 4x(ax^3 + 3) = 13x^4 - 12x$$

For the equation above, a is a constant. What is the value of a?

    A) −3   B) −2   C) 1   D) 2

Solution: This question is a bit more difficult than the first two we have seen so far. As with before, it is critical to remember that both sides need to be equal. We can start by distributing the $4x$, so the equation looks like this:

$$x^4 - 4ax^4 - 12x = 13x^4 - 12x$$

The x-terms are already equal on both sides since both sides of the equation have $-12x$, so we just need to make the x^4 terms equal to solve.

$$x^4 - 4ax^4 = 13x^4$$

Combining like terms we get

$$-4ax^4 = 12x^4$$

$$a = -3$$

The answer is A.

Example 4: $\qquad\qquad \frac{1}{4}(mx + 38) + 2x = \frac{23}{4}x + \frac{19}{2}$

For the equation above, m is a constant. What is the value of m?

    A) 21   B) 15   C) 13   D) 9

Solution: As in the last example, we need to make sure both sides are identical. We can start by distributing the $\frac{1}{4}$ to get

$$\frac{1}{4}mx + \frac{19}{2} + 2x = \frac{23}{4}x + \frac{19}{2}$$

The numbers are already equal on both sides, so we just need to make the x-terms equal to solve.

$$\frac{1}{4}mx + 2x = \frac{23}{4}x$$

To get rid of the fractions, multiply both sides by 4 to get

$$mx + 8x = 23x$$

$$mx = 15x$$

$$m = 15$$

The answer is B.

Solving for Constants in Equivalent Equations with Multiple Unknowns

Solving for constants questions can include multiple unknowns in the same equation. While these questions may look more difficult, we will solve them the same way. The key is to identify the terms that each unknown constant value is involved in and make sure these terms are identical on both sides of the equation.

Example 5: $\qquad\qquad ax - 5(x + 7) = 13x + b + 3$

For the equation above, a and b are constants. What is the value of $a + b$?

    A) -56 B) -20 C) 20   D) 56

Solution: To solve this question, we need to first multiply out the left side of the equation.

$$ax - 5x - 35 = 13x + b + 3$$

Now, we can use the fact that the x-terms and numbers on each side of the equation must be equal to solve for the values of a and b.

$$\text{To solve for } a: \qquad\qquad\qquad \text{To solve for } b:$$

$$ax - 5x = 13x \qquad\qquad\qquad -35 = b + 3$$

$$ax = 18x \qquad\qquad\qquad -38 = b$$

$$a = 18$$

So $a + b = 18 + (-38) = -20$. **The answer is B.**

The SAT can also present questions with multiple unknown variables in a question with multiplying polynomials. To solve these questions, we need to identify how the factored binomials multiply to become the expanded equation.

Example 6: $\qquad\qquad (bx - 6)(3x + 3) = 12x^2 - cx - 18$

For the equation above, what is the value of bc?

Solution: To solve this question, we begin with solving for b. Using our rules for multiplying binomials, we know that

$$(bx)(3x) = 12x^2$$

Here, we find that $b = 4$. Once we know the value of b, our equation looks like this

$$(4x - 6)(3x + 3) = 12x^2 - cx - 18$$

Now this looks just like the questions with one unknown. We need to multiply out the left side of the equation to solve for c.

$$12x^2 + 12x - 18x - 18 = 12x^2 - cx - 18$$

$$12x^2 - 6x - 18 = 12x^2 - cx - 18$$

For these equations to be equal, $c = 6$. We now know that

$$bc = (4)(6) = 24$$

The answer is 24.

Solving for Constants with No Solution

The SAT also includes questions with constants in equations that have no solution. **For an equation to have no solution, the equation must have the same coefficients for the variables on both sides and the numbers must be different.** Some examples of equations with no solution are below:

$$6x - 12 = 6x + 1 \qquad\qquad 7x^2 = 7x^2 + 10 \qquad\qquad x - 5 = x + 5$$

Notice that the terms with variables (the terms with x or x^2 in the above examples) are equal but the numbers are not. Anytime an equation looks like this, there is no solution.

The trick to solving constants with no solutions questions is to make the values of terms with the variable equal.

Example 7:
$$a(3x + 6) = 12x - 2$$

For the equation above, the value of a is constant. If the equation has no real solution, what is the value of a?

    A) 12   B) 4   C) 0   D) −4

Solution: To solve, we first distribute the 3 on the left side of the equation to get

$$3ax + 6a = 12x - 2$$

Now, we need to make the x-terms equal on both sides to have no solution.

$$3ax = 12x$$
$$3a = 12$$
$$a = 4$$

The answer is B.

Example 8:
$$4x^2 + 2(ax^2 - b) = 20x^2 - 17$$

In the equation above, a and b are constants and $b \neq 8.5$. If the equation has no real solution, what is the value of a?

    A) 2   B) 4   C) 6   D) 8

Solution: To start, we can distribute the 2 to get

$$4x^2 + 2ax^2 - 2b = 20x^2 - 17$$

For no real solution, we need the x^2 terms to be equal on both sides of the equation, so

$$4x^2 + 2ax^2 = 20x^2$$
$$2ax^2 = 16x^2$$
$$2a = 16$$
$$a = 8$$

The answer is D.

As we see in both of these examples, if you remember that the terms with variables need to be equal for no solution, these questions only require simple algebra to solve.

Solving for Constants with Infinite Solutions

The SAT includes questions about constants in equations that have infinite solutions. **For an equation to have infinite solutions, both sides of the equation must be identical.** Some examples of equations with infinite solutions are below:

$$6x - 12 = 6x - 12 \qquad 7x^2 = 7x^2 \qquad x^3 - 4x + 5 = x^3 - 4x + 5$$

For infinite solutions, both the terms with variables (the terms with x, x^2, and x^3 in the examples above) and the numbers must be equal. Anytime an equation looks like these, there are infinite solutions.

The trick to solving constants with infinite solutions questions is simple: make the values of all terms identical on both sides of the equation.

Example 9: $$19x - 5x(a + 3) = -11x$$

For the equation above, a is a constant. What value of a makes the equation have infinite solutions?

   A) 3   B) 2   C) 1   D) −1

Solution: We start by distributing the $5x$ to get

$$19x - 5ax - 15x = -11x$$

Then, by combining the x-terms we get

$$4x - 5ax = -11x$$
$$-5ax = -15x$$

To have infinite solutions, we need to solve for the value of a that makes both sides equal. So

$$-5ax = -15x$$
$$-5a = -15$$
$$a = 3$$

The answer is A.

Example 10: $$4(ax + b) - 13x = 15x - 36$$

For the equation above, a and b are constants. If the equation has infinite solutions, what is the value of $b - a$?

   A) −16   B) −2   C) 2   D) 16

Solution: To start, let's distribute the 4 to get

$$4ax + 4b - 13x = 15x - 36$$

We need to solve for two unknowns. The a is involved in the x-terms, and the b is involved with the numbers. Since we are told this equation has infinite solutions, we need to make sure that the x-terms and numbers are identical on both sides of the equation. Let's start by focusing on the x-terms and solving for a.

$$4ax - 13x = 15x$$
$$4ax = 28x$$
$$4a = 28$$
$$a = 7$$

We have solved for a. Next, we can solve for b by making the numbers equal on both sides.

$$4b = -36$$
$$b = -9$$

Now, we can finish the question.

$$b - a = (-9) - 7$$
$$b - a = -16$$

The answer is A.

Not too bad, right? The key to solving constants with infinite solutions questions is to remember that both sides need to be identical. If you remember that, you will be able to solve these questions quickly and easily on test day.

Solving for Constants Practice: A calculator may NOT be used on the following questions. Answers on page 252.

1. In the equation below, $a, b,$ and c are constants. If the equation is true for all values of x, what is the value of $a - b + c$?

$$x(2x - 2) - 2(-x - 4) = ax^2 + bx + c$$

$2x^2 - 2x + 2x + 8 = ax^2 + bx + c$

A) 2
B) 4
C) 8
D) 10

$a - b + c$

$2 - 0 + 8$

5. $$(3x - b)(x + 2) = 3x^2 + 4x - 4$$

For the equation above, b is a constant. If the equation has infinite solutions, what is the value of b?

A) -2
B) -1
C) 1
D) 2

2. The equation below has no solution, and a is a constant. What is the value of a?

$$8x + 6 = a(-3x + 2) - x$$

A) -3
B) $-\frac{8}{3}$
C) 0
D) 3

6. In the function below, a is a constant. If -5 is a zero of the function, which of the following is a possible value of a?

$$F(x) = x^2 - ax + 15$$

A) -3
B) -5
C) 8
D) -8

$F(-5) = 0$

$0 = (-5)^2 - a(-5) + 15$

$0 = 25 + 5a + 15$

$-40 = 5a$ $\boxed{-8 = a}$

3. In the equation below, a and b are constants. If the equation has infinite solutions, what is the value of $a + b$?

$$ax + 3(3x - 2) = 5x + b$$

A) -4
B) -6
C) -10
D) 5

7. $$(ax - 6)(bx + 3) = -2.75x^2 - 14.25x - 18$$

For the equation above, a and b are constants. What is the value of ab?

A) -2.75
B) 2.75
C) 14.25
D) 18

4. $$6(2x - 17) = a(5x + 1)$$

In the equation above, a and b are constants. If there is no real solution to the equation, what is the value of a?

A) 1.25
B) 2.4
C) 3.75
D) 5

8. $$ax^2 + 4(3x^2 + 2b) = 15x^2 + 24$$

In the equation above, a and b are constants. If the equation has no real solution, what is the value of a?

A) 2
B) 3
C) 5
D) 12

9. $-7x^4 + 4x(ax^3 + b) = 13x^4 + 24x$

For the equation above, a and b are constants. What is the value of $a + b$?

A) 11
B) 6
C) 5
D) 1

10. In the equation below, a is a constant. For which of the following values of a does the equation have no real solution?

$$3x^2 + 12 = 6 + ax^2$$

A) -3
B) -1
C) 0
D) 3

11. The expression below can be rewritten in the form $\frac{1}{3}(a - b)(a + b)$, where b is a positive constant. What is the value of b?

$$\frac{1}{3}a^2 - 5$$

A) $\frac{5}{3}$
B) $\sqrt{5}$
C) $\sqrt{15}$
D) 5

12. In the equation below, a and b are constants. If the equation is true for all values of x, what is the value of ab?

$$(x^3 + ax^2 + 5ax - 4) + (2x^3 + bx^2 - bx - 3) = 3x^3 + 8x^2 + 10x - 7$$

A) -2
B) 3
C) 5
D) 15

(handwritten work)
$3x^3 + ax^2 + bx^2 + 5ax - bx - 7 = 3x^3 + 8x^2 + 10x - 7$
$ax^2 + bx^2 = 8x^2$
$a + b = 8$
$3 + b = 8$
$b = 5$
$5ax - bx = 10x$
$5a - b = 10$
ab $(3)(5) = 15$

(left margin handwritten)
$a + b = 8$
$5a - b = 10$
$6a = 18$
$a = 3$

Solving for Constants Practice: A calculator may be used on the following questions.

13. In the equation below, a is a constant. If the equation has infinite solutions, what is the value of a?

$$23x - 5x(a + 2) = 4x$$

A) $-\frac{17}{5}$
B) $-\frac{9}{5}$
C) $\frac{9}{5}$
D) $\frac{17}{5}$

14. $\qquad 5x - 3(ax + b) = -31x + 30$

For the equation above, a and b are constants. If the equation has infinite real solutions, what is the value of $b - a$?

A) -22
B) -2
C) 2
D) 22

15. In the equation below, a is a constant. If $x = 5$ is a solution to the equation, what is the value of a?

$$ax^2 + 5x = 115 - 5a$$

16. In the equation below, a is a constant. If no value of x satisfies the equation, what is the value of a?

$$\frac{1}{3}ax - 12 = 3(x + 4) - 3(1 - 3x)$$

A) 4
B) 8
C) 12
D) 36

$$\frac{1}{3}ax - 12 = 3x + 12 - 3 + 9x$$

$$\frac{1}{3}ax - 12 = 12x + 9$$

$$\frac{1}{3}ax = 12x$$

$$a = 36$$

Chapter 15: Functions

A function is defined as a mathematical relationship between a variable x and the function $f(x)$. For every value of x, there is exactly one value of $f(x)$. For any function, there will be an input x, which appears as the term in the parentheses of a function, and an output, which will be the value that $f(x)$ equals.

For basic functions questions, you need to know where to properly plug in the input to a function. For the function

$$f(x) = 5x - 2$$

you plug in the input for x. You are likely used to the input being a number, but the input can include variables as well. No matter what the input, just plug it in for the x in the equation:

$$f(3) = 5(3) - 2 = 13$$

$$f(-2x) = 5(-2x) - 2 = -10x - 2$$

$$f(a - 11) = 5(a - 11) - 2 = 5a - 57$$

Example 1: If $f(x) = 3\sqrt{x} + 11$, what is the value for $f(25)$?

Solution: To solve, plug in the input to the function.

$$f(25) = 3\sqrt{25} + 11 = 3(5) + 11 = 15 + 11 = 26$$

The answer is 26.

Example 2: If $f(x) = \frac{10x}{x+4}$, for what value of x does $f(x) = 5$?

Solution: If you are given the output, which is 5 in this question, and need to find the input, plug in the output for $f(x)$ and solve for the input x.

$$5 = \frac{10x}{x + 4}$$

$$5(x + 4) = 10x$$

$$5x + 20 = 10x$$

$$20 = 5x$$

$$4 = x$$

The answer is 4.

Example 3: If $f(x) = 3x + 10$ and $g(x) = x - 5$, what is the value of $f(g(8))$?

Solution: The SAT will ask you to work with composite functions. If you are given these functions, work from the inside out. For composite functions, there are two methods to solve: (1) solve for the composite function or (2) work inside out. Both methods are shown below.

Method #1 - Solve for the composite function: We want to solve for the function $f(g(x))$. To do so, we plug the entire $g(x)$ function in for the x in the $f(x)$ function.

$$f\big(g(x)\big) = 3(x - 5) + 10 = 3x - 15 + 10 = 3x - 5$$

Now that we know the composite function, we can plug in 8 for x and solve.

$$f\big(g(8)\big) = 3(8) - 5 = 24 - 5 = 19$$

The answer is 19.

Method #2 - Work inside out: Rather than solve for the composite function, we can also work from the inside out to solve for $f(g(8))$. To start, we can solve for $g(8)$.

$$g(8) = 8 - 5 = 3$$

We now know that $g(8) = 3$, so we can simplify the function we are solving for.

$$f\big(g(8)\big) = f(3)$$

Now, we solve for $f(3)$.

$$f(3) = 3(3) + 10 = 19$$

The answer is 19.

Example 4: If $f(x) = 2x^2 - 7$ and $g(x) = x + 3$, what is $f(g(x - 1))$?

   A) $2x^2 + 2$ B) $2x^2 + 8x + 1$ C) $2x^2 + 12x + 11$ D) $2x^2 - 3$

Solution: This question looks more difficult since we now have $x - 1$ as the input, but you should still treat this as a composite function. Both of the methods outlined in Example 3 work to solve. Below, we will use the inside out method. First, we solve for $g(x - 1)$:

$$g(x - 1) = (x - 1) + 3 = x + 2$$

We now know that $g(x - 1) = x + 2$, so we can simplify the function that we are solving for.

$$f\big(g(x - 1)\big) = f(x + 2)$$

Now, solve for $f(x + 2)$

$$f(x + 2) = 2(x + 2)^2 - 7 = 2(x^2 + 4x + 4) - 7 = 2x^2 + 8x + 8 - 7 = 2x^2 + 8x + 1$$
$$f\big(g(x - 1)\big) = 2x^2 + 8x + 1$$

The answer is B.

**Common Mistake to Avoid: Remember that $(x + 2)^2 \neq x^2 + 4$. You need to multiply out the terms because $(x + 2)^2$ is the same as $(x + 2)(x + 2)$.

Example 5:

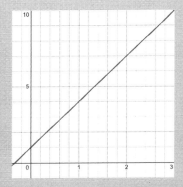

The function $f(x)$ is graphed above. A second function g, not shown, is modeled by the equation $g(x) = (x - 1)^2 + 3$. If $f(a) = 7$, what is the value of $g(a)$?

Solution: **When a function is graphed, the input, x, is on the x-axis and the output, $f(x)$, is on the y-axis.** Another way to better understand how functions appear on a graph is to remember that for any function

$$f(x) = mx + b \quad \text{is the same as} \quad y = mx + b$$

Now let's apply this principle to Example 5. We are told that $f(a) = 7$. To find the value of a, we need to find what value of x makes $f(x) = 7$. On the graph, we want to find where on the graph $y = 7$, which is at the point $(2, 7)$. The point $(2, 7)$ shows that $f(2) = 7$ so $a = 2$.

Now that we know the value of a, we can solve for $g(a)$:

$$g(a) = g(2) = (2 - 1)^2 + 3 = 4$$

The answer is 4.

Example 6: Given the function $f(x) = \frac{10x-7}{2}$, what is the value for $f^{-1}(6.5)$?

Solution: To find the inverse of a function, switch the input x and the output $f(x)$. Most students find it easiest to start by replacing $f(x)$ with y, so our function becomes

$$y = \frac{10x-7}{2}$$

To find the inverse function, switch the x and y and then solve for y.

$$x = \frac{10y-7}{2}$$

$$2x = 10y - 7$$

$$2x + 7 = 10y$$

$$\frac{2x+7}{10} = y$$

Once we have solved for y, we have found the inverse function.

$$f^{-1}(x) = \frac{2x+7}{10}$$

Now that we know the inverse, we can find $f^{-1}(6.5)$ by plugging in 6.5

$$f^{-1}(6.5) = \frac{2(6.5)+7}{10} = \frac{20}{10} = 2$$

$$f^{-1}(6.5) = 2$$

The answer is 2.

Functions Practice: A calculator may NOT be used on the following questions. Answers on page 253.

For questions 1-15, use the functions below.

$$f(x) = 2x^2 - 7$$
$$g(x) = -3x + 10$$
$$h(x) = x - 3$$

1. What is the value of $f(4)$?

2. What is the value of $g(-31)$?

3. What is the value of $f(-10)$?

4. What is the value of $h(-19)$?

5. What is the value of $f(3x)$?

6. What is the value of $g(x-3)$?

7. For what value of x does $h(x) = -5$?

8. For what value of x does $g(x) = 31$?

9. For what value of x does $f(x) = 43$?

10. For what value of x does $g(x) = -11$?

11. What is the value of $g(h(-11))$?

12. What is the value of $f(h(2x))$?

13. What is the value of $f(h(-4))$?

14. For what value of x does $g(h(x)) = 18$?

15. What is the value of $g(f(3x))$?

16. The function f is defined as $f(x) = x^2 - 4x$. What is the value of $f(2)$?

    A) -12
    B) -4
    C) 0
    D) 12

17. For functions f and g defined by $f(x) = 2x^2 + x$ and $g(x) = 2x - 1$, what is the value of $g(f(2))$?

    A) 10
    B) 15
    C) 19
    D) 22

18. For the function $f(x) = \frac{x+1}{3}$, what is the value of $f^{-1}(x)$?

    $y = \frac{x+1}{3}$

    A) $\frac{3x-1}{3}$
    B) $3x - 1$ $x = \frac{y+1}{3}$
    C) $\frac{x+1}{3}$ $3x = y+1$
    D) $\frac{-x-1}{-3}$ $3x-1 = y$

19. The function $f(x) = 3x + 7$ and the function $g(x) = 2x - 3$. What is the value of $f(g(5))$?

    A) 11
    B) 22
    C) 28
    D) 41

20. $(x+12)(x-2)$
    $$f(x) = x^2 + 10x - 24$$
    $$g(x) = x^2 - 4$$

    Which of the following expressions is equivalent to $\frac{f(x)}{g(x)}$ for $x > 2$?

    A) $\frac{x+12}{x+2}$ $\frac{(x+12)(x-2)}{(x-2)(x+2)} = \frac{x+12}{x+2}$
    B) $\frac{1}{x-2}$
    C) $\frac{x+12}{x-2}$
    D) $\frac{x(x+2)}{x-2}$

21.
$$f(x) = -5x + 2$$
$$g(x) = 10 - f(x)$$

The functions f and g are defined above. What is the value of $g(3)$?

A) -13
B) -3
C) 7
D) 23

22. If $h(x) = 4x - 7$, what is the value of $h(-2x)$ equal to?

A) $-8x - 7$
B) $8x - 14$
C) $8x - 7$
D) $-8x + 7$

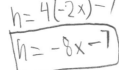

$h = 4(-2x) - 7$

$h = -8x - 7$

23.

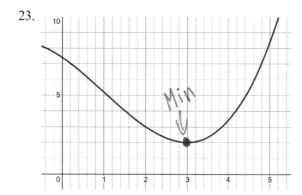

Min

The graph of the function f is shown above. The function f has a <u>minimum</u> value when $x = k$. If $g(x) = 2x - 7$, what is the value of $g(k)$?

$g(3) = -1$

A) -3
B) -1
C) 3
D) 7

24. A function g satisfies $g(5) = 11$ and $g(6) = 8$. A function h satisfies $h(8) = -3$ and $h(6) = 5$. What is the value of $g(h(6))$?

A) -3
B) 5
C) 8
D) 11

25.

x	$t(x)$	$p(x)$
1	-3	4
2	0	3
3	2	-1
4	9	-7

The table above shows some values for the functions t and p. For what value of x does $t(x) + p(x) = 2$?

A) 1
B) 2
C) 3
D) 4

$t(x) + p(x) = 2$

$9 - 7 = 2$

26.
$$p(x) = x^2 + 2x - b$$

For the function p defined above, b is a constant and $p(2) = 5$. What is the value of $p(-3)$?

A) -18
B) 0
C) 5
D) 12

Functions Practice: A calculator may be used on the following questions.

27. What is the value of $f(-3)$ given $f(x) = 3x^2 + 3x + 10$?

A) -46
B) -26
C) 28
D) 36

28. The function f is defined as $f(x) = -6x^3 + 2x^2$. What is $f(-3)$?

A) -180
B) -144
C) 144
D) 180

29.

x	$g(x)$
2	11
4	23
6	35

Some values of a linear function g are shown above. Which of the following defines $g(x)$?

A) $g(x) = 4x + 3$
B) $g(x) = 6x - 1$
C) $g(x) = 4x + 7$
D) $g(x) = 5x + 5$

30. The domain of $f(x) = \dfrac{5}{x^3 - 16x}$ is the set of all real numbers except?

A) $\dfrac{5}{16}$
B) -4 and 4
C) 0 and -4
D) 4, 0, and -4

31. A function is defined as $f(z) = 3z - 13$, and its domain is the set of integers from $1 - 20$ inclusive. For how many values of z is $f(z)$ negative?

A) 0
B) 4
C) 5
D) 12

32. If $f(x) = x + \dfrac{1}{2x}$ and $g(x) = \dfrac{1}{x}$ what is the value of $f(g(\frac{1}{4}))$?

A) -6
B) -4
C) 4
D) $4\frac{1}{8}$

$f(g(\frac{1}{4})) = \dfrac{1}{\frac{1}{4}} + \dfrac{1}{2(\frac{1}{4})} = \dfrac{33}{8}$

$32 \quad 4\frac{1}{8}$

33.

x	$k(x)$
-2	10
1	19
7	37

Some values of the linear function k are shown in the table above. What is the value of $k(4)$?

A) 22
B) 25
C) 27
D) 28

34. $f(x) = 2ax^2 - 5x - 4$

In the xy-plane, the point $(3, 17)$ lies on the graph of the function $f(x)$. What is the value of a?

A) 2
B) 4
C) 9
D) 36

35.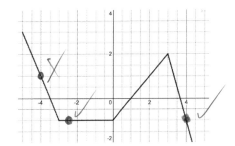

The complete graph of the function f is shown in the xy-plane above. Which of the following are equal to -1?

I. $f(-4)$
II. $f(-\frac{5}{2})$
III. $f(4)$

A) III only
B) II only
C) I and III only
D) II and III only

PrepPros

36. Consider the functions $f(x) = \sqrt{x}$ and $g(x) = 4x + b$. In the standard coordinate plane, the function $y = f(g(x))$ passes through $(5, 4)$. What is the value of b?

A) -4
B) 0
C) 4
D) 16

37. The function f is defined by $f(x) = 3x^2 - 5x + 10$. If the function $f(x - 2)$ is written in the form $ax^2 + bx + c$, what is the value of $a + b + c$?

38.

Graphs of the functions f and g are shown in the xy-plane above. For which value(s) of x does $f(x) = g(x)$?

A) 6
B) 5.5 and 8.5
C) 12
D) 6 and 12

39. The table below shows values of a quadratic function $f(x)$ for specific values of x. Which of the following could define $f(x)$?

x	$f(x)$
1	3
3	-1
5	3

A) $f(x) = (x - 3)^2 - 1$
B) $f(x) = (x - 3)^2 + 1$
C) $f(x) = (x + 3)^2 - 1$
D) $f(x) = (x + 3)^2 + 1$

40. In the xy-plane, the point $(3, 18)$ lies on the graph of the function f. If $f(x) = k - 2x^2$, where k is a constant, what is the value of k?

41. In the xy-plane, the point $(2, 8)$ lies on the graph of the function $f(x) = 2x^3 - tx - 6$. What is the value of t?

42. For all values of x, there is a function g such that $3g(x) = g(5x)$. If $g(20) = 18$, what is the value of $g(4)$?

43. $f(x) = \frac{(x-2)^4 - 3}{(x-3)^2 - 4(x-2) + 8}$

For what value x is the function above undefined?

Chapter 16: Mean, Median, Mode, and Range

To start, let's review the basic definitions of mean, median, mode, and range:

Mean (average): The sum divided by the number of items.

Median: The middle number in a list of numbers when ordered from smallest to largest.

Mode: The number that appears most often.

Range: The difference between the smallest and the largest numbers.

On the SAT, you are most commonly asked to solve average questions. For these questions, remember that:

$$Average = \frac{Sum}{Number\ of\ Items}$$

Example 1: The five students who sit in the front row of Ms. Rashard's class averaged 24 points on last Friday's quiz. If the first four students received scores of 22, 28, 17, and 25, what was the score of the fifth student?

Solution: Let's call the unknown student's score x and set up the question using the average equation.

$$24 = \frac{22+28+17+25+x}{5}$$

$$24 = \frac{92+x}{5}$$

$$120 = 92 + x$$

$$x = 28$$

The answer is 28.

Example 2: The highest possible score on the biology final is 100 points. The first period class of 6 students has an average score of 85. The second period class of 9 students has an average score of 90. What is the average score for all of the students combined?

Solution: To solve this question, we need to find out the total number of points scored by all students from both classes and then divide by the total number of students (15).

In the equations below, x represents the sum of the test scores for students in the 1st period class and y represents the sum of the test scores for students in the 2nd period class. To start, we can find the total number of points that all students in the 1st period class received.

$$85 = \frac{x}{6}$$

$$x = 510$$

The first period students received a total of 510 points. Even though we do not know each student's test score, we know the total. We can repeat this same calculation for the 2nd period class.

$$90 = \frac{y}{9}$$

$$y = 810$$

The second period class received a total of 810 points. Now, we can solve for the average score for all students combined.

$$Average\ Score = \frac{Total\ Points}{Total\ Students} = \frac{510+810}{15} = \frac{1320}{15} = 88$$

The answer is 88.

Example 3: Erica's golden retriever gave birth twice in the last two years. Her first litter had 7 puppies with an average weight of p lbs. Her second litter had 5 puppies with an average weight of m pounds. Which of the following expressions correctly calculates the average weight w, in pounds, of all of the puppies that Erica's golden retriever gave birth to over the last two years?

A) $w = \frac{p+m}{12}$ B) $w = \frac{p}{7} + \frac{m}{5}$ C) $w = \frac{7p+5m}{12}$ D) $w = \frac{7m+5p}{12}$

Solution: Method 1 – "Math Teacher Way": To find the average puppy weight, we need to find the total weight of all the puppies and divide it by the total number of puppies. First, we can find the total weight of her first litter:

$$p = \frac{sum}{7}$$

$$7p = total\ weight\ of\ puppies\ in\ 1st\ litter$$

We can repeat this to find the total weight of the second litter:

$$m = \frac{sum}{5}$$

$$5m = total\ weight\ of\ puppies\ in\ 2nd\ litter$$

We know that there are 12 puppies total, so now we can calculate the average weight.

$$w = \frac{7p+5m}{12}$$

The answer is C.

Method 2 – Pick Numbers. For many students, this question is difficult because we are not given any values for the average weights of the litters. To make this question easier, we can use substitution and pick numbers. Let's say the first litter has an average weight of 1 pound ($p = 1$) and the second litter has an average weight of 3 pounds ($m = 3$). We can use our numbers to solve for the average weight of the puppies in both litters.

$$Total\ Weight\ of\ 1st\ Litter = 7 \times 1 = 7$$

The first litter had 7 puppies with an average weight of 1 pound, so the total weight of the litter is 7 pounds.

$$Total\ Weight\ of\ 2nd\ Litter = 5 \times 3 = 15$$

The second litter had 5 puppies with an average weight of 3 pounds, so the total weight is 15 pounds. Now, we can find the average weight of each puppy from these two litters.

$$w = \frac{7+15}{12} = \frac{22}{12} = \frac{11}{6}$$

With the values $p = 1$ and $m = 3$, we found that $w = \frac{11}{6}$. To find the correct answer choice, plug in $p = 1$ and $m = 3$ to the answer choices and see which one gives us $w = \frac{11}{6}$. Below, you can see how the correct answer choice C gives us the correct value for w.

$$w = \frac{7(1)+5(3)}{12} = \frac{22}{12} = \frac{11}{6}$$

The answer is C.

Example 4: The mean household income in a neighborhood with 80 residents is $90,250 per year. If a new family moves in with a household income of $1,859,000, which of the following values for the neighborhood will change the least?

    A) Mean   B) Median   C) Range   D) Standard Deviation

Solution: The new family has a much higher household income than the mean household income for the rest of the neighborhood. In statistics, we call values that are far higher or lower than any other numbers in the data set outliers. **Any outlier will greatly increase the range.** The new family's income is also so large that it will increase the mean household income for the neighborhood. The standard deviation, which is a measure of how close or far apart numbers in a data set are from the average, will also increase from an outlier. We have not learned about standard deviation yet in this book, but we will cover it in chapter 24 on statistics.

The median will change the least. Since the median is the middle value in a data set, **any outlier always has a minimal effect on the median.**

The answer is B.

Example 5: For her science fair experiment, Monica wanted to find out whether her tree frog or bullfrog jumps farther. She placed each frog on a starting spot and then measured how far the frogs jumped, in inches. The results for each frog, in inches, are below:

Tree Frog: 41, 18, 30, 8, 14, 33
Bullfrog: 38, 19, 66, 48, 45, 33, 10

If f is the median jump length for the tree frog and h is the median jump length for the bullfrog, what is the value of $h - f$?

Solution: To start, we need to reorder the numbers in each data from smallest to largest.

Tree Frog: 8, 14, 18, 30, 33, 41
Bullfrog: 10, 19, 33, 38, 45, 48, 66

Next, we cross out numbers from both sides to find the median. For data sets with an odd number of numbers, such as the bullfrog data in this question, the median is just the middle value. For data sets with an even number of numbers, such as the tree frog data in this question, we need to take the average of the two middle numbers to find the median.

Tree Frog: ~~8~~, ~~14~~, 18, 30, ~~33~~, ~~41~~   Bullfrog: ~~10~~, ~~19~~, ~~33~~, 38, ~~45~~, ~~48~~, ~~66~~

Tree Frog median $= f = \dfrac{18+30}{2} = 24$ Bullfrog median $= h = 38$

$$h - f = 38 - 24 = 14$$

The answer is 14.

Finding the Median in a Table

The SAT will also ask you to find the median value in a frequency table. For these questions, we need to use a more efficient method than listing all of the values and crossing off to find the median value.

Example 6: The school newspaper recently surveyed 51 students about their monthly consumption of cheeseburgers. The results of the survey are summarized in the table below. What was the median number of cheeseburgers eaten each month by the students in the survey?

Number of Burgers Eaten	Number of Students
0	7
1	19
2 - 3	8
4 - 5	13
6 +	4

A) 0   B) 1   C) 2 - 3   D) 4 - 5

Solution: The trick to solving this question is to identify what term represents the median in the data set. To find the median term in a table, there are three quick steps:

1. Add 1 to the total number of items in the data set.

2. Divide that number by 2.

   - If you have a data set with an odd number of items, the number you get will be the term that it is the median. For example, if we have a group of 31, we will get 16 in step 2. This tell us that the 16th term is the median.

   - If you have a data set with an even number of items, you will get an answer that ends in 0.5. In this case, the median will be the average of the two middle terms. The two middle terms will be the integers right above and below the value that we get from our first two steps. For example, if we have a group of 20, we will get 10.5 in step 2. This tell us that two middle terms will be the 10th and 11th terms. We find the median by finding the average of the 10th and 11th terms.

3. Find where the term is in the table.

In this question, we have 51 students who were surveyed, so following Step 1 above

$$\frac{51+1}{2} = 26$$

we find the 26th student will be the median data point in the set. To find where the 26th student is in the table, start at the top of the table and add up the students until you find the 26th student. Here, there are 7 students who ate 0 burgers and 19 who ate 1 burger. If we add 7 and 19 together, we get 26, so we can tell that the 26th student ate 1 burger. The median is 1, and **the answer is B**.

Mean, Median, Mode and Range Practice: A calculator may **NOT** be used on the following questions.
Answers on page 255.

1. If James scored 10 touchdowns in the first 7 games of the year, how many touchdowns does he need to score in the 8th game to average 2 touchdowns per game?

   A) 6
   B) 8
   C) 10
   D) 16

2. If $a < b < c < d < e$, which of the following cannot affect the median of the set of numbers?

   A) Increasing the value of a
   B) Decreasing the value of e
   C) Increasing the value of b
   D) Decreasing the value of a

3. John and Karen work at the bakery. John works 7 hours per day, and Karen works 6 hours per day. John produces x brownies per hour and Karen produced y brownies per hour. Which of the following expressions gives the average number of brownies John and Karen produce per hour?

   A) $\frac{x+y}{13}$
   B) $\frac{7x+6y}{13}$
   C) $\frac{xy}{13}$
   D) $\frac{6x+7y}{13}$

4. John and Aaron tracked their 400-meter race times, which are listed below in seconds. The median for John's race times is x and the median for Aaron's race times is y. What is the value of $x - y$?

   John: 76, 68, 62, 68, 79, 70
   Aaron: 63, 58, 68, 61, 67, 66

5. A survey was conducted on the value of the cars driven by Orange County residents and found that the mean car value was $65,000 and the median car value was $48,000. Which of the following could explain the difference between the mean and the median car values in Orange County?

   A) Some cars are valued much higher than the rest.
   B) Some cars are valued much lower than the rest.
   C) Many cars have values between $48,000 and $65,000.
   D) The majority of cars have values that are close to each other.

6. A data set of 27 different numbers has a mean of 18 and a median of 18. A new data set is created by adding 20 to all of the values greater than the median while leaving all other numbers in the data set unchanged. Which of the following values will not change?

   A) Mean
   B) Range
   C) Median
   D) Sum of the numbers

7. Harold is writing a book. To finish by his deadline, he needs to write an average of 3,000 words per week for 4 weeks. He wrote 4,500 words in the first week, 2,800 words in the second week, and 2,400 words in the third week. Which inequality represents the number of words, x, Harold needs to write in the 4th week to meet or exceed his goal?

   A) $4{,}500 + 2{,}800 + 2{,}400 + x \geq 4(3{,}000)$
   B) $\frac{4{,}500+2{,}800+2{,}400}{3} + x \geq 3{,}000$
   C) $4{,}500 + 2{,}800 + 2{,}400 \geq x(3{,}000)$
   D) $\frac{4{,}500}{4} + \frac{2{,}800}{4} + \frac{2{,}400}{4} + x \geq 3{,}000$

8. The scores for the 43 students in AP Biology were reported, and the mean, median, range, and standard deviation were found. The teacher made an error in grading, and the student with the highest score actually scored 8 points higher. Which of the following will not change after the student's score is corrected?

A) Range
B) Mean
C) Standard Deviation
D) Median

9. Number of iPhones per Household

iPhones	Frequency
0	6
1	3
2	1
3	5
4	4
5	2

A recent survey asked 21 households how many iPhones they owned. Based on the table above, what was the median number of iPhones?

A) 1
B) 2
C) 3
D) 4

10. If x is equal to $k + 8$ and y is equal to $3k + 12$, which of the following expresses the average of x and y in terms of k?

A) $k + 10$
B) $2k + 10$
C) $4k$
D) $4k + 20$

11. 80 people each bowled one game at a Brick Alley Bowling last Friday. 60 people scored between 50 and 100, 18 people scored score between 101 and 185, and the remaining two players bowled a score between 280 and 300. Which of the following statements about the mean and median of the 80 scores is true?

A) The mean is less than the median.
B) The median is less than the mean.
C) The median and mean are equal.
D) There is not enough information to determine whether the mean or median is greater.

12. Production Run A of axles results in 35 axles with an average weight of a pounds. Production run B of axles results in 15 axles with an average weight of b pounds. Which of the following expressions gives the average weight w of all axles that are produced during two runs of Production run A and one run of Production Run B?

A) $w = \frac{35b + 15a}{50}$
B) $w = \frac{2a + b}{3}$
C) $w = \frac{70a + 15b}{85}$
D) $w = \frac{35a + 15b}{85}$

13. There is a list of 29 numbers, all of which are unique. Which of the following would definitely NOT affect the median?

A) Increasing the largest number in the data set.
B) Increasing all numbers in the data set by 10.
C) Making the smallest value in the data set the largest value in the data set.
D) Increasing the smallest value in the data set by 5.

Mean, Median, Mode, and Range Practice: A calculator may be used on the following questions.

14. If 4 apartments are rented for $280, $360, $240, and $320, what is the mean rent?

    A) $260
    B) $280
    C) $300
    D) $320

15. What is the difference between the mean and the median of the data set $\{4, 7, 8, 9, 12\}$?

    A) 0
    B) 1
    C) 2
    D) 3

16. Ashley wanted to save an average of $20 per week over the past 15 weeks. For the first 5 weeks, she saved an average of $15 per week. For the next 5 weeks, she saved an average of $19 per week. For the last 5 weeks, she saved an average of $23 per week. How much more should she have saved each week to hit her goal?

    A) $0.75
    B) $0.80
    C) $1.00
    D) $1.50

17. The average of 6 numbers is 93. What is the 6th number if the first 5 are 99, 86, 93, 89, 92?

    A) 88
    B) 93
    C) 95
    D) 99

18. The mean score of 10 students on a 36-point test is 23.8 points. If the student with the highest score is removed, the mean score for the other 9 students is 23 points. How many points did the student with the highest score have?

    A) 28
    B) 31
    C) 33
    D) 36

19. As part of a social studies project, Tommy surveyed 50 of his friends about their daily use of Snapchat. The results are shown in the table below.

Number of Snapchats Viewed	Number of Students
0 − 3	4
4 − 6	11
7 − 10	8
11 − 15	9
> 15	18

Which category contains the median number of Snapchats viewed for the survey?

    A) 4 − 6
    B) 7 − 10
    C) 11 − 15
    D) > 15

Questions 20-21 refer to the table below.

Points	Frequency
0	3
10	0
20	1
30	2
50	3
100	1

A student playing Skee-Ball tracked the points he received from each of his 10 throws.

20. What was his total score?

    A) 200
    B) 280
    C) 330
    D) 350

21. What was the median value of the points scored from the 10 throws?

    A) 20
    B) 25
    C) 30
    D) 50

22.

	Masses (g)				
Mike	8.3	7.8	9.2	7.6	8.1
Aaron	5.2	3.5	4.4	3.9	x

Mike and Aaron both conducted a chemistry experiment where they tried to isolate a mystery compound Z. They each ran the experiment 5 times and recorded the mass, in grams, of compound Z that they obtained. The mean of the masses of compound Z that Mike obtained is twice the mean of the masses of compound Z that Aaron obtained. What is the value of x?

23. In order for Mr. Walsh's class to get a pizza party, the class average on the final must be at least 85%. The first fifteen students received an average of 82%. What is the lowest possible score that the 16th student can receive to still allow the class of 20 students to get a pizza party?

Chapter 17: Geometry Part 1 - Angles

In this chapter, we will cover all of the rules that you need to know for angles on the SAT. For angles questions, we recommend finding and labeling any unknown angles. The more angles you label, the easier it will be to find the angle that you need to answer the question.

Intersecting Lines

If two lines intersect, what do we know about the relationships between the angles?

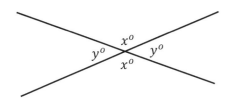

1. **Vertical angles are equal.**

2. **Adjacent angles are supplementary ($\angle x$ and $\angle y$ add to 180°).**

Parallel Lines

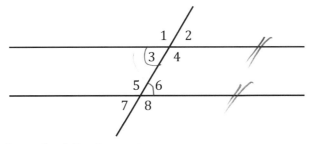

Given two parallel lines, we know the following are true:

1. **Vertical angles are equal (ex: $\angle 1 = \angle 4$).**
2. **Alternate interior angles are equal (ex: $\angle 3 = \angle 6$).**
3. **Opposite interior angles are supplementary (ex: $\angle 3 + \angle 5 = 180°$ and $\angle 4 + \angle 6 = 180°$).**
4. **Corresponding angles are equal (ex: $\angle 2 = \angle 6$).**

All of those rules and fancy terms are nice, but all you really need to know is that one line intersecting two parallel lines creates two sets of identical angles.

$$\angle 1 = \angle 4 = \angle 5 = \angle 8$$

$$\angle 2 = \angle 3 = \angle 6 = \angle 7$$

Any of the angles from the first list will be supplementary with any of the angles from the second list. For example, $\angle 1 + \angle 6 = 180°$ and $\angle 4 + \angle 7 = 180°$. As long as you memorize which angles are identical, you will be able to handle parallel lines questions.

Example 1:

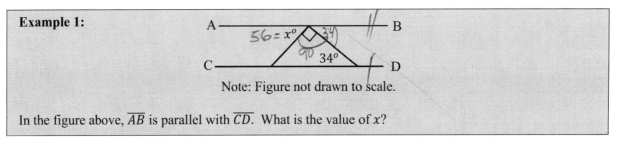

Note: Figure not drawn to scale.

In the figure above, $\overline{AB}$ is parallel with $\overline{CD}$. What is the value of x?

Solution: We know that all angles in a triangle add up to $180°$, so we can find the unknown third angle in the triangle above.

$$Third\ angle = 180^o - 34^o - 90^o = 56^o$$

The third angle and x^o are alternate interior angles, so they must be equal. **The answer is 56.**

TIP – Extend Parallel Lines

Often on the SAT, questions with parallel lines will not always look like the parallel lines in the figure on the previous page (the one with angles 1-8 labelled). If the lines just hit and stop (ex: the corner of a parallelogram), take your pencil and extend the lines yourself. Then, it will be much easier to tell which angles are identical.

Exterior Angle Theorem

The exterior angle of a triangle is the angle outside of the triangle when any side is extended. In the triangle below, a^o is an exterior angle. The exterior angle theorem states:

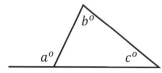

        The exterior angle is equal to the sum of the two opposite interior angles. For the triangle above, $a^o = b^o + c^o$.

Example 2:

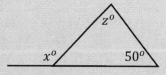

Which of the following equations expresses x in terms of z?

    A) $180 - z$ B) $130 - z$ C) $50 + z$ D) $z - 50$

Solution: By definition, x^o is an exterior angle, so it must be equal to the sum of the two opposite interior angles 50° and z^o. **The answer is C.**

Interior Angles in Polygons

You need to know the sum of the interior angles of a...

Triangle	Quadrilateral	Pentagon	Hexagon
180°	360°	540°	720°

For any polygon,

        Sum of Interior Angles $= 180^o(n - 2)$ where n is the number of sides.

It does not matter what the shape looks like. All that matters for the sum of the interior angles is the number of sides. You can see how this works with the examples below:

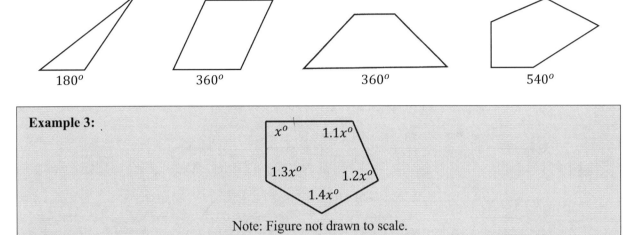

180° 360° 360° 540°

Example 3:

x^o $1.1x^o$

$1.3x^o$ $1.2x^o$

$1.4x^o$

Note: Figure not drawn to scale.

For the figure above, what is the value of x?

Solution: The figure above has 5 sides, so the sum of the interior angles is equal to $180^o(5-2) = 540^o$.

$$x^o + 1.3x^o + 1.4x^o + 1.2x^o + 1.1x^o = 540^o$$

$$6x^o = 540^o$$

$$x = 90$$

The answer is 90.

TIP – Note: Figure Not Drawn to Scale.

If you see a question with "Note: Figure not drawn to scale," do not trust the figure! The SAT often draws the figure incorrectly to trick you. On the other hand, **if a figure has no note below it, the figure is drawn to scale and you can trust the angles and side lengths in the figure.** If a figure is drawn to scale and you do not know how to solve the question algebraically, look at the answer choices to see if you can make an educated guess on which answer looks correct.

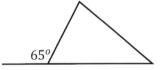   

Note: Figure not drawn to scale.

In the figures above, we see that the angle labelled as 65° in the figure on the left is clearly incorrect. Make sure that you do not trust what this figure looks like, as it may be trying to trick you. On the other hand, the figure on the right has no note, so we know the 115° is correct and know that the figure is drawn to scale.

Angles Practice: A calculator may NOT be used on the following questions. Answers on page 257.

1. In the triangle below, what is the value of x?

A) 30
B) 35
C) 45
D) 90

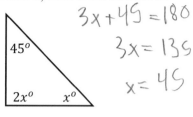

$3x + 45 = 180$
$3x = 135$
$x = 45$

2. In the figure below, two parallel lines are intersected by $\overline{AB}$. What is the measure of angle x in degrees?

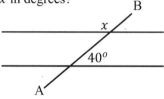

A) 40
B) 80
C) 130
D) 140

3. What is the value of x in the figure below?

A) 25
B) 30
C) 35
D) 40

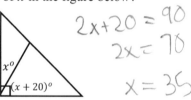

$2x + 20 = 90$
$2x = 70$
$x = 35$

4. In the figure below, $AE = DE$, $BE = CE$, and $\overline{BC}$ is parallel to $\overline{AD}$. If $x = 32$, what is the measure of $\angle BCE$?

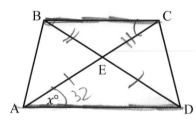

A) 28
B) 32
C) 48
D) 64

5. In the figure below, what is the measure of $\angle JKL$?

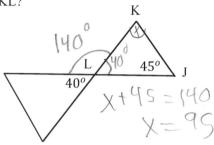

Note: Figure not drawn to scale.

A) 40
B) 45
C) 85
D) 95

$x + 45 = 140$
$x = 95$

6.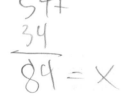

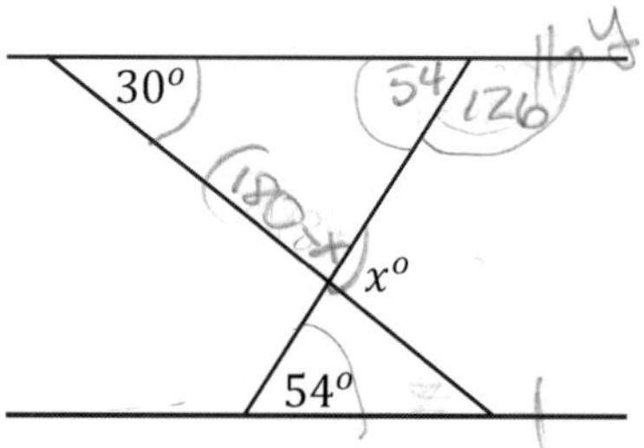

Note: Figure not drawn to scale.

What is the value of x in the figure above?

A) 150
B) 126
C) 96
D) 84

$54 +$
34
$\overline{\quad\quad}$
$84 = x$

7.

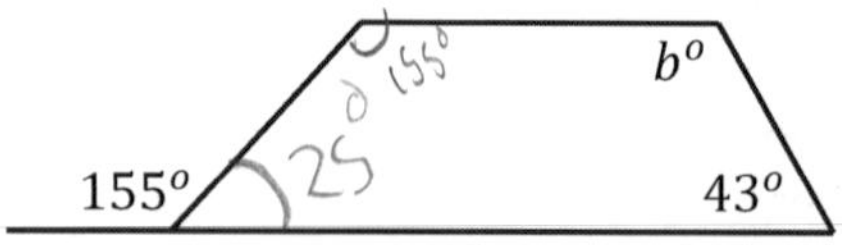

Note: Figure not drawn to scale.

In the figure above, the shape is a trapezoid. What is the value of b?

A) 43
B) 112
C) 137
D) 155

$155 +$
43
25
$\overline{\quad}$
223

$360 -$
223
$\overline{\quad}$
137

8.

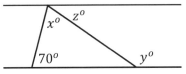

Which of the following expressions is correct for the figure above?

A) $x + y + z = 180$
B) $x + 70 = y$
C) $x + 70 + z = 180 - y$
D) $z - 70 = x$

9.

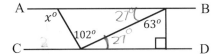

Note: Figure not drawn to scale.

In the figure above, $\overline{AB}$ and $\overline{CD}$ are parallel. What is the value of x?

$$x = 129$$

10.

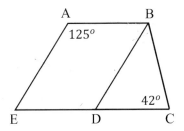

Note: Figure not drawn to scale.

In the figure above, $\overline{AB}$ and $\overline{EC}$ are parallel, $\overline{AE}$ and $\overline{BD}$ are parallel. What is the measure of $\angle ABC$ in degrees?

A) 138
B) 125
C) 97
D) 83

11.

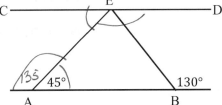

In the figure above, what is the measure of $\angle AED$ in degrees?

$$135^o$$

Angles Practice: A calculator may be used on the following questions.

12.

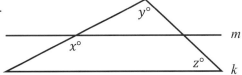

Note: Figure not drawn to scale.

In the figure above, lines k and m are parallel. If $x = 148$ and $y = 70$, what is the value of z?

A) 102
B) 78
C) 44
D) 32

13.

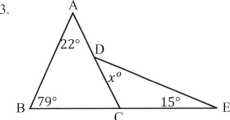

Note: Figure not drawn to scale.

In the figure above, what is the value of x?

A) 101
B) 86
C) 79
D) 64

14. In the figure below, if $y = 54$, what is the value of x?

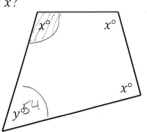
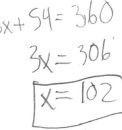

$$3x + 54 = 360$$
$$3x = 306$$
$$x = 102$$

Note: Figure not drawn to scale.

A) 102
B) 108
C) 112
D) 126

15. Triangle LMN and the collinear points L, N, and P are shown below. What is the measure of ∠M?

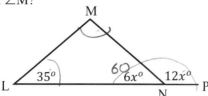

Note: Figure not drawn to scale.

A) 55
B) 65
C) 85
D) 95

(handwritten left margin: 18x = 180, x = 10, 180 − 95 = 85)

16.

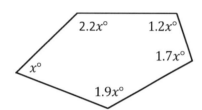

Note: Figure not drawn to scale.

In the figure above, what is the value of x?

A) 58.5
B) 60
C) 62.25
D) 67.5

17. In the figure below, $\overline{AB}$ is parallel to $\overline{DE}$. What is the measure of ∠CDE?

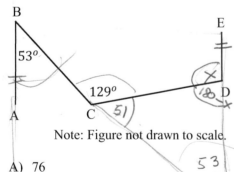

Note: Figure not drawn to scale.

A) 76
B) 94
C) 104
D) 139

(handwritten: x = 51 + y)

18. The measures of four of the interior angles of a hexagon are 65°, 70°, 95° and 110°. What is the sum of the last two interior angles?

A) 180
B) 340
C) 380
D) 440

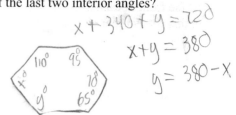

(handwritten: x + 340 + y = 720, x + y = 380, y = 380 − x)

19.

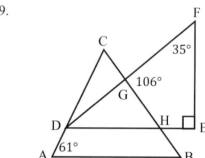

Note: Figure not drawn to scale.

In the figure above, $\overline{AB}$ is parallel to $\overline{DE}$. What is the measure of ∠ACB?

A) 51
B) 55
C) 68
D) 74

20.

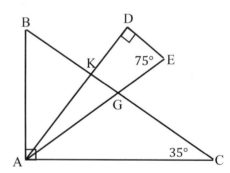

In the figure above, $AG = CG$. What is the measure of ∠AKB?

A) 70
B) 75
C) 80
D) 85

Chapter 18: Geometry Part 2 - Shapes

At the front of each SAT Math Test, you are given equations for certain shapes. There are additional equations in this chapter that you need to have memorized for test day as well. Whether the SAT gives you the equations or not, you should have all of the equations in this chapter memorized, as it will help you solve questions more quickly on test day.

Area and Volume

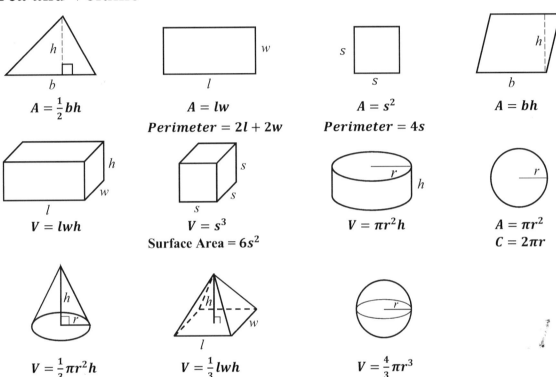

$$A = \frac{1}{2}bh$$

$$A = lw$$
$$Perimeter = 2l + 2w$$

$$A = s^2$$
$$Perimeter = 4s$$

$$A = bh$$

$$V = lwh$$

$$V = s^3$$
$$Surface\ Area = 6s^2$$

$$V = \pi r^2 h$$

$$A = \pi r^2$$
$$C = 2\pi r$$

$$V = \frac{1}{3}\pi r^2 h$$

$$V = \frac{1}{3}lwh$$

$$V = \frac{4}{3}\pi r^3$$

Example 1:

Amanda is freezing ice cream in the cake tin above to make an ice cream cake. The cake tin has a diameter of 25 cm. If Amanda uses 2,000 cm^3 of ice cream to make the ice cream cake, which of the following is closest to the height, in centimeters, of the ice cream cake?

    A) 12   B) 8   C) 4   D) 2

Solution: To solve, we will use the equation for the volume of a right circular cylinder. We know the volume is equal to 2,000 cm^3. The radius of a circle is equal to half of the diameter, so the radius is equal to 12.5 cm. Now, we can solve for the height.

$$V = \pi r^2 h$$

$$2000 = \pi(12.5)^2 h$$

$$\frac{2000}{\pi(12.5)^2} = h$$

$$4.07 = h$$

The height is equal to 4.07 cm, which is closest to 4. **The answer is C.**

Example 2: Morgan is making a poster for her room. The original poster did not fit on her wall, so she is changing the dimensions by tripling the width and halving the length. If the original area of the poster was 4*A*, what is the area of the new poster in terms of *A*?

A) $\frac{3}{2}A$ B) 4*A*   C) 6*A*   D) 9*A*

Solution: Method #1 – The Math Teacher Way: We know the area of the original poster is 4*A*, so

$$4A = lw$$

Now, we need to see how the area changes with the new length and width:

$$New\ Area = (3l)(0.5w) = 1.5lw$$

The new area is 1.5 times as large as the old area. From the first equation, we know that $4A = lw$, so plugging in the 4*A* for *lw*, we can find the new area in terms of *A*.

$$New\ Area = 1.5(4A) = 6A$$

The answer is C.

Method #2 – Substitution: If solving this question algebraically seems confusing, that's because it is! To make this question easier, use the substitution method we learned in Chapter 2 and pick values for the length and width of the original poster. Let's say the length is 2 and the width is 3, so the original poster has an area of 6. Now, use the numbers we picked to solve the rest of the question.

$$New\ Width = 3(3) = 9$$

$$New\ Length = 2(0.5) = 1$$

$$New\ Area = lw = (9)(1) = 9$$

The original area was 6 and the new area is 9. The new area is 1.5 times larger than the original area, so we can apply that same change to the poster's original area of 4*A*.

$$New\ Area = 1.5(Original\ Area) = 1.5(4A) = 6A$$

The answer is C.

Right Triangles

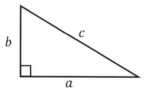

All right triangles follow the Pythagorean theorem:

$$a^2 + b^2 = c^2$$

where *a* and *b* are the lengths of the legs and *c* is the hypotenuse. Remember that **you can only use the Pythagorean theorem for right triangles.**

Example 3:

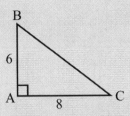

In the triangle above, point D (not shown) is the midpoint of BC. What is the length of CD?

Solution: We first need to use the Pythagorean theorem to find the length of BC.

$$6^2 + 8^2 = c^2$$

$$100 = c^2$$

$$10 = c$$

We now know $BC = 10$. Since D is the midpoint of BC, the length of CD is half of BC, so CD is 5. **The answer is 5**.

TIP – Pythagorean Triples

Pythagorean triples are sets of whole numbers that work in the Pythagorean theorem. On the SAT, you should look out for the two common Pythagorean triples.

3, 4, 5 Right Triangle   **5, 12, 13 Right Triangle**

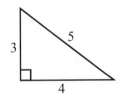   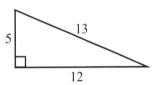

These triangles can also be scaled up by multiplying all of the side lengths by the same number to create more Pythagorean triples. For example, a 3, 4, 5 right triangle can be doubled to become a 6, 8, 10 right triangle, tripled to become 9, 12, 15, and so on.

Pythagorean triples appear most commonly in the no-calculator section. If you can spot any Pythagorean triples, it can save you some time.

Special Right Triangles

You need to be familiar with two special right triangles: $45^o - 45^o - 90^o$ and $30^o - 60^o - 90^o$. The side lengths of these triangles are always in a particular ratio.

$45^o - 45^o - 90^o$ **$30^o - 60^o - 90^o$**

        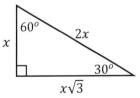

You are given the two pictures above at the beginning of each math section. It is still critical to memorize the ratio of the side lengths, so you can spot special right triangles questions.

Example 4:

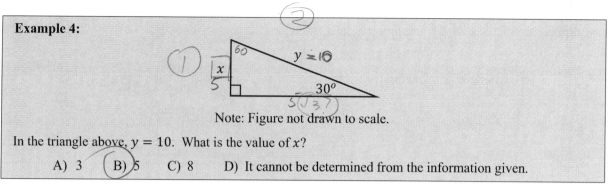

Note: Figure not drawn to scale.

In the triangle above, $y = 10$. What is the value of x?

    A) 3   B) 5   C) 8   D) It cannot be determined from the information given.

Solution: This is a $30^o - 60^o - 90^o$ right triangle, so we need to use the ratio of side lengths to solve. The shortest side, x, is always half the length of the hypotenuse, y. We know that $y = 10$, so $x = \frac{1}{2}(10) = 5$. **The answer is B.**

Example 5:

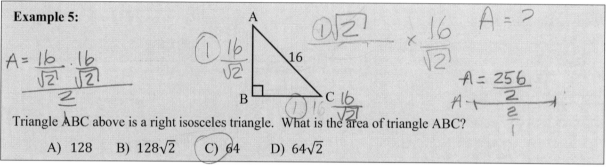

Triangle ABC above is a right isosceles triangle. What is the area of triangle ABC?

    A) 128   B) $128\sqrt{2}$ C) 64   D) $64\sqrt{2}$

Solution: A right isosceles triangle is the same as a $45^o - 45^o - 90^o$ right triangle. To find the area of triangle ABC, we need to know the side lengths AB and BC. To find these sides lengths, we can use the ratio from the $45^o - 45^o - 90^o$ right triangle. We are looking for the legs of the triangle, which are the x's, and we are given that the hypotenuse, which is the $x\sqrt{2}$. Since we know the hypotenuse is equal to 16, we can solve for x.

$$x\sqrt{2} = 16$$

$$x = \frac{16}{\sqrt{2}} = \frac{16}{\sqrt{2}} \times \frac{\sqrt{2}}{\sqrt{2}} = \frac{16\sqrt{2}}{2} = 8\sqrt{2}$$

We know that $AB = BC = 8\sqrt{2}$. Now that we know the lengths of the base and height of the triangle, we can solve for the area of triangle ABC.

$$\text{Area of ABC} = \frac{1}{2}\left(8\sqrt{2}\right)\left(8\sqrt{2}\right) = \frac{1}{2}(128) = 64$$

The answer is C.

Similar Triangles

Similar triangles are triangles with the same shape but different size. **All of the angles are identical, and the side lengths are proportional.**

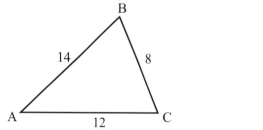

For similar triangles, the ratio of the side lengths is always the same:

$$\frac{AB}{DE} = \frac{BC}{EF} = \frac{AC}{DF}$$

Example 6:

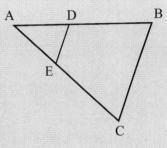

Note: Figure not drawn to scale.

In the triangle above, $\overline{DE}$ is parallel to $\overline{BC}$, $AE = 8$, $AC = 40$, and $AB = 28$. What is the length of AD?

Solution: Triangles ADE and ABC are similar triangles. Anytime a line that is parallel to one of the bases makes a smaller triangle, the smaller triangle will be similar to the larger triangle. Here, DE creates the smaller similar triangle. Since the triangles are similar, we know the sides must be proportional.

$$\frac{AD}{AB} = \frac{AE}{AC}$$

$$\frac{AD}{28} = \frac{8}{40}$$

$$40\,AD = 224$$

$$AD = \frac{224}{40} = \frac{28}{5} = 5.6$$

The answer is $\frac{28}{5}$ or **5.6**

More Triangles

An equilateral triangle is a triangle in which all three sides are equal, and all angles are equal to 60°.

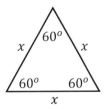

An isosceles triangle is a triangle in which two sides are equal and two angles are equal.

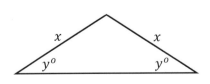
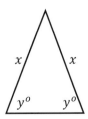

Example 7:

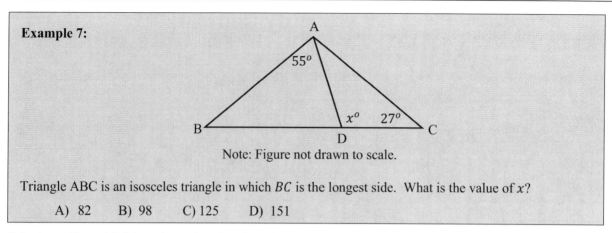

Note: Figure not drawn to scale.

Triangle ABC is an isosceles triangle in which BC is the longest side. What is the value of x?

A) 82   B) 98   C) 125   D) 151

Solution: Since ABC is an isosceles triangle and BC is the longest side, we know $AB = AC$. That means we can find $\angle B$:

$$\angle B = \angle C = 27^o$$

Once we know $\angle B = 27^o$, we can find $\angle ADB$ because we know the other two angles in triangle ADB.

$$\angle ADB = 180^o - 27^o - 55^o = 98^o$$

The angle x^o that we are looking for is adjacent to $\angle ADB$, so we can solve:

$$x^o = 180^o - 98^o = 82^o$$

The answer is A.

Remember that we cannot trust the figure when we see "Note: Figure not drawn to scale." The correct answer is an acute angle, but the figure makes it look like x^o should be obtuse. The question tried to trick you! The SAT Math Test may include curveball questions like this, so make sure you always read questions and figures carefully.

Third Side of a Triangle

Can you make a triangle with side lengths of 4, 5, and 10? What about one with side lengths of 4, 5, and 9? Or one with side lengths of 4, 5, and 8? While this may at first seem confusing, there is a simple rule:

> **The sum of the two shorter sides of a triangle, *a* and *b*, must be greater than the longest side of a triangle, *c*.**
> $$a + b > c$$

Let's use this rule to review the three potential triangles introduced above. We will start with a triangle with side lengths of 4, 5, and 9.

$$4 + 5 \not> 9$$

$$\frac{\overline{\quad 5 \quad \ \ 4 \quad}}{9}$$

Since the sum of the shorter side lengths are equal to the longest side, we cannot make a triangle.

Let's try side lengths of 4, 5, and 10.

$$4 + 5 \not> 10$$

Now, the two shorter sides cannot even reach the end of the longest side, so again we cannot make a triangle.

What about side lengths of 4, 5, and 8?

$$4 + 5 > 8$$

Since the smaller sides are greater than the longest side, we can finally make a triangle!

Example 8: Triangle ABC has two sides of length 10 and 15. Which of the following could NOT be the third side of triangle ABC?

A) 5   B) 13   C) 19   D) 23

Solution: To solve, we just need to test each answer choice to find which one does not work with our third side of the triangle rule. For answer choices A and B, the longest side would be 15. For answer choices C and D, the number in the answer choice would be the longest side.

Let's start with answer choice A.

$$5 + 10 \not> 15$$

The sides of 5 and 10 are equal to 15, so no triangle can be formed.

If we test the rest of the answer choices, we see that each of them works.

For B: $13 + 10 > 15$

For C: $10 + 15 > 19$

For D: $10 + 15 > 23$

The answer is A.

Shapes Practice: A calculator may NOT be used on the following questions. Answers on page 260.

1. If the area of rectangle ABCD below is 80, what is area of the shaded region?

A) 12
B) 18
C) 24
D) 36

2. What is the area of a circle with a circumference of 12π?

A) 12π
B) 24π
C) 30π
D) 36π

3. If a triangle has two sides with lengths 6 and 8 what is the length of the third side?

A) 2
B) 6
C) 8
D) Cannot be determined

4. In the figure below, the larger shaded circle has a radius of 10, and the smaller circles each have a radius of 2. What is the area of the shaded region?

A) 64π
B) 81π
C) 92π
D) 100π

5. Triangle ABC has two sides of length 7 and 12. Which of the following could NOT be the length of the third side of the triangle?

A) 5
B) 7
C) 12
D) 15

6. The circumference of a circle is 16π. What is the area of half of the circle?

A) 16π
B) 32π
C) 64π
D) 128π

7. Equilateral triangle ABC is shown below. What is the value of k?

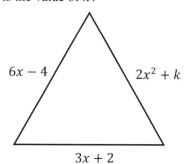

A) -2
B) 0
C) 4
D) 6

8.

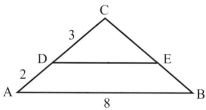

Note: Figure not drawn to scale.

In the figure above, $\overline{AB}$ is parallel to $\overline{DE}$. Which of the following is equal to the length of DE?

A) $\dfrac{16}{3}$
B) $\dfrac{13}{2}$
C) $\dfrac{24}{5}$
D) $\dfrac{40}{3}$

9.

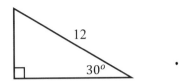

What is the area of the triangle above?

A) $36\sqrt{3}$
B) 36
C) $18\sqrt{3}$
D) 18

10.

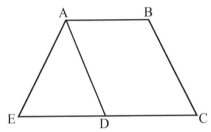

Note: Figure not drawn to scale.

In the figure above, $\overline{AB}$ and $\overline{EC}$ are parallel, $\overline{AD}$ and $\overline{BC}$ are parallel, $AD = AE$, and the measure of $\angle ABC$ is 110°. What is the measure of $\angle EAD$?

A) 110
B) 80
C) 50
D) 40

11.

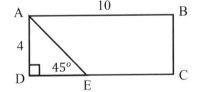

For the figure above, what is the perimeter of quadrilateral AECB?

A) $20 + 4\sqrt{2}$
B) $28 + 4\sqrt{3}$
C) $24 + 4\sqrt{2}$
D) 24

12. Ayesha is making a flowerpot for her Mom for Mother's Day. Her Mom's current favorite flowerpot, which is in the shape of a right circular cylinder, holds Q liters of water. Ayesha is going to make a new flowerpot with twice the width and twice the height. How many liters of water will the new flowerpot hold?

A) $2Q$
B) $4Q$
C) $6Q$
D) $8Q$

13. A triangle has interior angles with measures in the ratio of 4:8:12. If the shortest side of the triangle is 6, what is the length of the second longest side?

A) $6\sqrt{3}$
B) 9
C) 12
D) 18

14.

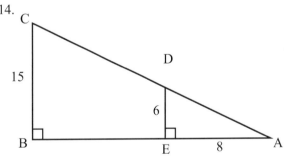

Note: Figure not drawn to scale.

In the figure above, $\overline{BC}$ is parallel to $\overline{DE}$. What is the length of AC?

- 119 -

Shapes Practice: A calculator may be used on the following questions.

15. In the shape below, all angles are right angles. Which of the following is closest to the area of the shape?

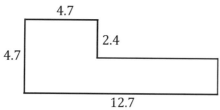

A) 40.5
B) 42.5
C) 53.5
D) 59.7

16. A swimming pool has a volume of 2,880 cubic feet. If the pool is 15 feet deep and 16 feet long, how wide, in feet, is the pool?

A) 12
B) 14
C) 15
D) 16

17. The perimeter of a parallelogram is 60 inches. One side is 20 inches. What are the other sides of the parallelogram?

A) 20, 10, 10
B) 20, 15, 15
C) 20, 14, 14
D) It cannot be determined

18. James is going to build a triangular bed for roses on the side of his house. He is going to put a fence around the rose bed. Two sides of the rose bed will be up against his house. A diagram of the rose bed is shown below. How many feet of fencing will he need to enclose the roses?

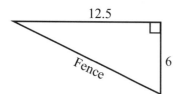

A) 3
B) 11
C) 14
D) 16

19. Simone is building a box to store all of her textbooks. She has a spot in the corner of her room to put a box that is 20 inches wide and 24 inches long. If the box must have a total volume of 7,400 cubic inches, what is the height of the box in inches? (Round your answer to the nearest tenth).

20. The length of the rectangular prism shown below is 3 times the width. The height and the width are the same. The volume of the prism is 81 cubic inches? What is the length, in inches, of the prism?

A) 3
B) 6
C) 9
D) 12

21. How many cubes with a side length of 5 can fit into a cube with a side length of 15?

A) 3
B) 10
C) 25
D) 27

22. In the figure below, the diameter of the circle is 10. What is the area of the square inside of the circle?

A) 25
B) 50
C) 80
D) 100

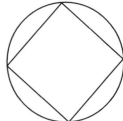

23. What fraction of a circle with an 8-inch diameter is equivalent to the area of one slice of a circle with a 16-inch diameter if the larger circle is cut into 8 equal pieces?

    A) $\frac{1}{8}$

    B) $\frac{1}{4}$

    C) $\frac{1}{2}$

    D) $\frac{3}{4}$

24.

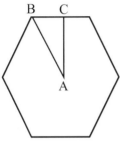

In the regular hexagon above, $AB = 20$. What is the area of $\triangle ABC$?

    A) 20
    B) $20\sqrt{2}$
    C) $50\sqrt{3}$
    D) 50

25.

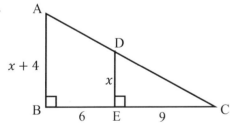

Note: Figure not drawn to scale.

In the figure above, $AC = \sqrt{a}$. What is the value of a?

26. Michelle is filling up a ball with water as part of a science fair project. If the ball can hold a total of 950 cubic inches of water when it is completely filled, approximately what is the radius of the ball?

    A) 6.1
    B) 8.9
    C) 20.1
    D) 26.7

27. In the figure below, the circle below has an area of 16π. What is the area of the equilateral triangle?

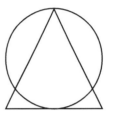

    A) 64

    B) $64\sqrt{3}$

    C) $\frac{64\sqrt{3}}{3}$

    D) $\frac{128\sqrt{3}}{3}$

28.

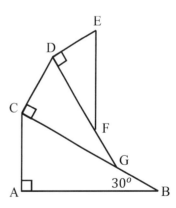

$\triangle ABC, \triangle CGD$, and $\triangle DFE$ are similar right triangles. If $CB = 40$, $DC = 18$, and the ratio of $DF : CG = 2 : 3$, what is the area of $\triangle DFE$?

    A) $72\sqrt{3}$
    B) $120\sqrt{2}$
    C) $144\sqrt{3}$
    D) $162\sqrt{3}$

Chapter 19: Arcs and Sectors

Arcs

The arc of a circle is a portion of the circumference. Arcs can be measured in two ways: the degree measure of the arc or the length of the arc.

Degree Measure of Arc AB

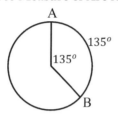

Length of Arc AB

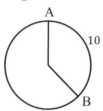

The degree measure of an arc is equal to the measure of the central angle intersecting the arc. The arc length is the actual distance covered moving from point A to point B along the circumference of the circle.

To solve arc questions, you will need to memorize the two equations below. These are different versions of the same equation. Being familiar with both the conceptual idea and the actual equation well help you solve different types of arc questions on the SAT.

$$\frac{Arc\ Length}{Circumference} = \frac{Angle\ Measure}{360\ degrees} \qquad \frac{L}{2\pi r} = \frac{\theta}{360} \qquad \begin{array}{l} L = \text{arc length} \\ \theta = \text{central angle} \\ r = \text{radius} \end{array}$$

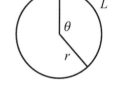

Example 1: In the circle to the right, the length of minor arc BC is 6π and the radius is 8. What is the measure of $\angle A$ in degrees? (Note: Figure not drawn to scale).

    A) 270   B) 180   C) 135   D) 100

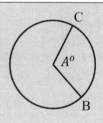

Solution: Using the arc equation, we can setup and solve for the measure of the central angle.

$$\frac{6\pi}{2\pi(8)} = \frac{\theta}{360}$$

$$\frac{6\pi}{16\pi} = \frac{\theta}{360}$$

Now, it is easiest to simplify the fraction on the left-hand side. This method will be particularly useful if you have to solve a question like this in the no-calculator section.

$$\frac{3}{8} = \frac{\theta}{360}$$

$$1080 = 8\theta$$

$$135 = \theta$$

The answer is C.

Example 2: Points X and Y lie on a circle. The length of arc XY is $\frac{1}{5}$ of the circumference of the circle. What is the measure of arc XY in degrees?

Solution: The proportion of the length of an arc to the circumference is equal to the proportion of the measure of an arc to 360°. Here, we know that the proportion of the arc length to the circumference is $\frac{1}{5}$, so we already know the left side of the equation.

$$\frac{1}{5} = \frac{\theta}{360}$$
$$360 = 5\theta$$
$$\theta = 72$$

The answer is 72.

For arc questions that measure the angle in radians, use the equation below. Remember that 2π radians $= 360^o$. If you are not familiar with radians, we will cover it later in chapter 26.

$$\frac{Arc\ Length}{Circumference} = \frac{Angle\ Measure}{2\pi\ radians} \qquad \frac{L}{2\pi r} = \frac{\theta}{2\pi}$$

Example 3: The length of arc AB is $\frac{5}{2}$ and the circle has a radius of 4. What is the measure of the central angle of arc AB in radians?

Solution: Using the arc equation above, we can setup and solve for the measure of the central angle.

$$\frac{\frac{5}{2}}{2\pi(4)} = \frac{\theta}{2\pi}$$
$$\left(\frac{5}{2}\right)2\pi = \theta(8\pi)$$
$$\frac{5\pi}{8\pi} = \theta$$

The central angle has a measure of $\frac{5}{8}$ radians. **The answer is $\frac{5}{8}$.**

TIP – Inscribed Angle Theorem

An inscribed angle is an angle that has its vertex on the circumference of a circle and whose sides are chords. While that fancy definition may seem confusing, all you need to know for the SAT is the following rule:

For an inscribed angle and central angle that intersect the same portion of the arc, the measure of the inscribed angle is half of the measure of the central angle.

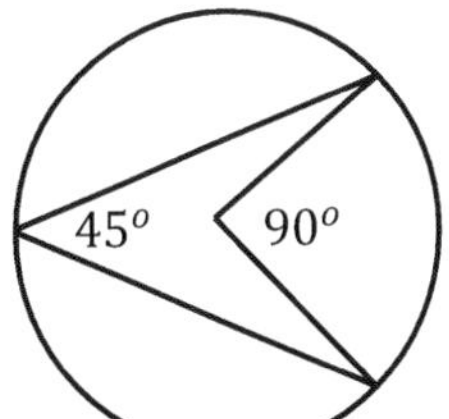

As you can see in the figure, the inscribed angle of 45° is half of the central angle of 90°. This rule does not show up often on the SAT, but you should still memorize it just in case.

Sectors

The sector is the measure of the area of a portion of a circle. To solve sector questions, you will need to memorize the equations below.

$$\frac{Sector\ Area}{Area\ of\ Circle} = \frac{Angle\ Measure}{360\ degrees} \qquad \frac{S}{\pi r^2} = \frac{\theta}{360}$$

S = sector area
θ = central angle
r = radius

Example 4: For the circle to the right, the radius is 6. If $\angle C = 150^o$, what is the area of sector BCD?

A) 8π B) 10π C) 12π D) 15π

Solution: Using the sector equation above, we can plug in the values from the question and solve to find the area of the sector.

$$\frac{S}{\pi(6)^2} = \frac{150}{360}$$

$$\frac{S}{36\pi} = \frac{150}{360}$$

Simplify the fraction on the right side we get

$$\frac{S}{36\pi} = \frac{15}{36}$$

Since both sides have 36 in the denominator, we can multiply both sides by 36 and cancel out the 36's to get

$$\frac{S}{\pi} = 15$$

$$S = 15\pi$$

The answer is D.

Example 5: Andrew bought a 12-inch diameter pumpkin pie and cut it into 12 equal slices. After eating 2 slices, he calculates that he consumed 480 calories. How many calories are in the entire pie?

Solution: The proportion of calories in two slices to calories in the entire pie is equal to the proportion of the area of the 2 slices of pie to area of the entire pie.

$$\frac{calories\ in\ 2\ slices}{calories\ in\ the\ entire\ pie} = \frac{2\ slices}{12\ slices}$$

$$\frac{480}{x} = \frac{2}{12}$$

$$480(12) = 2x$$

$$x = \frac{480(12)}{2}$$

$$x = 2,880$$

The answer is 2,880.

For sector questions that measure the angle in radians, you can use the equation below.

$$\frac{Sector\ Area}{Area\ of\ Circle} = \frac{Angle\ Measure}{2\pi\ radians} \qquad \frac{S}{\pi r^2} = \frac{\theta}{2\pi}$$

Example 6: Amanda is going to make a pie chart to display how she spends her time each day. She is going to print the pie chart on special circular paper that has a diameter of 12 inches. If Amanda spends 2 hours at volleyball practice each day, what will be the central angle, in radians, of the section of the pie chart that represents the number of hours for volleyball practice?

A) $\frac{\pi}{6}$ B) $\frac{\pi}{4}$ C) $\frac{\pi}{3}$ D) $\frac{\pi}{2}$

Solution: The proportion of hours spent playing volleyball to hours in the day is equal to the proportion of the central angle to the entire radian measure of the circle (2π radians). The diameter of 12 inches is just extra information to confuse you.

$$\frac{2\ hours\ playing\ volleyball}{24\ hours} = \frac{central\ angle}{2\pi\ radians}$$

$$\frac{2}{24} = \frac{x}{2\pi}$$

$$4\pi = 24x$$

$$\frac{4\pi}{24} = x$$

$$x = \frac{\pi}{6}$$

The answer is A.

Arc and Sectors Practice: A calculator may NOT be used on the following questions. Answers on page 263.

1. The circle below has a circumference of 30π. What is the length of minor arc AB?

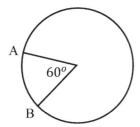

A) 5π
B) 6π
C) 8π
D) 10π

2. In the figure below, AC is a diameter of the circle and has a length of 12. What is the length of minor arc AB?

$3x = 45^\circ$
$4x = 60^\circ$
$5x = 75$

A) 4π
B) 6π
C) 8π
D) 12π

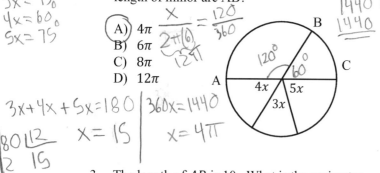

$\frac{x}{2+(6)} = \frac{120}{360}$ $2+(6)$ 12π

120° $\frac{1440}{1440}$ $\frac{360}{4}$

$3x+4x+5x = 180$ $360x = 1440$
$\frac{180}{12} \quad \frac{12}{15}$ $x = 15$ $x = 4\pi$
$\frac{60}{}$

3. The length of AB is 10. What is the perimeter of the semicircle below? $r = 5\pi$

A) 5π
B) $5\pi + 10$
C) $10\pi + 10$
D) 25π

4. The circle below has a radius of 6. What is the area of sector BAC?

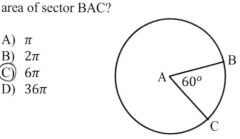

A) π
B) 2π
C) 6π
D) 36π

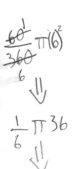

$\frac{60}{360}\pi(6)^2$
$\frac{1}{6}$

$\frac{1}{6}\pi 36$

6π

5. Points C and D lie on a circle with a radius of 2. Arc CD has a length of $\frac{\pi}{2}$. What is the measure of the central angle of arc CD?

A) $30°$
B) $45°$
C) $60°$
D) $90°$

6. The circle below has a radius of 9. The measure of $\angle XZY$ is $120°$. The length of the minor arc XY is equal to $a\pi$. What is the value of a?

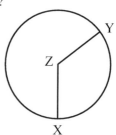

7. In the circle below, point B is the center of the circle, and the length of arc AC is $\frac{3}{10}$ of the circumference. What is the value of x?

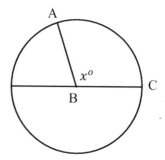

8. The circle below has a radius of 8. If the area of sector CAB is 16π, what is the measure of $\angle CAB$?

Note: Figure not drawn to scale.

Arcs and Sectors Practice: A calculator may be used on the following questions.

9. Dave is making a pie chart to represent the different fruits he currently has in the house. If he has 8 bananas, 6 apples, 4 oranges, and 6 plums, what is the central angle of the portion of the pie chart that represents the oranges?

   A) 45°
   B) 60°
   C) 90°
   D) 120°

10. Christine's famous chocolate cake contains 2,700 calories. If the cake is sliced evenly into 9 slices, what is the central angle of each of the slices?

11. In the circle shown below, chords LO and MN intersect at point P, which is the center of the circle. The circle has a radius of 6, what is the length of *arc NO*?

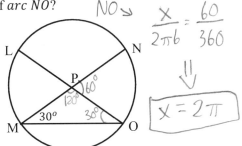

Note: Figure is not drawn to scale.

   A) 2π
   B) 3π
   C) 4π
   D) 6π

12. The length of AD is 6. What is the area of the shape ABCD below?

   A) 7π
   B) 14π
   C) 16π
   D) 21π

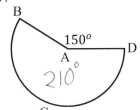

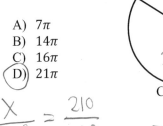

13. In the circle below, arc AB has a length of 4π. Which of the following is closest to the arc length of ADB?

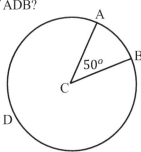

   A) 12π
   B) 18π
   C) 25π
   D) 29π

14. In the semicircle below, arc BC has a length of 3.2π, D is the midpoint of AB, and $DC = 8$. What is the measure of x?

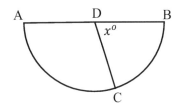

15. If the central angle of an arc is 135°, what proportion of the circumference does the arc intercept?

   A) $\frac{1}{4}$
   B) $\frac{1}{3}$
   C) $\frac{3}{8}$
   D) $\frac{3}{7}$

16. If the circumference of a circle is 18 and the length of arc AB is 6, what is the measure of the central angle that intercepts it?

   A) 30
   B) 60
   C) 120
   D) 240

$$\frac{6}{18} = \frac{X}{360}$$

$$120 = X$$

Chapter 20: Lines

Many SAT questions will ask you how to use and solve linear functions, which is just a fancy term for lines. Linear functions appear in the form $y = mx + b$. In this chapter, we will cover all of the equations that you need to know and common types of lines questions on test day.

Slope

Given any two points on a line (x_1, y_1) and (x_2, y_2),

$$Slope = \frac{rise}{run} = \frac{y_1 - y_2}{x_1 - x_2}$$

The slope measures how steep a line is. A line with a higher slope is steeper while a line with a lower slope is flatter. The rise is the change in the y-coordinates, and the run is the change in the x-coordinates. For example, if a line has a slope of $\frac{1}{2}$, the line will go up 1 unit for every 2 units we move to the right or it will go down 1 unit for every 2 units we move to the left. Lines with a positive slope go up and to the right, and lines with a negative slope go down and to the right.

Example 1: Line l passes through points $(9, y)$ and $(-1, 3)$ and has a slope of 3. What is the value of y?

Solution: To solve, plug the given values into the slope equation

$$Slope = \frac{y-3}{9-(-1)} = 3$$

$$\frac{y-3}{10} = 3$$

$$y - 3 = 30$$

$$y = 33$$

The answer is 33.

Example 2:

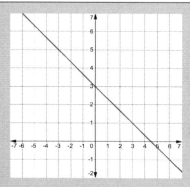

Line m is graphed above, what is the slope of line m?

A) $\frac{2}{3}$ B) $\frac{3}{2}$ C) $-\frac{2}{3}$ D) $-\frac{3}{2}$

Solution: To find the slope, we need to pick two points on the graph. We can see the graph includes the points $(3, 1)$ and $(0, 3)$.

$$Slope = \frac{1-3}{3-0} = \frac{-2}{3} = -\frac{2}{3}$$

The answer is C.

Slopes of Parallel and Perpendicular Lines

If two lines are parallel, the lines have the same slope. For example, if lines A and B are parallel and line A has a slope of 3, line B also has a slope of 3.

If two lines are perpendicular, the slopes of the lines are the negative reciprocals of one another. To find the negative reciprocal, take the slope of the initial line, flip the fraction, and make it negative. For example, if lines A and B are perpendicular and line A has a slope of $\frac{3}{2}$, the slope of line B is $-\frac{2}{3}$.

Example 3: Points $(4, 10)$ and $(1, 31)$ are located on line q. If line p is perpendicular to line q, which of the following equations could be the equation of line p?

A) $y = 7x + 28$ B) $y = \frac{1}{7}x - \frac{5}{2}$ C) $y = -7x + 10$ D) $y = -\frac{1}{7}x + 2$

Solution: To start, we need to find the slope of line q.

$$\text{Slope} = \frac{10-31}{4-1} = \frac{-21}{3}$$

$$\text{Slope} = -7$$

Line q has a slope of -7. Since line p is perpendicular to line q, line p must have a slope of $\frac{1}{7}$. **The answer is B.**

Slope-Intercept Form

Slope-intercept form is the simplest form of a line and the one that you are likely most comfortable with.

$$y = mx + b$$

where **m is the slope** and **b is the y-intercept**.

As an example, consider the graph of $y = 2x - 2$ below:

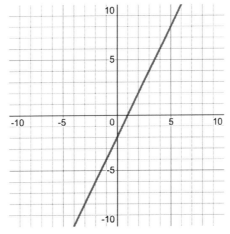

We can see both the slope and the y-intercept on the graph. The y-intercept is where the line crosses the y-axis, which we can clearly see at $y = -2$. We can also see the slope is 2 by tracing how the line moves: for every 2 units we move up (the rise), the graph moves one unit to the right (the run). **You need to be comfortable identifying the y-intercept and slope of a line from a graph.**

Example 4: Which of the following is the correct equation for the graph pictured in the xy-plane below?

A) $y = x + 5$
B) $y = x - 5$
C) $y = -x + 5$
D) $y = -x - 5$

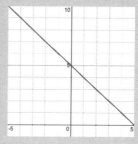

Solution: To solve, we need to find the y-intercept and the slope. The y-intercept is at $y = 5$. To find the slope, we can pick two points on the line. Here, we will use $(0, 5)$ and $(1, 4)$.

$$slope = \frac{5-4}{0-1} = \frac{1}{-1} = -1$$

The answer is C.

Point-Slope Form

If we only know the slope of a line and a point on the line, we will need to use point-slope form:

$$y - y_1 = m(x - x_1)$$

where (x_1, y_1) **is a point on the line and m is the slope**. Once we plug in the slope and point to point-slope form, we can then turn the equation back into slope-intercept form by solving for y.

Example 5: Line w passes through points $(2, 10)$ and $(5, -2)$. What is the y-intercept of line w?

Solution: To start, we need to find the slope of line w.

$$slope = \frac{10-(-2)}{2-5} = \frac{12}{-3} = -4$$

Now that we know the slope, we can use point-slope form. We can use either point. For this example, we will use the point $(2, 10)$.

$$y - 10 = -4(x - 2)$$
$$y - 10 = -4x + 8$$
$$y = -4x + 18$$

Once we have the equation in slope-intercept form, we see that the y-intercept is 18. **The answer is 18.**

TIP – Plug a point into $y = mx + b$ form.

When dealing with lines in $y = mx + b$ form, you can plug the (x, y) coordinates of a point on the line into the $y = mx + b$ equation and then solve for the slope or y-intercept. To see how this works, let's go back to example 5. Once we found the slope was -4, we could have set the equation up like this:

$$y = -4x + b$$

To solve for the b-value, we can plug in one of the points from the line. Here, we will use $(2, 10)$.

$$10 = -4(2) + b$$
$$b = 18$$

Both methods work, so you should use whichever one you feel more comfortable with.

Standard Form

Lines can also appear in standard form:

$$Ax + By = C$$

The coefficients in this form do not show the slope or the y-intercept. They actually show nothing, so standard form is not particularly useful. **To turn standard form into slope-intercept form, solve for y.** Once you have the equation in slope-intercept form, you can find the slope and the y-intercept for the line.

Example 6: Line n has an equation of $-4x + 3y = 15$. When written in $y = ax + b$ form, what is the value of $a + b$?

Solution: Convert line n from standard form to slope-intercept form.

$$-4x + 3y = 15$$
$$3y = 4x + 15$$
$$y = \frac{4}{3}x + 5$$

After putting line n in slope-intercept form, we see the slope (the value of a in this question) is $\frac{4}{3}$ and the value of the y-intercept (the value of b in the question) is 5.

$$a + b = \frac{4}{3} + 5$$
$$a + b = \frac{19}{3}$$

The answer is $\frac{19}{3}$ or 6.33.

Solving for Intercepts

The x-intercept is the point where a line crosses the x-axis. **To solve for the x-intercept, set $y = 0$ and solve for x.**

The y-intercept is the point where the line crosses the y-axis. **To solve for the y-intercept, set $x = 0$ and solve for y.**

Example 7: For the line $10 - 2y = 5x$, what is the sum of the x-intercept and the y-intercept?

Solution: To find the x-intercept, set $y = 0$ and solve for x.

$$10 - 2(0) = 5x$$
$$10 = 5x$$
$$x = 2$$

The x-intercept is 2.

To find the y-intercept, set $x = 0$ and solve for y.

$$10 - 2y = 5(0)$$
$$10 - 2y = 0$$
$$2y = 10$$

$$y = 5$$

The y-intercept is 5.

The sum of the x-intercept and y-intercept is $2 + 5$, so the **answer is 7**.

Midpoint Formula

Given any two points on a line (x_1, y_1) and (x_2, y_2),

$$\textbf{midpoint} = \left(\frac{x_1 + x_2}{2}, \frac{y_1 + y_2}{2}\right)$$

Example 8: C is the midpoint of AB. If point A is at $(3, 6)$ and point C is at $(5, 2)$, which of the following is point B?

    A) $(4, 4)$ B) $(1, 2)$ C) $(7, -2)$ D) $(1, 10)$

Solution: We are given the midpoint, point C, and one of the endpoints, point A. We can plug the values into the midpoint formula to solve for the coordinates of point B.

To solve for the x-coordinate of point B, plug in the x-coordinates that we are given for the midpoint ($x = 5$) and the endpoint at point A ($x = 3$) to the midpoint formula.

$$5 = \frac{3+x}{2}$$

$$10 = 3 + x$$

$$x = 7$$

The x-coordinate of point B is 7. If we look at the answer choices, **we can already tell that the answer is C.** Make sure that you always check the answer choices on questions like this. If we could not tell which answer is correct at this point, we would still need to solve for y, which we do below.

To solve for the y-coordinate of point B, plug in the y-coordinates that we are given for the midpoint ($y = 2$) and the endpoint at point A ($y = 6$) to the midpoint formula.

$$2 = \frac{6+y}{2}$$

$$4 = 6 + y$$

$$y = -2$$

The y-coordinate is -2. **The answer is C.**

Distance Formula

Given any two points (x_1, y_1) and (x_2, y_2),

$$\textbf{Distance} = \sqrt{(x_1 - x_2)^2 + (y_1 - y_2)^2}$$

The distance formula is used to solve for the distance between any two points.

If you do not like the distance formula, **you can also use the Pythagorean Theorem to find the distance between two points.** To do so, sketch a coordinate plane and draw a triangle, and solve for the hypotenuse. You can see how this works in the example below.

Example 9: The endpoints of line X are at $(-2, 1)$ and $(5, 4)$. The length, in coordinate units, of line X can be expresses as $\sqrt{a}$. What is the value of a?

Solution: We can solve for distance of line X using the distance formula or by sketching a triangle.

Method #1: Solve with the distance formula using $(-2, 1)$ as x_1 and $(5, 4)$ as x_2.

$$Distance = \sqrt{(-2 - 5)^2 + (1 - 4)^2}$$
$$Distance = \sqrt{(-7)^2 + (-3)^2}$$
$$Distance = \sqrt{58}$$

Since the distance can be expressed as $\sqrt{a}$, we see that $a = 58$. **The answer is 58.**

Method #2: Draw a coordinate plane and make a triangle.

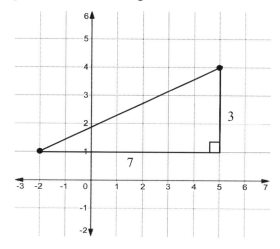

Using the triangle, we see that the base has a length of 7 and the height has a length of 3. To find the length of line X, use the Pythagorean Theorem:

$$7^2 + 3^2 = c^2$$
$$58 = c^2$$
$$c = \sqrt{58}$$

Since the distance can be expresses as $\sqrt{a}$, we see that $a = 58$. **The answer is 58.**

Lines Practice: A calculator may NOT be used on the following questions. Answers on page 263.

1. A line in the standard (x, y) coordinate plane passes through the points $(-7, 5)$ and $(1, -4)$. The slope of the line is:

   (A) Negative
   B) Positive
   C) Zero
   D) Undefined

   $$\frac{5+4}{-7-1} = -\frac{9}{8}$$

2. In the xy-plane, what is the midpoint of the line segment with endpoints $(2, 6)$ and $(6, 10)$?

   A) $(3, 6)$
   B) $(4, -4)$
   (C) $(4, 8)$
   D) $(8, 16)$

   $$\left(\frac{2+6}{2}, \frac{6+10}{2}\right)$$

   $(4, 8)$

3. Which of the following statements is true about the graph of the equation $3y - 4x = -6$ in the xy-plane?

   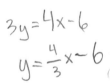

   $3y = 4x - 6$
   $y = \frac{4}{3}x - 6$

   A) The line has a negative slope and a negative y-intercept.
   B) The line has a negative slope and a positive y-intercept.
   (C) The line has a positive slope and a negative y-intercept.
   D) The line has a positive slope and a positive y-intercept.

4. In the standard xy-plane, what is the slope of the line with the equation $7x - 3y = 4$?

   $-3y = -7x + 4$
   $-y = -\frac{7}{3}x + 4$
   $y = \frac{7}{3}x - 4$

   $$\frac{7}{3}$$

5. When the point Y $(2, 4)$ is graphed in the standard xy-plane, the midpoint of XY is at $(-2, 3)$. What are the coordinates of point X?

   A) $(0, 3.5)$
   B) $(4, 0)$
   C) $(6, 5)$
   D) $(-6, 2)$

6. Which of the following is the correct equation for the graph below?

   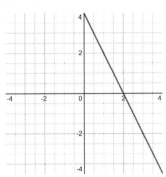

   A) $y = 4x + 2$
   B) $y = -\frac{x}{2} + 4$
   C) $y = -2x + 4$
   D) $y = 2x + 4$

7. Line k passes through the points $(-2, 10)$ and $(4, 28)$. Which of the following is the equation for line k?

   A) $y = 3x + 16$
   B) $y = 3x + 4$
   C) $y = \frac{1}{3}x + 12$
   D) $y = \frac{1}{3}x + 15$

Questions 8 and 9 refer to the graph below.

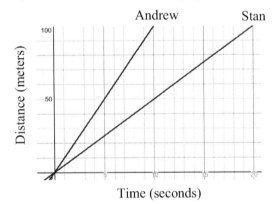

The graph above shows the positions of Andrew and Stan during a 100m rowing race.

8. According to the graph, what is the rate that Stan rowed at during the race in meters per second?

   A) 2
   B) 5
   C) 10
   D) 20

9. If Andrew and Stan want to cross the finish line at the exact same time, how many meters of a head start will Stan need to be given before Andrew and Stan begin rowing?

   A) 10
   B) 25
   C) 40
   D) 50

10. A line in the standard xy-plane is parallel to the y-axis and 4 units to the left of y-axis. What is the equation of the line?

    A) $y = 4$
    B) $y = -4$
    C) $x = -4$
    D) $y = x - 4$

11. Line m is shown in the xy-plane below.

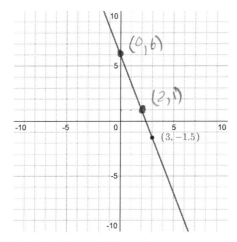

What is the slope of line m?

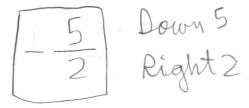

12. The graph below shows the function $f(x)$. $f(x)$ and $g(x)$ (not shown) are perpendicular lines. Which of the following could define $g(x)$?

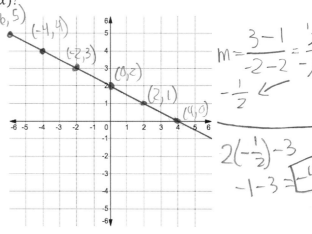

    A) $g(x) = -2x - 2$
    B) $g(x) = -\frac{1}{2}x + 4$
    C) $g(x) = \frac{1}{2}x + 2$
    D) $g(x) = 2x - 3$

13. Which of the following equations represents the line in the xy-plane that passes through the point $(-6, -7)$ and has a slope of $\frac{1}{3}$?

    A) $x - 3y = 15$
    B) $3x + y = 15$
    C) $2x + 5y = -15$
    D) $x + y = 5$

14. The line the with equation $\frac{5}{4}x + \frac{1}{2}y = 3$ is graphed in the xy-plane. What is the x-intercept of the line?

15. In the xy-plane below, line a is parallel to line b (not shown). Which of the following could be the equation of line b?

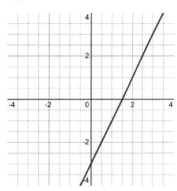

   A) $y = x - 3$
   B) $y = \frac{1}{2}x - 2$
   C) $y = 2x + 4$
   D) $y = -2x - 5$

16. Lines t and v are perpendicular in the xy-plane. The equation of line t is $4x + 3y = 10$, and line v passes through the point $(-3, 3)$. What is the y-intercept of line v?

17. The graph of a line in the xy-plane passes through the point $(4, 6)$ and crosses the y-axis at the point $(0, 10)$. The line crosses the x-axis at the point $(a, 0)$. What is the value of a?

18. Lines l and k are parallel in the xy-plane. The equation for line l is $x + 4y = -5$, and line k passes through the point $(2, 8)$. What is the x-intercept for line k?

19. The graph of the line $y = kx - 2$ is graphed in the xy-plane and k is a constant. If the line contains the point (a, b) and $a \neq 0$ and $b \neq 0$, what is the slope of the line in terms of a and b?

   A) $\frac{a+2}{b}$
   B) $\frac{b+2}{a}$
   C) $\frac{2-a}{b}$
   D) $\frac{b-2}{a}$

20. A line in the xy-plane has a slope of 3 and passes through the point $(2a, 6a)$, where a is a nonzero constant. What is the y-intercept of the line in terms of a?

   A) $0a$
   B) $\frac{16}{3}a$
   C) $12a$
   D) Cannot be determined

Lines Practice: A calculator may be used on the following questions.

21. What is the length, in coordinate units, of a line with endpoints at $(-9,-2)$ and $(3,7)$?

    A) $\sqrt{81}$
    B) $\sqrt{144}$
    C) $\sqrt{169}$
    D) $\sqrt{225}$

    $\sqrt{(-9-3)^2+(-2-7)^2}$

    $\sqrt{144+81}$

    $\sqrt{225}$

22. When a roadmap is drawn in the xy-plane, one rest stop is drawn at $(-2,6)$ and a second rest stop is drawn at $(8,14)$. If 1 coordinate unit represents 10 miles, which of the following is the closest to the straight-line distance in miles between the two rest stops?

    A) 80
    B) 100
    C) 130
    D) 164

23. In the standard xy-plane, what is the slope of a line perpendicular to $6x=4y+10$?

    A) -1
    B) $\frac{2}{3}$
    C) $\frac{3}{2}$
    D) $-\frac{2}{3}$

    $-4y=-6x-10$

    $y=\frac{3}{2}x-\frac{5}{2}$

    $\frac{3}{2} \rightarrow -\frac{2}{3}$

24.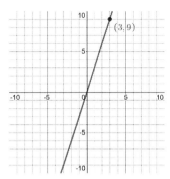

    In the graph above, point A (not shown) with coordinates (h,k) is on the line $y=f(x)$ shown above. If h and k are negative integers, what is the ratio of k to h?

    A) $-3:1$
    B) $1:3$
    C) $2:3$
    D) $3:1$

25. $$y=6x-4$$

    The equation of line m in the xy-plane is shown above. A second line, w, has half the slope of line m and twice the y-intercept. Where do lines m and w intersect?

    A) $\left(\frac{4}{3},4\right)$
    B) $\left(-\frac{3}{4},-\frac{9}{2}\right)$
    C) $\left(\frac{3}{4},\frac{1}{2}\right)$
    D) $\left(-\frac{4}{3},-12\right)$

26. $$4x-3y=10$$

    In the xy-plane, the graph of which of the following equations is perpendicular to the graph of the equation above?

    A) $-4y+3x=3$
    B) $6x+8y=-7$
    C) $2x-3y=10$
    D) $-4x+3y=10$

Chapter 21: Interpreting Lines

The SAT includes questions that will ask you to interpret the meanings of the numbers in a linear equation. Interpreting lines questions will ask you to either (1) interpret the constant in a given equation or (2) select the equation that properly models a described situation. To answer these questions correctly, you need to understand what the constants in slope-intercept form represent.

$$y = mx + b$$

- m **is the slope. The slope represents the change in the y-value per unit of x.** In other words, **every time the x-value increases by 1, the slope tells you how much the y-value will increase or decrease**.

- b **is the y-intercept. The y-intercept is the value of y when $x = 0$.** You can think of this as **the initial value**.

These definitions can be very helpful when it comes to solving interpreting lines questions.

1) Interpreting the Constants in a Given Equation

The first type of interpreting lines question on the SAT will ask you to interpret the meaning of a constant in a given equation.

Example 1: The price, P, of a kayak purchased in 2010 is estimated by the equation $P = 2200 - 150t$, where t represents the number of years since the kayak was purchased. Which of the following is the best interpretation of the 2,200 in this context?

    A) The initial price of a kayak in 2010.
    B) The decrease in price of a kayak each year.
    C) The price of a kayak in 2019.
    D) The decrease in the price of a kayak from 2010 to 2019.

Solution: The 2,200 is the y-intercept of the given equation, so it represents the initial price when $t = 0$. The 2,200 is equal to the price of the kayak when $t = 0$ years after 2010, which is 2010. **The answer is A.**

It is important to also understand what each of the numbers in a linear equation represents. The -150 in the equation above is the slope. The slope of -150 tells us that the price of a kayak will decrease by \$150 each year. If the question above instead asked you "what is the best interpretation of -150 in this context?" the answer would have been B.

Example 2: The number of bacteria in a colony is modeled by the equation $b(x) = 12.5 + 0.5x$, where x represents the number of weeks and b represents the thousands of bacteria present in the colony. What is the best interpretation of the number 0.5 in this context?

    A) The number of bacteria in the colony will increase by 50% each week.
    B) The number of bacteria in the colony will increase by 0.5 bacteria each week.
    C) The number of bacteria in the colony will increase by 500 bacteria each week.
    D) The initial number of bacteria in the colony is 500 bacteria.

Solution: The 0.5 is the slope in this equation. Since the unit of x is in weeks, we see that every 1 week the value of b will increase by 0.5. Since the unit of b is thousands of bacteria, the slope 0.5 shows an increase of 0.5 thousand each week. $0.5 \times 1000 = 500$, so the number of bacteria in the colony will increase by 500 each week. **The answer is C.**

For these types of questions, you need to read carefully and keep an eye out for tricks like this one. The SAT will change the units on more difficult questions, just like we saw here, so it is important to make close reading a habit in the math sections.

2) Selecting the Right Equation

The second type of interpreting lines question will ask you to select which equation properly models the situation described in the question.

> **Example 3:** Tasty Alley Bakery makes their famous apple pie by adding layers of 3 mm apple slices between two pieces of 8 mm crust. Which of the following gives the total thickness T, in mm, of an apple pie with n layers of apples?
>
> A) $T = 3n + 8$
> B) $T = 3n + 16$
> C) $T = 6n + 8$
> D) $T = 6n + 16$

Solution: Method 1 – "Math Teacher Way": The rate at which the thickness T increases is 3 mm per 1 layer of apple slices added, so 3 is the slope. The initial thickness of the pie when $n = 0$ (no apples) is 16 mm since the pie has 2 pieces of 8 mm crust, so the y-intercept must be 16. **The answer is B.**

Method 2 – Plug-In Points: Sometimes selecting the right equation can be difficult. **To make questions like this easier, select a point or points that you know must work in the equation and then plug that point or points into the answer choices.** You will then be able to tell which equation is correct.

For this question, let's say there are 2 layers of apples, so $n = 2$. That means there will be two 3 mm layers of apples for a total of 6 mm of apples. Now, we can determine that the total thickness of the pie is

$$6 \ mm \ of \ apples + 2(8 \ mm \ per \ layer \ of \ crust) = 22 \ mm$$

When $n = 2$, the total thickness must be 22 mm. We can then plug in $n = 2$ into the answer choices and look for which answer choice gives $T = 22$. **The answer is B.**

For more challenging questions where it is difficult to write the equation on your own, the plug-in points method outlined above can be even more helpful. If you can select a point or points that you know must work in the equation, you can use these points to help identify which answer choice is correct. It is usually easiest to start with an initial value, which will be the y-intercept, and then pick a second point if necessary. To see how this works in practice, take a look at the next example question.

> **Example 4:** An experiment collected data about the relationship between the pressure within a balloon and the balloon's altitude. The scientists found a linear relationship between pressure and altitude. On the ground, the pressure within the balloon was measured at 14.3 psi. For every 250-meter increase in elevation, the pressure within the balloon dropped by 1.8 psi. Which of the following equations best models the pressure within the balloon, p, at h meters above the ground?
>
> A) $p = 14.3 - 1.8h$
> B) $p = 14.3 - 0.0072h$
> C) $p = (250)(1.8) - 14.3h$
> D) $p = 14.3h$

Solution: This question can be solved using two different methods. Questions like this can appear in the no-calculator section, so it is actually more easily solved using the plug-in points method.

Method 1 – Plug in Points: Let's start with the point $(0, 14.3)$. We know that this point must be on the graph because when the balloon is on the ground ($h = 0$), the pressure is 14.3 psi ($p = 14.3$). We can plug the point $(0, 14.3)$ into the answer choices to see which answer choices work and which answer choices we can cross off as incorrect.

A. $p = 14.3 - 1.8(0)$ → $p = 14.3$ (A works)

B. $p = 14.3 - 0.0072(0)$ → $p = 14.3$ (B works)

C. $p = (250)(1.8) - 14.3(0)$ → $p = 450$ (C is incorrect)

D. $p = 14.3(0)$ → $p = 0$ (D is incorrect)

Since answer choices A and B both work with our first point, we need to select another point to determine if the answer is A or B.

For a second point, we can select $(250, 12.5)$. At a height of 250 m, we know that the pressure will have decreased by 1.8 psi from the original value of 14.3 psi, so the pressure at 250 m will be 12.5 psi.

A. $p = 14.3 - 1.8\,(250)$ → $p = -435.7$ (A is wrong)

B. $p = 14.3 - 0.0072\,(250)$ → $p = 12.5$ (B is correct)

Even without a calculator, we can tell that A will be a negative number and will not be equal to 12.5. **The answer is B.**

Method 2 – "Math Teacher Way": This question can also be solved using the more traditional approach of finding the slope and the y-intercept. Here, the y-intercept is easiest to find. When $h = 0$, the pressure is 14.3, so the y-intercept is 14.3.

The slope is a bit more difficult to find. In this equation, the slope represents the change in pressure per meter of elevation. We are told that the pressure decreases by 1.8 psi per 250 m of elevation, so the slope would be

$$\frac{change\ in\ pressure}{change\ in\ elevation} = \frac{-1.8}{250} = -0.0072.$$

The answer is B.

Interpreting Lines Practice: A calculator may NOT be used on the following questions. Answers on page 265.

1. $$x + y = 200$$

The equation above represents the number of hours, x, Andrew spends fishing each year and the number of hours, y, Andrew spends surfing each year. In the equation, what does the number 200 represent?

A) The number of hours spent fishing each year.
B) The number of hours spent surfing each year.
C) The total number of hours spent fishing and surfing each year.
D) The number of hours spent fishing for each hour spent surfing.

2. The maximum speed of an F1 racecar in miles per hour is a linear function of the temperature, t, in degrees Fahrenheit of the engine, given by $S(t) = 0.128t + 212.5$. Which of the following statements is the best interpretation of the number 212.5?

$S(0) = 0.128(0) + 212.5 = 212.5$

A) The increase in the speed of the car for each 1^oC increase in the temperature.
B) The increase in the speed of the car for each 0.128^oC increase in the temperature.
C) The speed of the car at 0^oC.
D) The speed of the car at 0.128^oC.

3. John makes his surfboard by starting with a 28 mm thick piece of foam. He then adds n layers of 2 mm fiberglass. Which of the following gives the total thickness, S, in millimeters for a surfboard with n layers of fiberglass?

A) $S = 2n + 28$
B) $S = n + 14$
C) $S = 28n + 2$
D) $S = 2n + 14$

4. A racecar completes a lap in 20 seconds. Which of the following functions models the number of laps, $n(m)$, the racecar can complete in m minutes?

$1l = 20_\Delta$
$3l = 60_\Delta$

A) $n(m) = 20m$
B) $n(m) = 3m$
C) $n(m) = \frac{1}{3}m$
D) $n(m) = 60m$

$\frac{60}{20} = 3m$

5. Max begins working at a bakery on January 1st. His job is to make chocolate croissants. The number of chocolate croissants that Max can make each day is estimated by the equation $y = 2.2x + 60$, where x is the number of weeks since January 1st and y is the number of croissants he makes per day. Which of the following is the best explanation of 2.2 in this context?

A) The increase in the estimated number of croissants that Max makes each week with each additional week of experience.
B) The increase in the estimated number of croissants Max makes each day with each additional week of experience.
C) The total number of croissants that Max makes during his first week.
D) The total number of croissants that Max makes during his first day.

6. The Lakewood Country Club plans to increase its membership by a total of m families per year. At the beginning of this year, there were p families with memberships. Which function best models the total number of families, f, the Lakewood Country Club plans to have as members x years from now?

A) $f = px + m$
B) $f = mx + p$
C) $f = m(p)^x$
D) $f = mxp$

7. $$w = 9a + 19.5$$

A doctor uses the model above to estimate the weight, w, of a boy in terms of the boy's age, a, in years. Based on the model, what is the expected increase in the boy's weight, in pounds, from his 3rd to 7th birthday?

A) 9
B) 19.5
C) 27
D) 36

$9(3) + 19.5 \qquad 9(7) + 19.5$
$27 + 19.5 \qquad 63 + 19.5$
$46.5 \qquad 82.5$

$82.5 -$
46.5
36

8. A moving company estimates the price of a job, in dollars, using the equation $P = 150 + 25mh$, where m represents the number of movers and h is the total number of hours the job will take using m movers. Which of the following is the best interpretation of the number 25 in the equation?

A) The company charges 25 dollar per hour for each mover.
B) The price of every job increases by 25 dollars each hour.
C) Each mover works for an average of 25 hours per week.
D) A maximum of 25 movers can be used for the same job.

9.

Total Calories Burned During Exercise

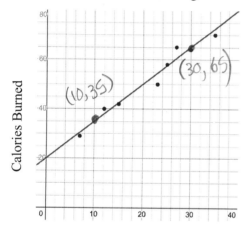

Minutes of Exercise

The scatterplot above shows the number of calories burned by eight people who exercise for various amounts of time. The line of best fit for the data is also shown. According to the line of best fit, which of the following is the closest to the predicted increase in calories burned for every 1-minute increase in exercise time?

$$\frac{65-35}{30-10} = \frac{30}{20} => 1.5$$

A) 1.0
B) 1.5
C) 2.0
D) 2.5

10.
$$C = 8x + 6y$$

The formula above gives the weekly cost, C, in dollars for employing a personal driver when the driver works x hours and uses y gallons of gas. If, in a particular week, the weekly cost is no more than \$800 and the driver uses at least 40 gallons of gas, what is the maximum number of hours the driver could have worked?

A) 50
B) 60
C) 70
D) 80

11.
$$W(b) = 0.62b + 5$$

Paleontologists can estimate the wingspan, W, of a Pterosaurs in feet based on beak length, b, in inches using the formula above. What is the correct interpretation of 0.62 in the equation?

A) The estimated beak length, in inches, of a Pterosaurs at birth.
B) The estimated increase of a Pterosaurs' wingspan, in feet, for each increase of 5 inches of beak length.
C) The estimated increase of a Pterosaurs' beak length, in inches, for each one-foot increase in wingspan.
D) The estimated increase of a Pterosaurs' wingspan, in feet, for each one-inch increase in its beak length.

12. Kyle measured the internal temperature of his brisket while it was being smoked. The temperature of the brisket before being placed in the smoker was 48°F. Kyle discovered that the temperature of the brisket rose at a constant rate. Two and a half hours after being placed in the smoker, the brisket's temperature was 93°F. Four hours after being placed in the smoker, the brisket's temperature was 120°F. Which of the following equations models the temperature $T(h)$ in degrees Fahrenheit h hours after being placed in the smoker?

$$(0, 48)$$

A) $T(h) = 45h + 48$
B) $T(h) = 30h + 48$
C) $T(h) = 48h + 45$
D) $T(h) = 18h + 48$

$$(2.5, 93)$$
$$(4, 120)$$

$$\frac{120-48}{4} = \frac{72}{4} = 18$$

13. The amount of juice that the average orange from Mitch's farm produces when juiced can be modeled by the equation $x = -19h + 290$, where x is the milliliters of juice produced and h is the weeks since harvest. Which of the following statements is true based on the equation?

   A) On average, an orange produces 19 milliliters less juice at harvest than one week after harvest.
   B) Two weeks after harvest, each orange on average produces 252 milliliters of juice.
   C) Each orange loses exactly 19 milliliters of juice per week after harvest.
   D) One week before harvest, each orange would have produced 308 milliliters of juice.

14. The effective oxygen level in the air is 21% at sea level. For every 1000 feet above sea level, the effective oxygen level in the air drops by 0.9%. Which of the following gives the effective oxygen level O, in percent, at h feet above sea level?

   $m = \dfrac{0.9}{1000} = 0.0009$

   A) $O = 21 - 0.0009h$
   B) $O = 21 - 0.9h$
   C) $O = 21h$
   D) $O = 21(0.09) - 1000h$

15. Annie paid $65 to sign up for a food delivery service that sends her ingredients for 5 meals each week. After the sign-up fee, Annie pays $200 every 4 weeks for the food. Which of the following models how much Annie pays, m, for k meals?

   A) $m = 65 + 10k$
   B) $m = 200 + 65k$
   C) $m = 5k + 65$
   D) $m = 65 + 50k$

Interpreting Lines Practice: A calculator may be used on the following questions.

16. The number of turtles that went to a certain beach in Costa Rica to lay their eggs from 2005 to 2015 can be modeled by the equation $y = 5.21x + 150$, where x represents the number of years since 2005 and y represents the total number of turtles each year. Which of the following best describes the meaning of the number 5.21 in the equation above?

   A) The estimated increase in the number of turtles that came to the beach each year from 2005 until 2015.
   B) The total number of turtles who came to the beach in 2005.
   C) The estimated difference between the number of turtles in 2005 and in 2015.
   D) The average number of turtles who arrived each year.

Questions 17 and 18 refer to the following information.

$$S(P) = 2P + 30$$
$$D(P) = 100 - \frac{3}{2}P$$

The quantity of new track shoes supplied and demanded is estimated by the functions above. The function $D(P)$ gives the quantity of track shoes demanded when the price is P dollars, and the function $S(P)$ gives the quantity of track shoes supplied when the price is P dollars.

17. How will the quantity of track shoes demanded change if the price is increased by 6 dollars?

   A) The quantity demanded will decrease by 12 units.
   B) The quantity demanded will decrease by 9 units.
   C) The quantity demanded will increase by 12 units.
   D) The quantity demanded will decrease by 21 units.

18. Which of the following best describes the meaning of the 2 in the supply function?

    A) The initial number of track shoes supplied at any price.
    B) The estimated increase in the number of track shoes demanded that corresponds with a $1 increase in the price.
    C) The estimated increase in the number of track shoes supplied that corresponds with $1 increase in the price.
    D) The estimated difference in the number of shoes supplied for each $10 increase in the price of the track shoes.

Questions 19 and 20 refer to the following information.

Total Cost of Renting a Kayak by the Hour

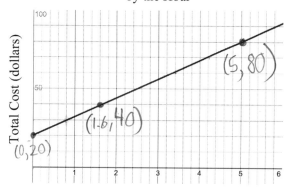

Time (hours)

The graph above shows the total cost C, in dollars, of renting a kayak for x hours.

19. What does the y-intercept on the graph represent?

    A) The initial cost of renting a kayak.
    B) The total number of hours the kayak was rented.
    C) The total number of kayaks rented.
    D) The increase in cost to rent the kayak for each additional hour.

20. Which of the following represents the relationship between x and C?

    A) $C = 12x$
    B) $C = 12x + 20$
    C) $C = 50 + 5x$
    D) $x = 8C + 20$

    $\dfrac{80-20}{5} = \dfrac{60}{5} = 12$

---

21. $$27000 - 180m = v$$

    The current value, v, of Jill's car m months after she purchased the car is modeled by the equation above. Which of the following statements is correct?

    A) The value of Jill's car at purchase was $26,820.
    B) Every year, the current value of Jill's car decreases by $180.
    C) Every 6 months, the current value of Jill's car decreases by $1,080.
    D) In ten years, the value of Jill's car will be $25,200.

22. A research team tracked the diameter of the trunk of a redwood tree, w, in inches over seventy-two years. When the study began in 1940, the redwood tree's trunk had a diameter of 46 inches. When the study was completed in 2012, the redwood tree's trunk had a diameter of 104 inches. Which of the following best models the diameter of the redwood tree, w, for y years since 1940?

    A) $w = 46 + 0.806y$
    B) $w = 104y$
    C) $w = 104y - 46$
    D) $w = 58y + 46$

Chapter 22: Exponential Growth and Decay

Any quantity that grows or decays at a fixed rate over time is said to experience exponential growth or decay. Some examples that you may be familiar with include money in a bank account earning 3% interest each year or the number of bacteria on a plate doubling every week. To solve exponential growth and decay questions, we use the equations below:

Growth: $A = P(1+r)^t$

Decay: $A = P(1-r)^t$

P = initial value
A = current value
r = rate of the growth or decay
t = time interval

To see how these equations work and appear on a graph, let's examine the equation for a bank account that has an initial balance of $500 and a 3% annual interest rate.

$$A = 500(1 + 0.03)^t$$
$$A = 500(1.03)^t$$

The $500 is the initial value, and the 3% is the growth rate. 3% is expressed as 0.03 in decimal form, so we get a value of 1.03 inside the parentheses. A represents the current value after t time intervals. Since the amount of money in the bank account is increasing at a non-linear rate over time, we have **exponential growth**.

Now, let's see how this exponential growth equation appears on a graph.

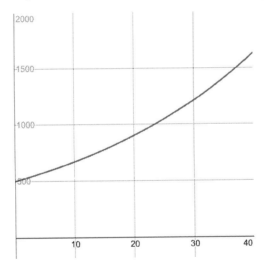

Note that **the graph is NOT linear**. Even though the growth rate remains constant at 3%, the annual increase in the amount of money in the account will not be the same. For any exponential growth equation, the graph will have an upward curve like this one. **The y-intercept of the graph shows the initial value**, which in this example is $500.

Now let's consider an example of **exponential decay**. A new car purchased for $20,000 loses 10% of its value each year after the purchase date.

$$A = 20,000(1 - 0.1)^t$$
$$A = 20,000(0.9)^t$$

The $20,000 is the initial value, and the 10% is the rate of decay. 10% can be expressed as 0.1 in decimal form, so we get a value of 0.9 inside the parentheses. A represents the current value after t time intervals.

Now, let's see how this exponential decay equation appears on a graph.

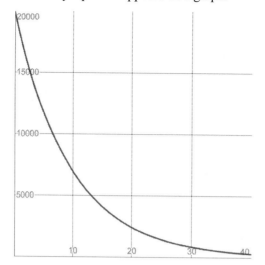

Again, note that the graph is NOT linear. The car continues to lose 10% of its value each year, but the numerical decrease in the car's value is not the same every year. Anytime we have an exponential decay equation, the graph will have a downward curve like this one. **The y-intercept of the graph shows the initial value**, which in this example is the purchase price of $20,000.

Example 1: Julia estimates that the numbers of bees in a hive increases by 30% every month. If Julia buys a hive with 50 bees, which of the following properly models Julia's estimate for how many bees, B, will live in the hive in m months?

A) $B = 50 + 30m$
B) $B = 50(0.3)^m$
C) $B = 50m^2 + 30$
D) $B = 50(1.3)^m$

Solution: The initial number of bees in the colony is 50, and the growth rate is 30%. Since the growth is 30% each month and not a fixed numerical value, we have exponential growth and not linear growth. A, which is linear, and C, which is quadratic, are incorrect. The value in the parentheses must be 1.3 and not 0.3 since the growth rate is 30%. The 1.3 comes from the $(1 + 0.3)$ in the growth equation. **The answer is D.**

The SAT will also ask you to interpret constants in a given exponential equation.

Example 2: A paper published in 1980 estimated that the number of ranchers in the United States can modeled by the equation $r = 10.5(0.92)^t$, where r is the number of ranchers, in thousands, and t is the number of years since 1980. Which of the following is the best interpretation of 10.5 in this context?

A) The estimated number of ranchers, in thousands, in 1980.
B) The estimated number of ranchers, in thousands, t years after 1980.
C) The estimated annual decrease in the number of ranchers, in thousands, for each year after 1980.
D) The estimated percent by which the number of ranchers decreased each year after 1980.

Solution: The 10.5 represents the initial number of ranchers at $t = 0$. Since the paper was published in 1980, the value of 10.5 represents the estimated number of ranchers, in thousands, in the United States in 1980. **The answer is A.**

More difficult questions will include different units of time in the exponential equation and the answer choices. Let's take a look at how this might appear with the next example.

> **Example 3:** A chemist is growing fungi as part of an experiment. At the beginning of the experiment, there are 105 fungi on the plate. The chemist discovers that the fungi population doubles every 20 minutes. Which of the following equations best models the number of fungi, f, on the plate h <u>hours</u> after the start of the experiment?
>
> A) $f = 105(2)^{3h}$
>
> B) $f = 105(2)^{\frac{h}{20}}$
>
> C) $f = 105(1 + \frac{h}{20})$
>
> D) $f = 105(1 + 3h)$

Solution: The best way to solve a question like this is to find a value that must appear on the graph and plug that value into the answer choices. For this question, we know that the population doubles every 20 minutes, so after 20 minutes, the population will be 210 fungi. 20 minutes is $\frac{1}{3}$ hours, so we can plug in $h = \frac{1}{3}$ to the answer choices and see which one will gives $f = 210$. **The answer is A.**

Exponential Growth and Decay Practice: **A calculator may NOT be used on the following questions.** Answers on page 266.

1. Trayvon is buying 5,436 fish to start his fish farm. The number of fish in his pond are estimated to increase at a rate of 3% per year. Which equation models the total number of fish, P, in the pond t years from now?

   A) $P(t) = 5,436(1.03)^t$
   B) $P(t) = 5,436(0.03)^t$
   C) $P(t) = 0.03(5,436)^t$
   D) $P(t) = 1.03(5,436)^t$

2. The value of a motorcycle depreciates at an annual rate of 14 percent. If the initial value is $20,000, which of the following models the value of the motorcycle, in dollars, in t years?

   A) $f(t) = 1.14t + 20,000$
   B) $f(t) = 0.86t + 20,000$
   C) $f(t) = 20,000(1.14)^t$
   D) $f(t) = 20,000(0.86)^t$

3. A surfboard depreciates at an annual rate of 15%. If the initial value of the surfboard is $995, which of the following functions P correctly models the price of the surfboard t years from purchase?

   A) $P(t) = 0.15(995)^t$
   B) $P(t) = 0.85(995)^t$
   C) $P(t) = 995(1.15)^t$
   D) $P(t) = 995(0.85)^t$

4. The function $f(x) = 75,000(b)^x$ models the annual value for a stock, in dollars, x years after being placed on the stock market, where b is a constant. If the stock's value increases 6% per year, what is the value of b?

   A) 0.06
   B) 0.6
   C) 1.06
   D) 1.6

5. The number of phosphorescent algae at Moonlight Beach on April 1, 2020 is P_0. For every 5-day period after April 1st, 2020, the number of phosphorescent algae will decrease by 7%. Which of the following equations represents the number of phosphorescent algae at Moonlight Beach, P_t, after t days?

   A) $P_t = P_0(0.07)^{5t}$
   B) $P_t = P_0(0.07)^{\frac{t}{5}}$
   C) $P_t = P_0(0.93)^{\frac{1}{5}t}$
   D) $P_t = P_0(0.93)^{5t}$

6. A hedge fund is offering a guaranteed investment return of 7% every three months. If you were to invest $50,000 today, which of the following equations gives the value of the investment, $V(t)$, y \underline{years} from today?

A) $V(y) = 50,000(1.07)^y$
B) $V(y) = 50,000(1.07)^{4y}$
C) $V(y) = 50,000(1.07 + \frac{y}{4})$
D) $V(y) = 50,000(1.07)^{3y}$

$\frac{12}{3} = 4$

$3m = \frac{1}{4}y$

7. The function below can be used to estimate the millions of people living within 15 miles of San Diego, where n is the number of years since 2017. Which of the following is the best explanation for 7.86?

$$F(n) = 7.86(1.02)^n$$

A) The number of people, in millions, living in San Diego in 2017.
B) The number of people, in millions, living within 15 miles of San Diego in 2017.
C) The estimated annual increase in the number of people, in millions, living within 15 miles of San Diego after 2017.
D) The estimated annual increase in the number of people, in millions, living in San Diego after 2017.

8. The equation below models the number of bacteria, in thousands, on a petri dish h hours after the dish has been inoculated. According to the model, the number of bacteria is predicted to increase by 2% every n minutes. What is the value of n?

$$F(h) = 62(1.02)^{\frac{h}{5}}$$

A) 12
B) 60
C) 120
D) 300

Exponential Growth and Decay Practice: A calculator may be used on the following questions.

9. A flu medicine has been shown to kill 50% of the viral load every 24 hours. If a sick individual has a viral load of x when they are given the medicine and the equation $N = x(b)^d$ models viral load, N, present after d days, what value should be used for b?

A) $b = 0.125$
B) $b = 0.25$
C) $b = 0.5$
D) $b = 1.5$

10. Which of the following describes an exponential relationship between the pair of variables listed?

A) For every 5% in medicine X taken, the number of inflammation markers drops by 15%.
B) For every 5% increase in medicine X taken, the number of inflammation markers drops by 30.
C) For every z grams of medicine X taken, inflammation markers decrease by a constant value p.
D) For every additional 10 grams of medicine X taken, inflammation markers drop by 50 units.

11. Starting in 1950, the number of people living in Alaska doubled every 20 years. The population of Alaska was 150,000 in 1950. Which of the following expressions gives the population of Alaska in 2010?

A) $150,000(2)^3$
B) $150,000(2)^{20}$
C) $150,000(2)^{60}$
D) $150,000(2)(60)$

12. Each year after a car is purchased, the price is estimated to be 15% less than the value the previous year. If the initial purchase price of a car was $29,500, which of the following is closest to the price of the car 3 years after it was purchased?

    A) $13,000
    B) $16,000
    C) $16,225
    D) $18,100

13. The US population has grown at an average rate of 0.8% per year since 1975. There were 236 million people in the US in 1980. Which of the following functions represents the US population N, in millions of people, y years since 1980?

    A) $N(y) = 236(1.008)^y$
    B) $N(y) = 236(1.08)^y$
    C) $N(y) = 236 + 1.008y$
    D) $N(y) = 236 + 1.08y$

14. From the 2nd month to the 6th month of its life, a golden retriever experiences exponential growth. The table below shows the weight of a golden retriever every 2 months.

Age (months)	Weight (pounds)
2	8
4	18
6	40.5

    Which of the following equations most closely models the weight of the golden retriever, $W(m)$, m months after 2 months from the ages of 2 months to 6 months?

    A) $W(m) = 8(2.25)^{\frac{m}{2}}$
    B) $W(m) = 8(2.25)^{2m}$
    C) $W(m) = 8(1.25)^{\frac{m}{2}}$
    D) $W(m) = 8(1.25)^{2m}$

$\frac{18-8}{8} = 1.25$

$(1 + 1.25) = 2.25$

15. San Diego estimates that the city's population will increase 8% every 16 years. If the current population is 3 million people, which of the following represents the city's estimate of the number of people, P, in millions that will live in San Diego y years from now?

    A) $P = 3(1.08)^y$
    B) $P = 3 + 1.08y$
    C) $P = (3y)^{1.08}$
    D) $P = 3(1.08)^{\frac{y}{16}}$

16. The doubling time for bacterial colonies on a petri dish from March 1st to May 1st is 14 days. Which of the following exponential functions models the number $N(d)$ of bacterial colonies d days after March 1st if the petri dish had 250 colonies on March 1st?

    A) $N(d) = 14(2)^{\frac{d}{250}}$
    B) $N(d) = 14(2)^{250d}$
    C) $N(d) = 250(2)^{\frac{d}{14}}$
    D) $N(d) = 250(2)^{14d}$

17. The equation below models the number of students, N, who have joined the choir y years after the choir was started. Which of the following equations models the number of students who have joined the choir m months after it started?

$$N = 25(1.15)^y$$

    A) $N = 25(1.15) + 12m$
    B) $N = 25(1.15)^{12m}$
    C) $N = 25(1.15 + \frac{m}{12})$
    D) $N = 25(1.15)^{\frac{m}{12}}$

18. NASA has just finished building a new ion thruster that will power a spaceship on a mission to Pluto. By using continuous small thrusts, the engine is able to accelerate at an exponential rate of 0.096% per day. When the ion thruster is turned on, the spaceship is moving at 35,000 meters per second. The spaceship will double its speed every 73 days. Which of the following exponential functions models the speed $S(y)$ of the spaceship, in meters per second, y years after the ion thruster is turned on? (1 year = 365 days)

A) $S(y) = 35{,}000(1.0096)^y$

B) $S(y) = 35{,}000(1.0096)^{2y}$

C) $S(y) = 35{,}000(2)^{\frac{1}{5}y}$

D) $S(y) = 35{,}000(2)^{5y}$

$365d = 1y$

$73d = ?$

$\Downarrow$

$\dfrac{1}{5}\ year$

Chapter 23: Scatter Plots and Lines of Best Fit

Scatter plots show the relationship between two variables in a data set. **Each data point appears as a dot on the scatter plot. A line of best fit is a line (or curve) that best represents the data on a scatter plot.** This line may pass through some of the points, none of the points, or all of the points. Let's see how this works with an example scatter plot:

The scatterplot below shows the root depth and plant height for the tomato plants in Bill's garden one month after the seeds were planted.

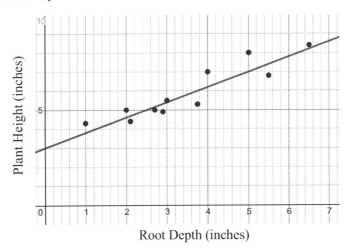

Each of the points in the scatter plot represents a single tomato plant in Bill's garden. The location of the dot corresponds with the root depth and plant height of the tomato plant. Since there are 11 dots, we know there are 11 tomato plants in Bill's garden. This brings us to the first two principles you need to know about scatter plots.

   Principle #1 – Each point on a scatter plot represents one data point in the set.

   Principle #2 – The total number of points on a scatter plot is equal to the total number of data points in the set.

The line of best fit can be used to make an estimate for data points that are not part of the original data set. For example, on the scatter plot above when the root depth is 5 inches, the line of best fit predicts the plant height will be 7 inches. The actual value of the height of the plant with a root depth of 5 inches is 8 inches (see the dot at $(5, 8)$). This brings us to our second important principle to understand about scatter plots and the line of best fit.

   Principle #3 – The predicted value is on the line of best fit while the actual value is at the point in the scatter plot.

We will use the scatter plot above to go over the various ways that the SAT will test you on scatter plots and lines of best fit.

Example 1: Based on the line of best fit, if the value of root depth is 6 inches, what is the predicted plant height in inches?

   A) 3.8   B) 5.2   C) 6.7   D) 7.8

Solution: To find the predicted plant height, we want to find the point on the line of best fit where root depths is 6 inches. On the line of best fit, this is at the point $(6, 7.8)$. **The answer is D.**

Example 2: For the tomato plant with a root depth of 4 inches, which of the following is closest to the positive difference between the actual plant height and the plant height predicted by the line of best fit?

    A) 1.5   B) 1.2   C) 0.8   D) 0.4

Solution: We first need to find which point the question is directing us to look at, which is where the root depth is 4 inches. The plant height is on the x-axis, so if we look at where $x = 4$, we find a point at $(4, 7)$. This point shows one of the tomato plants had a root depth of 4 inches and a height depth of 7 inches. The 7 inches is the actual height. To find the predicted height, we find the point on the line of best fit where the root depth is 4 inches. We can estimate this point to be at $(4, 6.2)$. The 6.2 inches is the plant height predicted by the line of best fit. The positive difference between the actual height and predicted height is $7 - 6.2 = 0.8$. **The answer is C.**

Notice that even though we had to estimate the value for the predicted value, the answer choices made clear which one is correct. Even if we estimated the point to be at $(4, 6.1)$, we would get an answer of 0.9, which is closest to 0.8.

Example 3: The scatter plot above shows the depth of the tomato plant roots, x, and the height of the tomato plants, y, for 11 tomato plants in Bill's garden. A line of best fit is also shown. Which of the following could be the equation of the line of best fit?

    A) $1.4x + 3$ B) $0.8x + 3$ C) $1.4x + 1.2$ D) $0.8x + 1.2$

Solution: For a question like this, start by solving for the slope. To find the slope, find for two points on the line of best fit. Here, we will use $(5, 7)$ and $(0, 3)$.

$$slope = \frac{7-3}{5-0} = \frac{4}{5} = 0.8$$

Next, find the y-intercept. For the line of best fit, we see the y-intercept is at $y = 3$. **The answer is B.**

TIP – Is that really the y-intercept?

When asked to find the equation of a line of best fit on a scatter plot, make sure that the point that looks like the y-intercept is actually the y-intercept. **Scatter plots may have the axes scaled so that the bottom left of the graph will not be when $x = 0$. When this occurs, the point that looks like the y-intercept is just another point on the graph.**

For example, let's take a look at the same graph from above but the left side of the graph has now been cut off.

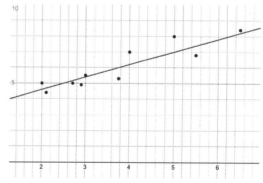

At first glance, it looks like the y-intercept is at $y = 4$, but that would be incorrect. **The graph does not include $x = 0$, so we cannot see the y-intercept.** Make sure that you do not fall for this common trick on test day.

Scatter Plots Practice: A calculator may NOT be used on the following questions. Answers on page 267.

1.

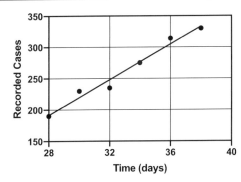

The graph above models the number of recorded flu cases in Somerton based on the number of days after the first recorded case. For how many days was the number of recorded flu cases greater than the line of best fit predicted?

A) 0
B) 1
C) 2
D) 4

3.

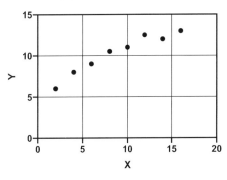

Which of the following equations best models the line of best fit for the scatterplot above?

A) $y = 0.6x + 5$
B) $y = x + 5$
C) $y = 2x$
D) $y = 3x + 5$

2.

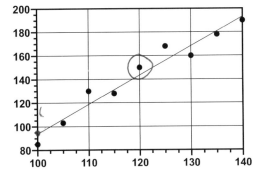

On the graph above, the x-axis represents the pounds of steel used in a new building and the y-axis represents the price of a new building in thousands of dollars. For the building that used the median pounds of steel, which of the following is closest to the difference between the actual price and the predicted price of the building in thousands of dollars?

A) −3
B) 0
C) 6
D) 11

$$\frac{150 - 120}{100 - 95} = \frac{30}{5} = 6$$

4.

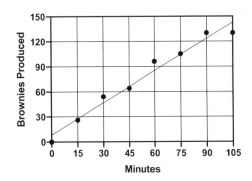

The graph above displays the number of brownies produced at a bakery at different numbers of minutes after opening. Based on the line of best fit, how many minutes after opening is the number of brownies produced expected to be 60?

A) 40
B) 45
C) 85
D) 95

5.

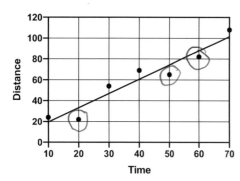

The graph above plots Paula's runs last week. What is the number of times that the line of best fit predicted a distance greater than the actual distance?

6.

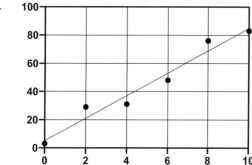

The graph above plots the height, in cm, of a Great Dane on the y-axis and the age, in months, on the x-axis. Which of the following is closest to the difference in centimeters between the actual height of the Great Dane at 8 months and the height of the Great Dane predicted by the line of best fit?

A) 2
B) 7
C) 12
D) 15

7.

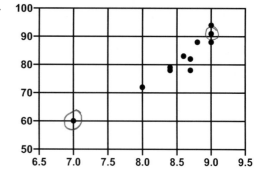

Which of the following could be the equation for the line of best fit for the data shown in the scatterplot above?

A) $y = 14x + 50$

B) $y = 14x - 40$

C) $y = \frac{1}{2}x + 50$

D) $y = \frac{1}{2}x$

$(7, 60)$

$(9, 90)$

$\frac{90-60}{9-7} = 15$

$60 = 14(7) + b$

$-38 = b$

8. Tijuana Daily Border Crossings

Year	Average Number of People Crossing
2007	13,400
2008	14,300
2009	15,500
2010	16,400
2011	17,500

The table above shows the average number of people crossing the Tijuana border per day for the different years listed. If these data points were displayed on a scatter plot with the years after 2007 on the x-axis and the average number of people crossing on the y-axis, which of the following best models the line of best fit?

A) $y = 13,400 + 1,000x$
B) $y = 13,400 + 800x$
C) $y = 13,400(1.1)^x$
D) $y = 13,400(1.1)^{\frac{x}{5}}$

9.

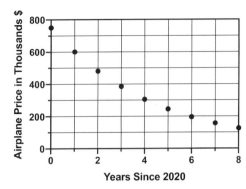

The graph above models the relationship between the price, in thousands of dollars, of an airplane since it was purchased in 2020. Let x equal the years since 2020. Which of the following is the equation for the line of best fit?

A) $y = 750 - 150x$
B) $y = 750 - 80x$
C) $y = 750(0.2)^x$
D) $y = 750(0.8)^x$

10.

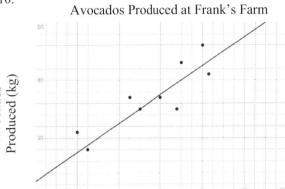

Height of the Avocado Tree (ft)

The scatterplot above shows the relationship between the height of the avocado trees (h) and the kilograms of avocados produced (p) at Frank's farm. A line of best fit for the data is shown. Which of the following is the equation of the line of best fit?

A) $p = \frac{5}{2}h + 22$

B) $p = \frac{5}{2}h - 2.5$

C) $p = \frac{2}{5}h + 22$

D) $p = \frac{2}{5}h$

Chapter 24: Statistical Analysis

The SAT loves to ask questions about various statistics terms, proper sampling methods, and the assumptions that can be made from a given data set. Statistical analysis is a topic that many students have not learned before taking the SAT, so it is common to struggle with statistics questions. The good news is we have everything you need to know about statistics in this chapter, so you will be ready for any statistical analysis questions on test day.

Sampling

Data collection in statistical analysis is most commonly gathered through surveying (or sampling) a population. There are 3 important things to remember about sampling:

1. **In order to have reliable data, a survey must be conducted on randomly selected members of the population.**

2. **A larger sample size is better than a smaller sample size as long as both samples are randomly selecting members from the population.**

3. **The findings of a survey can be generalized to the entire population that is being randomly sampled.**

The most important thing to look for in any sampling question is that the sample is random. Any sample that is not random is not reliable (more on this shortly).

So what is the point of all of this sampling? The findings of a survey conducted with random sampling can be generalized to the entire population that is being sampled. In other words, sampling is a powerful tool to help predict what the actual value might be for a larger population without having to sample the entire population.

I know this wording seems confusing, so let's use an example to make this clearer:

Blue Top Middle School has 2,500 total students and 700 6th grade students. 40 6th grade students are randomly selected and asked how many pairs of shoes they own. The survey found the 40 randomly selected 6th grade students on average own 5 pairs of shoes.

The survey randomly selects students, so we have a reliable data set. **From this survey, we can estimate that the average number of pairs of shoes owned by each student for the 700 6th grade students at Blue Top Middle School is close to 5.** Even though we did not survey all 700 6th grade students, we can make an educated guess that the average number of pairs of shoes owned by 6th graders at Blue Top Middle School is close to the average from the survey. This is the entire point of conducting a survey! Since we were sampling from the 700 6th grade students at Blue Top Middle School, we can generalize the findings to all 700 students.

Now, **we can NOT assume that the average number of pairs of shoes owned by each student for all 2,500 students at Blue Top Middle School is close to 5.** We can only generalize the survey data to the group that we are randomly sampling. Since we did not randomly sample from all students at Blue Top Middle School, we cannot make any predictions about the average number of pairs of shoes owned for all 2,500 students at Blue Top Middle School.

In addition, we cannot apply the findings to any other groups of 6th grade students. If there was another Middle School, let's call it Red Top Middle School, down the street from Blue Top Middle School, we cannot apply the findings and say that Red Top Middle School's 6th graders on average own close to 5 pairs of shoes. There may be something different about the students at Red Top Middle School that make them own more or fewer pairs of shoes. Again, we can only apply the findings of a survey to the population that is being randomly sampled.

If you understand the three principles and how they apply to this example, you know everything you need to correctly answer sampling questions on test day.

Example 1: The teachers at Iron Ridge High School want to find out how students use their phones. Which of the following will produce the most reliable data about all of the students at the high school?

    A) Listing students' last names alphabetically and then conducting a survey of the last 80 students on the list.
    B) Randomly selecting 30 students to complete an online questionnaire.
    C) Assigning each student a number and then using a random number generator to select 200 students to complete a survey.
    D) Setting up a table with free pizza and getting 75 students to fill out a survey.

Solution: For this survey to have reliable data, we need a random sample. A is not a random sample because we organized the students alphabetically. D is not random because students volunteered for the survey. B and C are both random samples. A larger sample size produces better data than a smaller sample size, so **the answer is C**.

It is important to recognize that A is not a random sample. Even though it may seem random at first, **any type of organization in selecting a sample makes it non-random**.

Example 2: A study about the quality of the health care system is conducted by polling 110 nurses who work at different hospitals in Austin, Texas. The survey found the average rating for the overall quality of the current health care system is 6.5 out of 10. Which of the following is the biggest group that the findings of this study can be applied to?

    A) The 110 nurses polled in the study.
    B) All of the nurses that work in hospitals in Austin, Texas.
    C) All of the nurses in Austin, Texas.
    D) All of the nurses who work in hospitals in Texas.

Solution: The results of a study can be generalized to the population that is being randomly survey. In this question, the study surveys nurses who work in hospitals in Austin, Texas, so we can generalize the findings to that group. The study did not survey nurses who did not work in hospitals, so we cannot include all nurses in Austin, Texas. The study also did not include nurses from other parts of Texas, so we cannot assume nurses from the rest of Texas would respond similarly to those in Austin, Texas. **The answer is B.**

Standard Deviation

Standard deviation is a measure of the spread of values in a data set. A low standard deviation indicates the numbers tend to be closer to the average of a data set while a high standard deviation indicates that numbers tend to be farther from the average of a data set. You will not need to know how to compute standard deviation on the SAT, but you will need to understand the concept. All that you need to know is

    A set of values that are closer together has a lower standard deviation, and a set of values that are farther apart has a higher standard deviation.

All you need to do to correctly answer standard deviation questions correct is memorize this rule. Let's take a look at some examples to see how this might come up on test day.

Example 3:
Company A: 18, 25, 26, 26, 27, 35, 36, 38
Company B: 64, 66, 66, 66, 68, 68, 68, 70
Company C: 22, 40, 78, 78, 88, 90, 90, 96

Three water filtration companies (A, B, and C) each provided 8 samples of water to be tested for purity. The purity scores are listed above. Which of the following statements about the standard deviation of the purity scores is correct?

A) Company A has the lowest standard deviation.
B) Company B has the lowest standard deviation.
C) Company C has the lowest standard deviation.
D) It cannot be determined which company has the lowest standard deviation.

Solution: To find out which company has the lowest standard deviation, look for which set of numbers is the closest together. The purity scores for company B are the closest together, so company B has the lowest standard deviation. **The answer is B.**

Notice that the actual values of the numbers do not affect standard deviation. It does not matter how big or small the numbers are; all that matters is how close the values are to each other.

Standard deviation questions can also include a table or graph. If you are given a table or graph, you are still looking for how spread apart the data points are. Data points that are more closely clustered have a lower standard deviation while data points that are more spread apart have a higher standard deviation.

Example 4: The tables below give the distribution of weekly rainfall for City A and City B over 17 weeks during the summer of 2012.

Weekly Rainfall	City A	City B
0.00-0.99 inches	6	3
1.00-1.99 inches	2	11
2.00-2.99 inches	3	2
3.00-3.99 inches	1	1
>4 inches	5	0

Which of the following is true about the data shown for these 17 weeks?

A) The standard deviation of weekly rainfall in city A is greater.
B) The standard deviation of weekly rainfall in city B is greater.
C) The standard deviation of weekly rainfall in city A is the same as in city B.
D) The standard deviation of weekly rainfall cannot be calculated with the data provided.

Solution: To determine standard deviation, we need to see how spread out the data points are. The values for the weekly rainfall for city A are very spread out, with 6 weeks having less than 1 inch of rainfall and 5 weeks having greater than 4 inches of rainfall. City B has very consistent rainfall, with 11 of the 17 weeks falling between 1 and 1.99 inches, so the weekly rainfall is not very spread out. City A is much more spread out than city B, so the standard deviation of weekly rainfall in city A is greater. **The answer is A.**

TIP – Dot Plots

The SAT occasionally includes standard deviation questions with dot plots. Dot plots are a way to efficiently display a data set visually. The dot plot below shows the results of a survey that asked how many hours students spend on their phones per week.

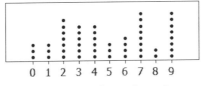

Time on phone (hours)

This dot plot shows that 3 students said they spent 0, 1, or 5 hours on the phone (3 dots for each), seven students spent 2 hours on the phone, 6 students spend 3 or 4 hours on the phone, etc.

Margin of Error

Margin of error is a statistic expressing the amount of random sampling error in a survey. The margin of error is the amount by which the findings of a survey may vary from the true value. I know that wording seems confusing, so let's take a look at an example to clarify how margin of error is actually used.

At Smithfield High School, 50 students are randomly selected to complete a survey about their homework habits. The survey found that the estimated mean number of hours spent on homework per week was 9.5 with a margin of error of 2.

From this survey, **an appropriate interpretation of the data would be that it is plausible that the mean number of hours spent on homework per week for all high school students at Smithfield High School is between 7.5 and 11.5 hours.**

The margin of error identifies the range in which we expect the true value of the mean to fall. **The true value of the mean would be the value if you surveyed every student at Smithfield High School and calculated the mean.** However, we do not have time to survey every student, so the margin of error helps us more quickly find out what the mean number of hours students spend on homework each week likely is.

Be sure to notice that we are talking about the mean here. **The margin of error does NOT tell us that all students spend between 7.5 and 11.5 hours of homework per week.** Some students may be lazy and only do 3 hours of homework per week, and others may study much more and spend 15 hours on homework each week. The margin of error just says the mean number of hours spent on homework each week for all students at Smithfield High School is between 7.5 and 11.5 hours.

Example 5: A quality control manager at Clark's Candies is testing to see how many chocolates are in each jar. The quality control manager randomly selects 200 jars that day and counts the number of chocolates in each jar. He finds that the mean number of chocolates in each jar is 58 with an associated margin of error of 4. Which of the following is the most appropriate conclusion based on the data?

A) All of the jars of chocolate ever produced at Clark's Candies have between 54 and 62 chocolates.

B) All of the jars of chocolate produced that day at Clark's Candies have between 54 and 62 chocolates.

C) It is plausible that the mean number of chocolates in each jar produced that day at Clark's Candies is between 54 and 62 chocolates.

D) It is plausible that the mean number of chocolates in each jar ever produced at Clark's Candies is between 54 and 62 chocolates.

Solution: Given the mean and margin of error, it is plausible that the mean number of chocolates in each jar for all of the jars produced that day is between 54 and 62 chocolates. The margin of error does not mean that all of the jars fall within that range; there could have been an error and a jar with only 40 candies could have been produced, so B is incorrect. Also, the sample can only give data about the day when it was conducted, so answer choices A and D, which talk about all of the jars ever produced, are incorrect. **The answer is C.**

*Test Day Tip: For any margin of error question, look for the word "plausible" in the answer choices. The correct answer almost always has the word plausible in it.

Example 6: Researchers want to find the output of orange trees at George's farm in Vero Beach, Florida by randomly selecting 80 orange trees in his grove and counting the number of oranges each tree produces. After gathering the data, the researchers discovered that the trees on average produced 310 oranges per tree with a margin of error of 22 oranges. Which of the following statements is the most appropriate conclusion from these findings?

A) The mean number of oranges produced per tree for all farms in Vero Beach, Florida is between 288 and 332 oranges.

B) The number of oranges per tree on all trees on George's farm is between 288 and 332 oranges.

C) It is plausible that the mean number of oranges produced by each tree on George's farm is between 288 and 332 oranges.

D) All trees in Vero Beach, Florida produce between 288 and 332 oranges.

Solution: Given the mean and margin of error, it is plausible that the mean number of oranges produced by each tree at George's farm is between 288 and 332. We can only apply the data to George's farm since all of the trees selected were on his farm, so A, which talks about all farms in Vero Beach, is incorrect. The margin of error tells us about the mean value for all trees, not the exact value on each individual tree, so answer choices B and D are incorrect. **The answer is C.**

Again, notice here how we see the word "plausible" in the correct answer choice.

There is one other important principle to understand for margin of error:

A larger data set will most likely have a smaller margin of error, and a smaller data set will most likely have a larger margin of error.

If you think about sampling, this makes perfect sense. The more data points you gather, the more likely you are to be closer to the true mean. For example, let's say that Joe and Tommy are trying to find out how many watches are owned by each student in the 11th grade. If Joe only asks 5 students and Tommy asks 60, the mean value of Tommy's data set will likely be much closer to the true mean value for all students than the mean from Joe's data set. In other words, Tommy's data set will have a much smaller margin of error than Joe's.

Here is an example of how this type of question may appear on the SAT.

Example 7: Rebecca and Simone survey people in their town and ask people to rank, on a scale of 1 to 10, how much they care about saving tigers in the wild. Rebecca surveys 125 people, and Simone surveys 52. Both Rebecca and Simone find that the mean survey response was 5.5. Which of the following statements is most likely to be true?

A) The range for Rebecca's survey responses is larger than the range for Simone's survey responses.
B) The range for Rebecca's survey responses is smaller than the range for Simone's survey responses.
C) The margin of error for Rebecca's survey responses is larger than the margin of error for Simone's survey responses.
D) The margin of error for Rebecca's survey responses is smaller than the margin of error for Simone's survey responses.

Solution: Rebecca surveyed a larger number of people, so the margin of error for her survey responses is most likely smaller. The mean survey response and size of the survey does not tell us anything about the range, as we have no way to know the largest and smallest values in the survey, so answer choices A and B are both wrong. **The answer is D.**

Statistical Bias

Statistical bias is when a model or statistic does not accurately represent the population that was surveyed. Below, we will cover the common surveying mistakes that can lead to a sample having bias and not accurately reflecting the general population. **If statistical bias occurs, the results of the survey will somehow be skewed because participants were not selected at random, and the findings cannot be applied to the general population.**

1. **Sampling bias occurs whenever the population is not randomly sampled.** Anytime the participants are not selected randomly, the results from the sample will not be representative of the population.

   For example, let's say you wanted to find the average number of kids in a neighborhood. If you go to the community pool and ask people how many kids they have, this creates sampling bias because individuals at the community pool are more likely to have kids. To do this survey correctly, you would need to randomly select houses in your neighborhood and then ask the people at these houses how many kids they have.

2. **Self-Selection bias occurs when individuals are selecting themselves to be part of a sample.** If a survey is voluntary, only certain people will take the effort to respond to the survey, but this choosing to respond may correlate with other behaviors. The results from any sample with self-selection bias will not be representative of the population.

   For example, let's say you want to find out why lawyers in San Francisco think they were successful. To do so, you send out an email to 500 lawyers in San Francisco and ask them to come in and answer a few questions about how they achieved success. This will generate self-selection bias. The most successful lawyers will likely be too busy to take time to come in for an interview for your survey. In addition, the lawyers who did come in may be likely to overexaggerate their success and not give honest feedback. To do this survey correctly, you would need to find a method that generates a completely random sample of lawyers to come in for the interview and gets honest responses to the survey questions.

3. **Cause-Effect bias occurs when a correlation between two variables leads us to incorrectly believe that there is a cause and effect relationship.**

For example, after selecting a group of 2,000 people and examining their breakfast diets and health, researchers found that those who ate fruit at breakfast had a lower rate of heart attacks. This does not mean that eating fruit for breakfast lowers the risk of a heart attack. Most likely, people who eat fruit with breakfast have a healthier lifestyle compared to those who eat less healthy options. This healthier lifestyle, not just the fruit at breakfast, more likely causes the lower rate of heart attacks.

Any survey with any of these three biases produces a data set that is not reliable. As a result, the findings cannot be generalized to a larger population.

Example 8: Three separate studies examined the number of countries a junior at Fenwick High could name in 30 seconds. The participants for the studies were selected as follows:

   I.   For Study 1, 200 juniors from Fenwick High volunteered to participate.
   II.   For Study 2, 150 juniors from Fenwick High were randomly selected to participate.
   III. For Study 3, 125 of the 250 juniors at Fenwick High who are currently enrolled in world history were selected at random to participate.

The results of which studies can appropriately be generalized to the entire population of juniors at Fenwick High?

   A) Study I   B) Study II   C) Studies II and III   D) Studies I, II, and III

Solution: Study I is not random since students volunteer, so Study 1 has self-selection bias. Study III has sampling bias because students who are enrolled in world history may have better knowledge of countries than a randomly selected student. Study II uses a randomly selected population, so we can generalize the results to the entire population of juniors at Fenwick High. **The answer is B.**

Example 9: Penelope wants to find out how much people spend on organic produce each week in her town. To do so, she goes to Mark's Organic Market, a market that specializes in selling organic items, and surveys people at the market. Penelope surveys 218 people and finds that the mean amount spent on organic produce each week is $43 with a margin of error of $4. Which of the following is the best interpretation of Penelope's finding?

   A) The mean number of dollars spent on organic produce each week for all of the people in Penelope's town is $43.
   B) It is plausible that the mean number of dollars spent on organic produce each week for all people in Penelope's town is between $39 and $47.
   C) If Penelope surveys another 218 people at Mark's Organic Market, the mean number of dollars spent on organic produce will be $43.
   D) Penelope's method for collecting data is flawed, so we cannot make any conclusions about the amount of money the rest of the town spends on organic produce.

Solution: Since Penelope conducts the survey at Mark's Organic Market, she is not sampling a random population and her findings cannot be generalized to the rest of the town. People shopping at Mark's Organic Market likely will spend more on organic produce than shoppers at other grocery stores. **The answer is D.**

Box and Whisker Plot

A box and whisker plot is another way that a data set can be visually displayed. The box and whisker plot gives a five-number summary of the data: the minimum, the maximum, the first quartile, the median, and the third quartile.

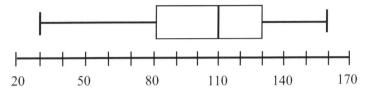

- **The whiskers display the minimum and maximum of the data.** For the example plot, the minimum is at 30 and the maximum is at 160.

- **The box ranges from the first quartile (25th percentile) to the third quartile (75th percentile) of the data.** In other words, the middle 50% of the data points, those from the 25th to 75th percentiles, all fall within the box. The first quartile, the lowest 25% of data points, is from the minimum to the left edge of the box. The fourth quartile, the largest 25% of data points, is from the right side of the box to the maximum.

- **The middle line in the box displays the median for the data.** For the example plot, the median is 110.

Example 10: Ms. Pearson's first and second period classes each sold brownies to raise money for charity after a forest fire destroyed many local businesses. There are 24 students in the second period class and 29 in the third period class. Each student in the class sold brownies and then reported the number of brownies they sold to Ms. Pearson. The data for the number of brownies sold by each student are displayed in the box and whisker plot below. If a represents the median for class 1 and b represents the median for class 2, what is the value of $a - b$?

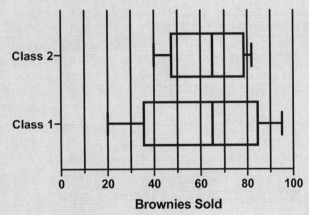

Solution: The median value is the line in the middle of the box. Since both lines are located at the same number of brownies, the median values for both classes are equal so $a = b$. Therefore, $a - b = 0$. **The answer is 0.**

Statistical Analysis Practice: A calculator may NOT be used on the following questions. Answers on page 268.

1. Everyone must pass a driver education test in order to get a driver's license. This year, California offered a new program where students could attend an additional review session for free before taking the test. The students who went to the additional review session scored higher on the test on average than those who did not. Which of the following is a valid conclusion based on this information?

   A) The extra review session caused the enrolled students to do better on the driving test.
   B) The extra review session will cause anyone to do better on the driving test.
   C) An extra review session will help anyone do better in any type of class.
   D) You cannot make a conclusion about the cause and effect of going to an extra review session before taking the driving test.

2. Which of the following is true about the standard deviations of the two data sets in the table below?

Set A	30	45	55	75	80	90
Set B	8	40	79	90	110	140

   A) The standard deviation of data set A is larger than the standard deviation of data set B.
   B) The standard deviation of data set B is larger than the standard deviation of data set A.
   C) The standard deviation of data set A is the same as the standard deviation of data set B.
   D) There is not enough information available to compare the standard deviations of the two data sets.

3. A San Diego marine biologist went to La Jolla and selected a random sample of 15 sea lions for a study about sea lion mass. The marine biologist found that the mean mass of the sea lions in the sample was 480 pounds, with an associated margin of error of 38 pounds. Which of the following is the best interpretation of the marine biologist's findings?

   A) All sea lions in the sample have a mass between 442 pounds and 518 pounds.
   B) Most sea lions have a mass between 442 pounds and 518 pounds.
   C) Any mass between 442 pounds and 518 pounds is a plausible value for the mean mass of the sea lions in La Jolla.
   D) Any sea lion at La Jolla shores has a mass between 442 pounds and 518 pounds.

4. Two hundred members at Axburry Golf Club will be selected to participate in a survey about the menu for the annual club championship dinner. Which of the following methods would result in a random sample of members of the Axburry Golf Club?

   A) Obtain an alphabetical list of all Axburry Golf Club members. Select the first two hundred people.
   B) Obtain a numbered list of all Axburry Golf Club members. Use a random number generator to select 200 members from the list. Give the survey to those members.
   C) Obtain a list of Axburry Golf Club members attending the club championship dinner. Give the survey to the first 200 members who arrive.
   D) Tell all Axburry Golf Club members that volunteers are needed to take a survey. Give the survey to the first 200 volunteers.

5. To determine if residents of Cardiff would support a measure to spend $50,000 to build a new skate park, Jonathan surveyed 100 people at a popular skate spot. 70% of them said they would support the measure. Which of the following statements must be true?

A) When the measure is voted on, 70% of Cardiff residents will vote yes.
B) The sample size is too small to have any useful data.
C) The margin of error is not provided, so we cannot make a valid conclusion.
D) The sampling method is flawed and will likely produce a biased result.

6. A news website invited readers to respond to a poll at the end of the article that asked, "Do you think the new federal budget will help our economy?" The survey found that 65% of respondents said "Yes" and 31% said "No". Which of the following best explains why these results are unlikely to represent the beliefs of the entire US population?

A) Those who responded to the poll do not represent a random sample of US residents.
B) The news website did not share how many people responded to the poll.
C) The percentages do not add up to 100%, so any possible conclusions from the data are invalid.
D) The poll was not posted on the website for a long enough time, so there is not enough data to make any valid conclusions.

7.

| Set A | 2,420 | 3,480 | 5,600 | 7,843 | 9,867 |
| Set B | 10,452 | 25,460 | 38,499 | 50,480 | 80,260 |

Which of the following is true about the standard deviations of the two data sets above?

A) The standard deviation for set B is larger than for set A.
B) The standard deviation for set A is larger than for set B.
C) The standard deviations for set A and for set B are equal.
D) There is not enough information to compare the standard deviations of the sets.

8.

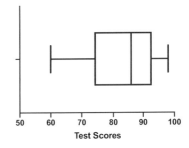

Test Scores

The box and whisker plot above displays information about the test scores for students on the final exam. Which of the following is the median test score on the final exam?

A) 60
B) 75
C) 87
D) 92

9. A researcher asked a randomly selected group of 5,000 oncologists if they believed that cancer will be cured in the next 50 years. Using the survey data, the researcher found that 18% of the scientists believe that cancer will be cured in the next 50 years with a margin of error of 3%. Which of the following is the most appropriate conclusion about all oncologists based on the given findings and margin of error?

A) It is plausible that the percentage of all oncologists who believe cancer will be cured in the next 50 years is between 15% and 21%.
B) The researcher is between 15% and 21% sure that most oncologists believe cancer will be cured in the next 50 years.
C) It is unlikely that less than 18% of oncologists believe cancer will be cured in the next 50 years.
D) At least 18% but no more than 21% of oncologists believe cancer will be cured in the next 50 years.

Questions 10 and 11 refer to the following information.

At a business with 3,000 employees, Chloe and Amy conduct a survey to find out how much money people spent on groceries each week. Both Chloe and Amy mailed out surveys to randomly selected employees. 180 people responded to Chloe's survey and 100 people responded to Amy's survey. The results from Chloe's and Amy's surveys are summarized below:

Chloe's Survey Results

Grocery Spending (USD)	Number of Employees
Less than 100	12
100-199	26
200-299	39
300-400	68
Greater than 400	35

Amy's Survey Results

Grocery Spending

10. Which of the following statements about the median values in Chloe's and Amy's survey results is accurate?

A) The median value in Chloe's results is higher than the median value in Amy's results.

B) The median value in Amy's results is higher than the median value in Chloe's results.

C) The median values in Amy's and Chloe's results are the same.

D) There is not enough information to determine whether the median value in Amy's or Chloe's results is higher.

11. Which of the following box and whisker plots correctly displays Chloe's survey results?

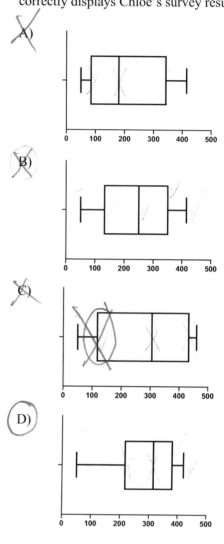

A)

B)

C)

D)

$\frac{180+1}{2} = 90.5$

$12+26+39=77$

$77+68=145$

12. Erica wants to predict if over 50% of seniors will vote to change the school mascot. A majority vote is needed to change the mascot. Erica randomly selects 140 of her classmates to ask about the vote, and 51% of her classmates say they will vote to change the mascot. The associated margin of error with Erica's survey is 2.5%. Based on the survey's results, which of the following is accurate?

    A) Erica's survey does not provide sufficient information to conclude if the seniors will vote to change the mascot.
    B) 51% of the seniors will vote to change the mascot.
    C) The seniors will vote to change the mascot, but the exact percentage of votes in favor cannot be predicted.
    D) The seniors will vote to change the mascot with at least 53.5% of the vote.

13. To determine if eating chocolate has an effect on men's standardized test scores, researchers surveyed a random population of 8,000 men. Study participants were identified as regular chocolate eaters or non-chocolate eaters and were given a standardized test. They found that the regular chocolate eaters had higher scores than the non-chocolate eaters. What is the most appropriate conclusion for this study?

    A) Eating chocolate regularly causes higher standardized test scores for men and women.
    B) Eating chocolate regularly causes higher standardized test scores for men but not necessarily for women.
    C) There is an association between eating chocolate and higher standardized test scores for men and women, but it is not necessarily a cause-and-effect relationship.
    D) There is an association between eating chocolate and higher standardized test score for men, but it is not necessarily a cause-and-effect relationship and it does not necessarily exist for women.

14. Donovan asked 47 of his classmates about their grades on the last US history test. Christina measured 124 tomato plants one month after sprouting and recorded their heights. Box and whisker plots of their results are below.

Donovan's Results

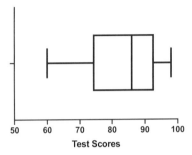

Test Scores

Christina's Results

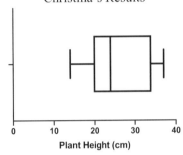

Plant Height (cm)

If d is the median test score from Donovan's survey and c is the median plant height from Christina's data and both d and c are integers, what is a possible value of $d - c$? (Note: median values must be estimated for this question, but there are multiple correct answers).

15.

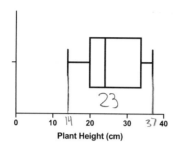

Plant Height (cm)

The box and whisker plot above displays information about the height of plants in a garden. Which of the following values is closest to the range for the heights of the plants in the garden?

A) 13
B) 18
C) 20
D) 24

16. A school librarian wants to predict how often students at Walker High School will want to use a new 3D printer. Which of the following study designs will most likely provide reliable results for the librarian?

A) Polling 120 random students who are in the library.
B) Using an online survey that gets responses from 30,000 high school students.
C) Randomly selecting 500 students at Walker High School to complete a questionnaire.
D) Asking 1,000 Walker High School students and parents to volunteer to complete a survey.

17. The principal of a local high school is conducting a survey on whether students felt online learning was still effective during the COVID-19 pandemic. Of the 200 students who were randomly sampled, 43% felt that online learning is still effective. Based on the margin of error, the principal expects that somewhere between 35% and 51% of all students feel that online learning is still effective during the COVID-19 pandemic. What is the margin of error?

A) 43%
B) 16%
C) 8%
D) 2%

18. A market researcher asked 150 randomly selected people who like a local market's tri tip sandwiches if they like the local market's new Reuben sandwich. 78% of the people said that they like the new Reuben sandwich. Which of the following inferences can be appropriately drawn from this survey?

A) Exactly 78% of people will like the new Reuben sandwich.
B) Exactly 78% of people who like the local market's tri tip sandwich will like the new Reuben sandwich.
C) Around 78% of people will like the new Reuben sandwich.
D) Around 78% of people who like the local market's tri tip sandwich will like the new Reuben sandwich.

Chapter 25: Probability

Probability is the likelihood of a desired outcome occurring compared to the total number of possible outcomes. On the SAT, probability is usually listed as a fraction or, less commonly, a decimal:

$$Probability = \frac{Desired\ Outcome}{All\ Possible\ Outcomes}$$

The SAT may phrase probability questions by asking you the "probability," the "chances," the "odds," or the "likelihood" of an event occurring. To answer these questions, consider the desired outcome that the question is asking about and compare it to the total number of possible outcomes.

To learn how probability works, let's work through a few questions with the following example:

Example 1: A bag has a total of 38 chocolate candies. 18 of the candies are blue, 10 are red, 5 are yellow, 3 are green, and 2 purple.

Question 1: Andy will reach into the bag and pick one candy. What is the probability that he will grab a yellow candy?

Solution: Of the 38 candies in the bag, 5 are yellow. Therefore, the probability of selecting a yellow candy is $\frac{5}{38}$. **The answer is $\frac{5}{38}$.**

Question 2: Evelyn is going to pick one piece of chocolate candy from the bag. What is the probability that she will NOT pick a blue candy?

Solution: There is a total of 18 blue candies in the bag, which means there are 20 candies that are not blue. The probability of selecting a chocolate candy that is not blue is $\frac{20}{38}$. **The answer is $\frac{20}{38}$.** This could also be simplified to $\frac{10}{19}$. Both answers are correct.

Pretty easy, right? Now, probability questions get a bit more difficult when you have probabilities that involve multiple events. **To calculate a probability involving multiple events, multiply the probabilities of each individual event.** Make sure that you remember to multiply the probabilities and not add them. Adding instead of multiplying the probabilities for multiple events is the most common mistake students make.

Question 3: Min will select 2 chocolate candies from the bag without replacement. What is the probability that Min will select a red candy and then a green candy?

   A) $\frac{13}{75}$ B) $\frac{15}{722}$ C) $\frac{15}{703}$ D) $\frac{13}{76}$

Solution: We have two probabilities: (1) the probability of selecting a red candy and (2) the probability of then selecting a green candy. For the red candy, there are a total of 38 candies in the bag and 10 red candies, so the probability of selecting a red candy is $\frac{10}{38}$. After selecting a red candy, there are 37 candies left in the bag since Min does not replace the first candy. There are still 3 green candies in the bag, so the probability of the second candy being green is $\frac{3}{37}$. Since we have multiple events occurring in a row, we multiply the probabilities together.

$$\frac{10}{38} \times \frac{3}{37} = \frac{30}{1,406}$$

Simplifying the fraction, we get an answer of $\frac{15}{703}$. **The answer is C.**

Probability and Data Tables

For the majority of probability questions on the SAT, you will be given a data table and asked to identify the probability of a certain event occurring. It is critical to read the question carefully and consider (1) what are the outcomes that you are being asked to identify (the numerator) and (2) what are the total outcomes you are choosing from (the denominator). For these questions, probability can be defined as

$$Probability = \frac{Number\ In\ Target\ Group}{Total\ Number\ To\ Select\ From}$$

Let's use the example below to see how this works:

The table below shows the results of a survey asking high school students in two different classrooms about their favorite school lunch.

	Tacos	Chicken Tenders	Vegetable Pasta	Total
Period 1	24	3	6	33
Period 2	9	5	15	29
Total	33	8	21	62

Question 1: Given that a student is in period 2, what is the probability that he or she picked chicken tenders on the survey?

Solution: We are asked to consider students from period 2, so we only look at the 29 students in period 2 not all 62 students at the school. Of the 29 students in period 2, 5 selected chicken tenders.

$$\frac{Selected\ Chicken\ Tenders\ in\ Period\ 2}{Total\ Students\ in\ Period\ 2} = \frac{5}{29}$$

The answer is $\frac{5}{29}$.

Questions 2: What is the fraction of students whose favorite school lunch is tacos?

Solution: We are not given any restrictions on which students to consider, so we include all 62 students in the total. The total number of students who selected tacos is 33.

$$\frac{Selected\ Tacos}{Total\ Students} = \frac{33}{62}$$

The answer is $\frac{33}{62}$.

Question 3: If a student's favorite school lunch is vegetable pasta, what is the probability the student is in period 2?

Solution: For this question, we only look at the 21 students who selected vegetable pasta. Of those 21 students, 15 are in period 2.

$$\frac{In\ Period\ 2\ and\ Selected\ Vegeable\ Pasta}{Total\ Students\ who\ Selected\ Vegetable\ Pasta} = \frac{15}{21}$$

Simplifying the fraction, **the answer is $\frac{5}{7}$.**

Probability Practice: A calculator may be used on the following questions. Answers on page 269.

1. Andy has a bag of marbles. If the bag has 30 blue marbles, 25 red marbles, and 15 green marbles, what is the probability that he will randomly select a red marble?

    A) $\frac{5}{14}$

    B) $\frac{6}{15}$

    C) $\frac{3}{7}$

    D) $\frac{5}{7}$

2. Jerry is in a rush and needs to grab one of the premade sandwiches at the market. Jerry's favorite is the Italian sub, but the sandwiches have no labels on them. If there are 27 total sandwiches and 10 are Italian subs, what is the probability that he does NOT get an Italian sub?

    A) $\frac{1}{10}$

    B) $\frac{10}{27}$

    C) $\frac{17}{27}$

    D) $\frac{17}{37}$

3. A box contains 1 red bead, 6 white beads, and 3 blue beads. Jorge will randomly remove one bead from the box, record its color, and place it back in the box. If Jorge repeats this experiment 150 times, what is the expected number of times that Jorge will record a bead that is blue?

    A) 30
    B) 45
    C) 75
    D) 120

4. A bowl contains 12 red marbles, 6 blue marbles and an unknown number of black marbles. The probability of choosing a blue marble out of the bowl is $\frac{1}{7}$. How many black marbles are in the bowl?

    A) 8
    B) 12
    C) 18
    D) 24

5. A bag contains 13 pieces of candy: 5 lemon, 2 strawberry, 3 orange, and 3 grape. What is the probability that one piece of candy randomly selected is not lemon?

    A) $\frac{3}{13}$

    B) $\frac{5}{13}$

    C) $\frac{8}{13}$

    D) $\frac{10}{13}$

6. Three squares with the same center have side lengths of 1, 2, and 3 respectively. What is the probability that a point randomly chosen in the interior of the largest square is also in the interior of the smallest square?

    A) $\frac{1}{3}$

    B) $\frac{1}{9}$

    C) $\frac{4}{9}$

    D) $\frac{6}{9}$

7. Julia runs out of time on her test and needs to guess on the last 4 questions. Each question has 5 answers. If Julia answers each one randomly, what is the probability she answers all 4 questions correctly?

    A) $\frac{1}{625}$

    B) $\frac{4}{625}$

    C) $\frac{1}{125}$

    D) $\frac{1}{5}$

Use the information below for questions 8 and 9.

The table below shows the impact of two diets on the weights of dogs.

Diet	Type of Weight Change		Total
	Gained	Lost	
A	50	100	150
B	75	75	150

8. Based on the results in the table, what fraction of the dogs who lost weight received diet B?

   A) $\frac{75}{175}$

   B) $\frac{75}{150}$

   C) $\frac{100}{175}$

   D) $\frac{100}{300}$

9. Based on the results in the table, what fraction of the dogs in the study received diet A and gained weight?

   A) $\frac{1}{2}$

   B) $\frac{1}{3}$

   C) $\frac{1}{6}$

   D) $\frac{5}{12}$

Use the information below for questions 10 and 11.

In a survey, biology and chemistry professors from local science departments were asked if their primary focus was teaching or research. The results are shown below.

Type of Professor	Primary Focus		Total
	Teaching	Research	
Biology	86	132	218
Chemistry	142	85	227
Total	228	217	445

10. A speaker for an upcoming event will be selected at random from the professors who participated in the survey. Which of the following is the closest to the probability that the selected professor is a chemistry professor whose primary focus is research?

    A) 0.191
    B) 0.392
    C) 0.488
    D) 0.510

11. Which of the following is the closest to the probability that a randomly selected professor whose primary focus is research is a chemistry professor?

    A) 0.374
    B) 0.392
    C) 0.413
    D) 0.488

Use the information below for questions 12-14.

		Thin	Deep Dish	Gluten Free
		Crust Style		
Topping	Cheese	12	19	7
	Pepperoni	8	25	9

The table above shows the pizza orders at Pete's Pizzeria for an hour on a Saturday afternoon.

12. What is the probability that a pizza ordered was a thin crust pizza?

A) $\frac{1}{4}$

B) $\frac{2}{5}$

C) $\frac{19}{40}$

D) $\frac{3}{5}$

13. What is the probability that a pizza ordered was thin crust or gluten free?

A) $\frac{19}{28}$

B) $\frac{1}{2}$

C) $\frac{19}{40}$

D) $\frac{9}{20}$

14. What is the probability that a cheese pizza ordered was gluten free?

A) $\frac{7}{80}$

B) $\frac{19}{40}$

C) $\frac{7}{38}$

D) $\frac{7}{16}$

Use the information below for questions 15 and 16.

	Decrease	Increase	Total
	Resting Heart Rate		
Weight Training	140	60	200
Cardio	160	20	180
Total	300	80	380

The table above shows adults who exercise with weight training or cardio and whether their resting heart rate increased or decreased.

15. What proportion of adults had an increase in resting heart rate?

A) $\frac{1}{9}$

B) $\frac{3}{10}$

C) $\frac{4}{19}$

D) $\frac{3}{4}$

16. What proportion of the adults exercising with weight training had a decrease in resting heart rate?

A) $\frac{7}{19}$

B) $\frac{3}{5}$

C) $\frac{7}{15}$

D) $\frac{7}{10}$

Use the information below for questions 17 and 18.

Beverage	Food	
	Purchased	No Purchase
Purchased	100	85
No Purchase	45	20

The table above shows the purchases made by a random sample of 250 people at a baseball game.

17. What is the probability that someone surveyed purchased both food and a beverage?

A) $\frac{100}{250}$

B) $\frac{45}{250}$

C) $\frac{85}{185}$

D) $\frac{100}{145}$

18. What is the probability that someone surveyed who purchased food did not purchase a beverage?

A) $\frac{45}{250}$

B) $\frac{45}{65}$

C) $\frac{45}{145}$

D) $\frac{85}{250}$

Chapter 26: Trigonometry

For the majority of trigonometry on the SAT, just remember **SOH-CAH-TOA,** which stands for sine is opposite over hypotenuse, cosine is adjacent over hypotenuse, and tangent is opposite over adjacent. This acronym makes it easy to memorize the sine, cosine, and tangent functions.

$$\sin x = \frac{opposite}{hypotenuse} = \frac{3}{5}$$

$$\cos x = \frac{adjacent}{hypotenuse} = \frac{4}{5}$$

$$\tan x = \frac{opposite}{adjacent} = \frac{3}{4}$$

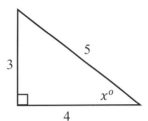

Remember that we can **only use SOH-CAH-TOA with right triangles.** On the SAT, you will most often need to use trigonometric functions to find missing sides of a right triangle when you know the angle.

Example 1: Which of the following is the value of x in the triangle below? (Round your answer to the nearest tenth).

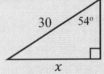

Solution: With the angle and two sides that we are given, we can use the sine function to solve for x.

$$\sin 54^o = \frac{x}{30}$$

$$30 \sin 54^o = x$$

At this point, we must plug in $30 \sin 54^o$ to the calculator to solve for x.

$$x = 24.3$$

The answer is 24.3. A grid-in question like this would only appear in the calculator section.

Example 2: In right triangle XYZ, the cosine of angle Y is 0.72. If the longest side of the triangle YZ has a length of 15, what is the length of XY?

    A) 10.4   B) 10.8   C) 13.4   D) 20.8

Solution: To start, we should draw the triangle.

    Test Day Tip – If you are ever given a trigonometry question without a drawing, always start by sketching and labelling a triangle.

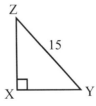

Now, we can use the cosine function to solve since we know

$$\cos Y = \frac{XY}{15}$$

and

$$\cos Y = 0.72$$

so we can set equal and solve for XY

$$\frac{XY}{15} = 0.72$$

$$XY = 10.8$$

The answer is B.

Questions like these first two examples should be pretty easy to solve. If you found either of those questions difficult, make sure you take some time to review the basics SOH-CAH-TOA.

It is important to understand that trigonometric functions only tell you the ratio of the side lengths and not the actual side lengths. For example, triangle ABC with $\sin C = \frac{3}{5}$ could look like any of these

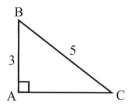 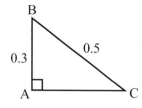 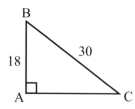

Since all right triangles with the same angles are similar triangles, the ratio of the sides will be the same. Many students make the mistake of labeling the side lengths of triangles from trigonometric functions and assume triangle ABC looks like the one on the left. We do not know what the triangle actually looks like until we are given the length of one of the sides. Understanding this concept can help with questions like example 3 below.

Example 3: For the right triangle below, $\tan A = \frac{2}{5}$. What is the value of z?

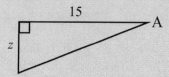

Solution: Even though we do not know any angles in this triangle, we can still use trigonometry to solve. We can see that

$$\tan A = \frac{z}{15}$$

The question tells us that

$$\tan A = \frac{2}{5}$$

so we can set them equal and solve for z.

$$\frac{z}{15} = \frac{2}{5}$$

$$z = 6$$

The answer is 6.

Example 4: In the figure below, $\overline{BC}$ is parallel with $\overline{DE}$ and $\tan A = \frac{4}{3}$. If $AB = 6$ and $DE = 30$, what is the length of AE?

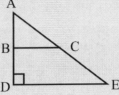

Note: Figure not drawn to scale.

A) 50   B) 42.5   C) 40   D) 37.5

Solution: Triangles ABC and ADE are similar triangles. Before we can find AE, we need to know the side lengths in triangle ABC. We know that

$$\tan A = \frac{BC}{6}$$

The question tells us that

$$\tan A = \frac{4}{3}$$

So we set them equal and solve for BC

$$\frac{BC}{6} = \frac{4}{3}$$

$$BC = 8$$

Now that we know BC, we can solve for AC using the Pythagorean theorem.

$$6^2 + 8^2 = c^2$$

$$AC = 10$$

Since triangles ABC and ADE are similar and we know that $DE = 30$, we can solve for AE. Remember that sides in similar triangles are proportional.

$$\frac{8}{30} = \frac{10}{AE}$$

$$AE = 37.5$$

The answer is D.

Shortcut Solution: Triangle ABC is a $3:4:5$ right triangle. Given that $\tan(A) = \frac{4}{3}$, we know the ratio of the two legs of the triangle is $4:3$. This is enough to tell that triangle ABC is a $3:4:5$ right triangle. Since triangle ABC is similar to triangle ADE, triangle ADE must also be a $3:4:5$ right triangle. From that, we know that

$$\frac{4}{5} = \frac{30}{AE}$$

$$AE = 37.5$$

The answer is D.

The shortcut method is more advanced and difficult to spot, so if this seems confusing stick with the first solution above.

For questions similar to this one, keep an eye out for $3:4:5$, $6:8:10$, and $5:12:13$ right triangles, especially in the no-calculator section.

Beyond the basic trigonometric functions, you should also know these two important identities:

$$sin\ x = cos(90^o - x)$$

$$cos\ x = sin(90^o - x)$$

In a right triangle, the sine of one acute angle in a right triangle is equal to the cosine of the other acute angle, and the cosine of one acute angle in a right triangle is equal to the sine of the other acute angle.

Example 5: In right triangle XYZ, the right angle is at Z. If $cos\ X = \frac{7}{9}$, what is the value of $sin\ Y$?

A) $\frac{2}{9}$ B) $\frac{7}{9}$ C) $\frac{4\sqrt{2}}{9}$ D) $\frac{9}{7}$

Solution: First, sketch and label triangle XYZ.

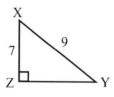

We are asked to solve for the $sin\ Y$, which is

$$sin\ Y = \frac{7}{9}$$

The answer is B.

Shortcut solution: In triangle XYZ, angles X and Y will add up to 90°. From the identity above, we know that

$$cos\ x = sin(90^o - x)$$

In our triangle, angle Y is equal to $90^o - x$, so

$$cos\ X = sin\ Y$$

The question tells us that $cos\ X = \frac{7}{9}$, so **the answer is B.**

Inverse Trigonometric Functions

You also need to know the inverse trigonometric functions ($sin^{-1}, cos^{-1}, tan^{-1}$). We use these functions when we know the sides of a triangle and are solving for an unknown angle.

$$sin^{-1}\left(\frac{opposite}{hypotenouse}\right) = angle$$

$$cos^{-1}\left(\frac{adjacent}{hypotenouse}\right) = angle$$

$$tan^{-1}\left(\frac{opposite}{adjacent}\right) = angle$$

Example 6: Find the value of x in the triangle below. (Round your answer to the nearest whole number)

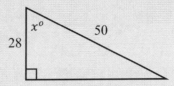

Solution: To find the missing angle, we need to use an inverse trigonometric function. We know the adjacent and opposite lengths in this triangle, so we can solve for x using the inverse cosine function.

$$cos^{-1}\left(\frac{28}{50}\right) = x$$

$$x = 55.95$$

The answer is 56. Make sure to follow the directions on free response questions. The question directs you to round your answer to the nearest whole number. If you bubble in 55.9 or 55.95, your answer will be marked as incorrect.

Example 7: Anthony is building a ramp from a spot in his backyard to the entrance to his tree house. The tree house is 18 feet off the ground, and the spot that Anthony is going to put the base of the ramp is 45 feet from the base of the tree, which is directly below the entrance to the tree house. What angle of elevation should Anthony use for his ramp? (Round your answer to the nearest tenth).

Solution: Start by sketching and labelling the triangle described in the question. The most difficult part of this word problem is getting the sketch correct.

The angle of elevation is the angle of the ramp, labeled above as x. We know the opposite and adjacent lengths in the triangle, so we can solve for the angle of elevation using the inverse tangent function.

$$tan^{-1}\left(\frac{18}{45}\right) = x$$

$$x = 21.801$$

The answer is 21.8. Again, make sure to follow the directions in the question telling you to bubble in the answer to the nearest tenth.

Radians

Radians are another unit to measure angles. Just like you can measure temperature in Fahrenheit or Celsius, you can measure an angle in degrees or radians. For the SAT, you will need to know how to convert between radians and degrees. At the front of each math section, the SAT will tell you

The number of degrees in a circle is 360.

The number of radians of arc in a circle is 2π.

That is a very complicated way of saying that

2π radians $= 360^o$

If we simplify this, we get

π radians $= 180^o$

Both of these are correct, so you can use either one of these when working on radians questions. For the rest of this section, we will use π radians $= 180^o$.

To convert from radians to degrees, multiply by

$$\frac{180^o}{\pi \, radians}$$

To convert from degrees to radians, multiply by

$$\frac{\pi \, radians}{180^0}$$

Example 8: Angle D has a measure of 200°. If angle D can be written as $a\pi$ radians, what is the value of a?

Solution: We need to convert angle D from degrees to radians. As in any unit conversion question, start with the given, which is 200°, and then use the conversion factor to change the units.

$$200^o \times \frac{\pi \, radians}{180^0} = \frac{10}{9}\pi \text{ radians} = 1.11\pi \text{ radians}$$

The answer is $\frac{10}{9}$ or 1.11. If the question does not specify how to bubble in your answer, round to the number that will lead you to using all four the spots on your answer sheet or just keep the answer as a fraction. Both answers will be marked as correct.

Example 9: Angle M has a measure of $\frac{13}{5}$ radians. If angle M is half of angle Q, what is the measure of angle Q in degrees? (Round your answer to the nearest whole number).

Solution: First, convert angle M to degrees.

$$\frac{13}{5} \, radians \times \frac{180^o}{\pi \, radians} = 148.96^o$$

Make sure that you notice the measure of angle M is $\frac{13}{5}$ radians and not $\frac{13}{5}\pi$ radians. Many students make that mistake on a question like this.

We know that angle M is half of angle Q, so we need to multiple angle M by 2 to get angle Q. **The answer is 298.**

Trigonometry Practice: A calculator may NOT be used on the following questions. Answers on page 270.

1. The side lengths of a triangle are given in the figure below. What does $\sin C$ equal?

   A) 2
   B) $\frac{2}{3}$
   C) $\frac{1}{2}$
   D) $\frac{3}{4}$

   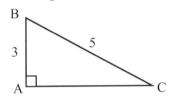

2. Two of the side lengths of a right triangle are given in the figure below. What is $\cos C$?

   B
   3   5
   A   C

   Note: Figure not drawn to scale.

   A) $\frac{3}{5}$
   B) $\frac{5}{3}$
   C) $\frac{5}{4}$
   D) $\frac{4}{5}$

3. Two acute angles have degree measures of x and y. If $\sin x = \frac{6}{10}$, what is the value of $\cos y$?

4. Triangle ABC has a right angle at point B. If $\sin A = \frac{2}{7}$, what is the value of $\tan C$?

   A) $\frac{7}{2}$
   B) $\frac{\sqrt{45}}{2}$
   C) $\frac{2}{5}$
   D) $\frac{2\sqrt{45}}{45}$

5. Triangle CAB has right angle A. If $\tan C = \frac{6}{8}$, what is the value of $\cos B$?

6. For an angle with measure θ, $\sin \theta = \frac{12}{13}$ and $\cos \theta = \frac{5}{13}$. What is the value of $\tan \theta$?

   A) $\frac{5}{12}$
   B) $\frac{13}{12}$
   C) $\frac{12}{5}$
   D) $\frac{5}{13}$

7. The side lengths of a triangle are given below. Which of the following expressions gives the measure of the angle θ?

   A) $\tan^{-1}\left(\frac{b}{a}\right)$
   B) $\sin^{-1}\left(\frac{b}{c}\right)$
   C) $\sin^{-1}\left(\frac{c}{b}\right)$
   D) $\cos^{-1}\left(\frac{b}{c}\right)$

   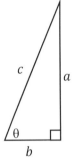

8. In the triangle below, $\cos x = \frac{5}{17}$. What is $\sin y$?

   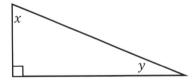

9. The figure below shows a 7-foot stick leaning against a vertical wall. The stick makes a 47° angle. Which of the following expressions gives the height where the top of the ladder hits the wall?

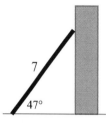

A) 7 tan 47°

B) 7 sin 47°

C) $\dfrac{7}{\cos 47°}$

D) $\dfrac{7}{\sin 47°}$

10. In the triangle below, the $\sin A = \frac{3}{5}$, what is tan B?

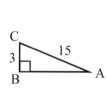

A) $\dfrac{4}{3}$

B) $\dfrac{3}{4}$

C) $\dfrac{4}{5}$

D) $\dfrac{3}{5}$

11. The two acute angles of a right triangle have degree measures of a and b. If $\sin a = 0.3$, what does $\cos b$ equal?

12.

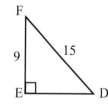

For the triangles above, which of the following expressions is true?

A) $\sin A = 3 \sin D$

B) $\sin A = \frac{1}{3} \sin D$

C) $\cos A = 3 \cos D$

D) $\cos A = \frac{1}{3} \cos D$

13. In the figure below, $AC = 5$. The measure of $\angle C$ is half the measure of $\angle A$, and $\overline{AB}$ is parallel to $\overline{ED}$. In triangle CDE, what is the measure of $\sin C$?

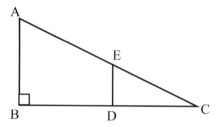

A) $\dfrac{1}{2}$

B) $\dfrac{3}{5}$

C) $\dfrac{4}{5}$

D) 2

Trigonometry Practice: A calculator may be used on the following questions.

14. If $\sin \theta = 0.8$ in the triangle, below what is the value of x?

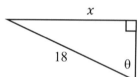

A) 3.6

B) 14.4

C) 21.6

D) 24

15. If $\cos x° = y$, which of the following must be true for all values of x?

A) $\sin x° = y$

B) $\sin (90° - x°) = y$

C) $\cos (90° - x°) = y$

D) $\sin (90° + x°) = y$

16. In triangle ABC, which expressions represents the length of AB?

    A) $7 \sin A$
    B) $7 \cos A$
    C) $\frac{\sin A}{7}$
    D) $\frac{\cos A}{7}$

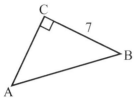

17. In the right triangle below, $\tan B = \frac{8}{6}$. What is $\cos C + \cos B$ equal to?

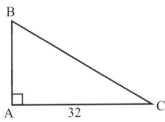

Note: Figure not drawn to scale.

18. In the figure below, $\cos(90 - x) = \frac{3}{11}$. What is the value of $\cos x$?

    A) $\frac{4\sqrt{7}}{11}$
    B) $\frac{11\sqrt{7}}{28}$
    C) $\frac{8}{11}$
    D) $\frac{11}{3}$

19. In the figure below, ABC is a right triangle. If $BC = 30$ and the tangent of $\angle BCA$ is equal to 0.75, what is the length of AC?

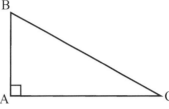

Note: Figure not drawn to scale.

20. In the figure below, $\cos C = \frac{4}{5}$. If $CB = 16$ and $ED = 6$, what is the length of EC?

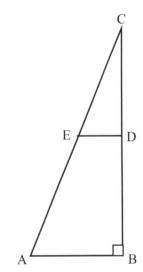

Note: Figure not drawn to scale.

Chapter 27: Circles

In order to answer circle questions on the SAT, you need to know the equation for a circle and how to graph a circle.

Equation for a Circle

The equation for a circle with a center at the origin and a radius r is

$$x^2 + y^2 = r^2$$

To make sure you understand this, let's go over this equation with numbers. Let's start with

$$x^2 + y^2 = 16$$

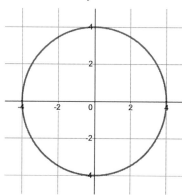

This equation represents a circle with its center at the origin and a radius of 4. Make sure that you remember that the number represents r^2. Many students forget this and mistakenly think the radius here is 16.

The equation for a circle with a center at (h, k) and a radius r is

$$(x - h)^2 + (y - k)^2 = r^2$$

We call this the standard form of a circle. This is the equation that you need to memorize, as questions using this form often appear on test day. Again, let's put some numbers into the equation to make sure we understand how this works.

$$(x - 3)^2 + (y + 5)^2 = 49$$

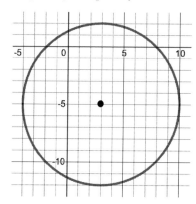

This equation is a circle with a center at $(3, -5)$ and a radius of 7. Make sure that you notice the sign of the h and k values in the equation is the opposite of the actual coordinate of the center (h, k). The term $(x - 3)^2$ shows the x-coordinate is at $x = 3$, not $x = -3$. The term $(y + 5)^2$ shows the y-coordinate is at $y = -5$ not $y = 5$. A common mistake is to think the center of this circle is at $(-3, 5)$.

Example 1: A circle in the xy-plane has a center of $(-9, 4)$ and a radius of 6. Which of the following is the equation of the circle?

A) $(x - 9)^2 + (y + 4)^2 = 36$
B) $(x + 9)^2 + (y - 4)^2 = 36$
C) $(x - 9)^2 + (y + 4)^2 = 6$
D) $(x + 9)^2 + (y - 4)^2 = 6$

Solution: For this question, we need to properly use the equation of a circle. The radius is 6, so the right side must equal 36. Since the center is at $(-9, 4)$, we need to see the opposite signs of h and k, which here are 9 and -4 respectively, in the circle equation. **The answer is B.**

Other types of circles questions ask you to somehow change the size or location of a circle. For these questions, we again just need to know how the equation of a circle works.

Example 2:
$$(x - 4)^2 + (y + 6)^2 = 25$$

The equation for Circle A is shown above. Circle B is drawn by shifting Circle A 3 units left, 8 units up, and increasing the radius by 2. Which of the following is the equation of Circle B?

A) $(x - 7)^2 + (y + 14)^2 = 49$
B) $(x - 1)^2 + (y - 2)^2 = 29$
C) $(x - 7)^2 + (y - 2)^2 = 49$
D) $(x - 1)^2 + (y - 2)^2 = 49$

Solution: Let's start by finding the radius of Circle B. Circle A has a radius of 5, which we know because 25 is equal to r^2. If we increase that radius by 2, the radius of Circle B is 7, so the right side of the equation must be 49. From this, we know that B is incorrect.

Next, we need to find where the center of Circle B is located. The center of Circle A is at $(4, -6)$. Again, remember that the signs of the numbers in the equation are opposite of the coordinates of the center of the circle. We shift the center of Circle A 3 units left and 8 units up to find the center of Circle B, so the center of Circle B is at $(1, 2)$. **The answer is D.**

TIP – Draw It Out: If this question is difficult for you, sketch the coordinate plane and draw the circle. The visual can help make sure that you shift the center to the correct point. It is easy to mistakenly shift in the wrong direction if you do not draw it out.

Example 3:
$$(x - 5)^2 + y^2 = 53$$

The equation above represents a circle in the xy-plane. Point $(11, a)$ lies on the circle. If a can be written as $\sqrt{n}$, what is the value of n?

Solution: Since point $(11, a)$ lies on the circle, we can plug the point in for x and y in the circle equation and solve for a.
$$(11 - 5)^2 + a^2 = 53$$
$$36 + a^2 = 53$$
$$a^2 = 17$$
$$a = \sqrt{17}$$

Since $a = \sqrt{17}$ and we are told that a can be written as $\sqrt{n}$, $n = 17$. **The answer is 17.**

For any question that gives a point on a circle, we can always plug the point back into the equation to solve for any missing values.

Example 4:	$(x + 9)^2 + (y + 2)^2 = k$

The equation above represents Circle M in the xy-plane. If point $(-3, 7)$ lies on Circle M, what is the value of k?

Solution: Since point $(-3, 7)$ lies on Circle M, we can plug that point into the equation to solve for k.

$$(-3 + 9)^2 + (7 + 2)^2 = k$$
$$6^2 + 9^2 = k$$
$$36 + 81 = k$$
$$117 = k$$

The answer is 117.

Completing the Square

The SAT can also ask questions with the general form of a circle. The general form of a circle is

$$x^2 + y^2 + Ax + By + C = 0$$

This form does not tell us anything helpful about what the circle looks like. In order to find the circle's center and radius, we will need to complete the square to get back to standard form.

The steps below will show you how to complete the square. For this example, we will use the equation

$$x^2 + y^2 - 6x + 2y - 15 = 0$$

Step 1: Move any numbers to the right side.

$$x^2 + y^2 - 6x + 2y = 15$$

Step 2: Group the x-terms and y-terms together. Leave yourself a space to complete the square.

$$(x^2 - 6x + \quad) + (y^2 + 2y + \quad) = 15$$

Step 3: Complete the square by dividing the coefficient of the middle term by 2 and squaring. For the x-terms, the middle coefficient is -6, so we divide -6 by 2, getting -3, and then square -3, getting 9. We write a 9 in the open space to complete the square. For the y-terms, the middle coefficient is 2, so we divide 2 by 2, getting 1, and then square 1, which is 1. We write a 1 in the open space to complete the square. Be sure to add 9 and 1 to the right side of the equation as well.

$$(x^2 - 6x + 9) + (y^2 + 2y + 1) = 15 + 9 + 1$$

Step 4: Factor both perfect squares. The whole point of completing the square is to create perfect squares. Here we get

$$(x - 3)^2 + (y + 1)^2 = 25$$

When completing the square, the value in the completed square, here the -3 and $+1$, are always equal to half of the middle terms, -6 and $+2$, that we had before factoring.

Once we have the circle in standard form, **we can see that the center is at $(3, -1)$ and the radius is 5.**

Example 5: Circle P can be written as $x^2 + y^2 + 10x - 4y - 71 = 0$. Which of the following is an equation of Circle P?

A) $(x+5)^2 + (y-2)^2 = 100$
B) $(x+5)^2 + (y+2)^2 = 71$
C) $(x+10)^2 + (y-4)^2 = 71$
D) $(x+5)^2 + (y-2)^2 = 42$

Solution: We need to convert Circle P from general form to standard form. To start we, need to add the 71 to the right side.

$$x^2 + y^2 + 10x - 4y = 71$$

Now, we need to organize the x-terms and y-terms. Remember to leave space to complete the square.

$$(x^2 + 10x + \quad) + (y^2 - 4y + \quad) = 71$$

Next, we complete the square.

$$(x^2 + 10x + 25) + (y^2 - 4y + 4) = 71 + 25 + 4$$

Factoring, we get

$$(x+5)^2 + (y-2)^2 = 100$$

The answer is A.

Advanced Circle Questions

For more difficult circle questions, the SAT will require a deeper understanding of some basic principles of how circles work. While these principles may at times seem simple, recognizing these principles will be critical to solving more advanced circle questions.

Principle #1: The two endpoints of any diameter on a circle have their midpoint at the center of the circle.

Try this on your own. Grab a piece of paper and draw a circle. No matter how you draw the diameter, the center of the circle will be the midpoint of the diameter.

Example 6: Circle P has its center at $(2,7)$. If AB is a diameter of circle P and point A is at $(-3,4)$, which of the following is point B?

A) $(7,10)$ B) $(-8,1)$ C) $(-\frac{1}{2}, \frac{11}{2})$ D) $(6,8)$

Solution: Using principle #1, we know that the center of the circle must be the midpoint of AB. Since we are given point A, we can use the midpoint formula to solve for point B. To solve for the x-coordinate, we set up

$$\frac{x + (-3)}{2} = 2$$

$$x = 7$$

If we can check the answer choices, we already know that **the answer is A**. Be sure to **always check the answer choices once you find either the x-coordinate or y-coordinate of a point.**

To finish solving this question algebraically, we solve for the y-coordinate.

$$\frac{y+(4)}{2} = 7$$

$$y = 10$$

Point B is at $(7, 10)$, so **the answer is A.** If you need to review how to use the midpoint formula, go back to chapter 20.

Principle #2: The distance between the center and any endpoint of a diameter of a circle is equal to the radius of the circle.

If this principle seems obvious, it is because it is. It is just the definition of a radius! However, it is helpful to recognize if you are only given two endpoints of a diameter and are asked to find the equation of the circle.

Example 7: In the xy-plane, point $(4, 2)$ and $(6, 10)$ are the endpoints of a diameter on the circle. Which of the following is the equation of the circle?

A) $(x - 1)^2 + (y - 4)^2 = 68$
B) $(x - 1)^2 + (y - 4)^2 = 17$
C) $(x - 5)^2 + (y - 6)^2 = 68$
D) $(x - 5)^2 + (y - 6)^2 = 17$

Solution: To find the equation of the circle, we need to find the center and the radius. To find the center, we just need to find the midpoint of the two endpoints of the diameter. The x-coordinate of the center is at

$$\frac{4+6}{2} = x$$

$$x = 5$$

The y-coordinate of the center is at

$$\frac{2+10}{2} = y$$

$$y = 6$$

The center of the circle is at $(5, 6)$. From this, we know that answer choices A and B are incorrect. Now that we know the center, we can find the radius using principle #2. The distance from the center to either of the endpoints is equal to the radius. Here, we will use point $(4, 2)$ to find the radius using the distance formula.

$$r = \sqrt{(5-4)^2 + (6-2)^2}$$

$$r = \sqrt{(1)^2 + (4)^2}$$

$$r = \sqrt{17}$$

If you need to review the distance formula, go back to chapter 20.

Now that we know the radius, we can finish this question. The right side of a circle equation is equal to r^2. Since $(\sqrt{17})^2 = 17$, **the answer is D**.

TIP – Draw It Out: For any questions like this, we recommend making a drawing. Sketching a coordinate plane, the endpoints of the diameter, and drawing the circle can help you identify what steps you need to take to solve the question. Even if you still cannot find the exact answer, you can often at least eliminate some incorrect answers and make a more educated guess after drawing it out.

Circles Practice: A calculator may NOT be used on the following questions. Answers on page 273.

1. In the standard xy-plane, what is the center of the circle $(x - 3)^2 + (y + 4)^2 = 16$?

   A) $(-3, 4)$
   B) $(3, 4)$
   C) $(3, -4)$
   D) $(4, 4)$

2. In the standard xy-plane, what is the radius of the circle $(x + 5)^2 + (y - 3)^2 = 36$?

   A) 3
   B) 5
   C) -5
   D) 6

3. The equation of a circle in the xy-plane is shown below. What are the coordinates of the center of the circle?

   $$x^2 + 4x + y^2 - 8y + 5 = 0$$

   A) $(2, -4)$
   B) $(-2, 4)$
   C) $(4, -8)$
   D) $(-4, 8)$

4. The equation of a circle in the xy-plane is shown below. If the circle is shifted two units to the left, one unit down, and the radius is increased by two, what is the new equation of the circle?

   $$(x - 6)^2 + (y + 2)^2 = 9$$

   A) $(x - 8)^2 + (y + 1)^2 = 25$
   B) $(x - 4)^2 + (y + 3)^2 = 25$
   C) $(x - 8)^2 + (y + 3)^2 = 11$
   D) $(x - 8)^2 + (y + 3)^2 = 25$

5. Circle A has a center at $(6, -2)$ and a radius of 2. Circle B is formed by moving Circle A down 6 units and to the left by 3 units. Which of the following gives the correct equation for Circle B?

   A) $(x - 3)^2 + (y + 8)^2 = 4$
   B) $(x - 3)^2 + (y - 1)^2 = 4$
   C) $(x)^2 + (y + 8)^2 = 4$
   D) $(x + 3)^2 + (y - 4)^2 = 4$

6. In the standard (x, y) coordinate plane, what is the area of the following circle?

   $$(x + 2)^2 + (y - 3)^2 = 144$$

   A) 10π
   B) 12π
   C) 64π
   D) 144π

7. In the xy-plane, circle A has an equation of $(x - 1)^2 + (y + 5)^2 = 16$, and circle B has an equation of $(x - 1)^2 + (y + 9)^2 = 16$. Which of the following describes the translation of circle B required to obtain circle A?

   A) Shift 4 units down
   B) Shift 4 units up
   C) Shift 4 units left
   D) Shift 4 units right

8. In the xy-plane, circle A is described by the equation $(x + 4)^2 + (y + 3)^2 = 16$ and circle B is described by the equation $(x - 1)^2 + (y + 3)^2 = 64$. What transformations can be applied to circle A to obtain circle B?

   A) Shift the center to the right 5 units and multiply the radius by 2
   B) Shift the center to the left 5 units and multiply the radius by 2
   C) Shift the center to the right 5 units and multiply the radius by 4
   D) Shift the center to the left 5 units and multiply the radius by 4

9. The equation below represents circle A in the xy-plane. If point, $(2, b)$ lies on circle A, what is the value of b?

$$(x + 4)^2 + (y + 3)^2 = 100$$

A) 2
B) 5
C) 6
D) 8

10. The equation of a circle in the xy-plane is shown below. What is the radius of the circle?

$$x^2 + 4x + y^2 - 6y = 12$$

11. $$(x + 2)^2 + (y - 10)^2 = j$$

The equation above represents Circle B in the xy-plane. If point $(4, 5)$ lies on Circle B, what is the value of j?

12. In the xy-plane, points $(-4, -2)$ and $(2, 6)$ are endpoints of the diameter of a circle. What is the equation of the standard form of the circle?

A) $(x + 1)^2 + (y - 2)^2 = 25$
B) $(x + 1)^2 + (y - 2)^2 = 100$
C) $x^2 + (y - 1)^2 = 25$
D) $x^2 + (y - 1)^2 = 100$

13. $$x^2 + y^2 + 4x + 8y - 16 = 0$$

For the circle above, the center is at point (a, b) and the radius is c. What is the value of $a + b + c$?

A) 0
B) 6
C) 12
D) 42

14. In the xy-plane, points $(-4, 3)$ and $(4, -3)$ are the endpoints of the diameter of a circle. Which of the following is the equation of the circle?

A) $x^2 + y^2 = 25$
B) $x^2 + y^2 = 100$
C) $(x - 4)^2 + (y + 3)^2 = 25$
D) $(x - 4)^2 + (y + 3)^2 = 100$

Circles Practice: A calculator may be used on the following questions.

15. Which of the following gives the equation of a circle tangent to $y = 6$ with a center of $(6, 3)$?

A) $(x - 3)^2 + (y + 6)^2 = 3$
B) $(x - 6)^2 + (y - 3)^2 = 3$
C) $(x - 6)^2 + (y - 3)^2 = 9$
D) $(x + 6)^2 + (y + 3)^2 = 9$

16. The equation of a circle in the xy-plane is shown below. What is the center of the circle?

$$x^2 + y^2 - 8x + 10y - 23 = 0$$

A) $(4, 5)$
B) $(-4, 5)$
C) $(4, -5)$
D) $(8, -10)$

17. In the xy-plane, points $(8, a)$ and $(-2, b)$ are the endpoints of the diameter of a circle. If the center of that circle is (h, k) and $hk = 18$, what is the value of $a + b$?

    A) 6
    B) 12
    C) 18
    D) 24

18. The equation below represents a circle in the xy-plane. If the circle is translated so that it is tangent to both the x-axis and y-axis, what is the new equation of the circle?

    $$(x - 8)^2 + (y + 4)^2 = 25$$

    A) $x^2 + y^2 = 25$
    B) $(x - 5)^2 + (y)^2 = 25$
    C) $(x - 5)^2 + (y + 5)^2 = 25$
    D) $x^2 + (y - 5)^2 = 25$

19. The equation below represents a circle in the xy-plane. If the point $(a, 9)$ lies on the circle and $a > 0$, what is a possible value of a?

    $$(x - 4)^2 + (y - 6)^2 = 34$$

20. The equation of a circle in the xy-plane is shown below. What is the radius of the circle?

    $$2x^2 + 2y^2 + 12x + 16y - 48 = 0$$

21. In the xy-plane, which of the following points does not lie in the interior of a circle with the equation $(x + 4)^2 + (y + 2)^2 = 36$?

    A) $(-6, -3)$
    B) $(-4, -7)$
    C) $(3, -4)$
    D) $(2, -2)$

22. In the xy-plane, which of the following points lies outside of the circle below?

    $$(x - 3)^2 + (y - 4)^2 = 64$$

    A. $(-5, 4)$
    B. $(-4, -4)$
    C. $(10, 7)$
    D. $(8, -1)$

23. In the xy-plane, which of the following points lies on a circle with the equation $(x + 3)^2 + (y - 4)^2 = 100$?

    A. $(-3, 4)$
    B. $(-7, 7)$
    C. $(5, 10)$
    D. $(6, 8)$

Chapter 28: Complex Numbers

Complex numbers are a combination of real and imaginary components expressed in the form $a + bi$, where a and b are real numbers and i is the imaginary unit. The imaginary unit is defined as

$$i = \sqrt{-1}$$

Since part of complex numbers are indeed "imaginary," it is difficult to grasp how they work. But do not worry, you just need to learn a few methods for how to handle $i = \sqrt{-1}$ when it appears on the SAT.

Addition and Subtraction with Complex Numbers

For addition and subtraction with complex numbers, just combine like terms. For example,

$$(8 + 5i) + (5 - 2i) = 13 + 3i$$

Simple right? For subtraction problems, always make sure that you distribute the negative sign to both terms.

$$(2 - 3i) - (5 - 7i) = 2 - 3i - 5 + 7i = -3 + 4i$$

Many students make the mistake of forgetting to distribute the negative sign and get $-3 - 10i$. Be careful because the SAT will have these common mistakes as incorrect answer choices.

Example 1: If $a = 22 - 14i$ and $b = 7 - 3i$, what is the value of $a - b$?

   A) $15 - 17i$ B) $15 - 11i$ C) $-15 + 11i$ D) $29 - 17i$

Solution: Set up the equation and combine like terms

$$a - b = (22 - 14i) - (7 - 3i) = 22 - 14i - 7 + 3i$$
$$a - b = 15 - 11i$$

The answer is B.

The Powers of i

You should memorize the following pattern of i powers.

$$i^1 = i$$
$$i^2 = -1$$
$$i^3 = -i$$
$$i^4 = 1$$

Knowing this pattern will be essential to solving certain imaginary numbers questions.

Example 2: $10i^4 + 6i^2 + 3 = x$

For the equation above, what is the value of x?

Solution: To solve, we just need to plug in the values of i^2 and i^4.

$$10(1) + 6(-1) + 3 = x$$
$$7 = x$$

The answer is 7.

As long as you memorize the pattern of i powers, solving questions like example 2 are easy!

The pattern repeats over and over again as you increase i to higher powers. Below, you can see the first 8 powers and how the pattern works.

$$i^1 = i \qquad\qquad i^5 = i$$
$$i^2 = -1 \qquad\qquad i^6 = -1$$
$$i^3 = -i \qquad\qquad i^7 = -i$$
$$i^4 = 1 \qquad\qquad i^8 = 1$$

Less commonly, questions may use higher powers of i.

Example 3: The expression $3i^8 - 5i^5 - 9i^3 + 6i^2 - 5$ is equivalent to which of the following?

A) $4 - 14i$ B) $-8 - 14i$ C) $4 + 4i$ D) $-8 + 4i$

Solution: Substitute in values for the various i terms.

$$3(1) - 5(i) - 9(-i) + 6(-1) - 5 = 3 - 5i + 9i - 6 - 5$$

Combine like terms to solve

$$-8 + 4i$$

The answer is D.

This is a more advanced question aimed to stump top math students. However, as long as you have the powers of i memorized, the math is actually relatively easy. As always, be very careful with negative signs in questions like this.

Multiplying Complex Numbers

Before we go into the details of how to multiply complex numbers, you need to know that

$$i^2 = -1$$

Multiplying imaginary numbers is just like multiplying binomials: use FOIL, which stands for First, Outer, Inner, Last. For example,

$$(3 - 5i)(2 - 2i) = 6 - 6i - 10i + 10i^2 = 6 - 16i + 10i^2$$

We are not done yet. Since there is an i^2 term when multiplying complex numbers and $i^2 = -1$, we plug in -1 for i^2

$$6 - 16i + 10(-1)$$

so we get the answer of

$$-4 - 16i$$

Example 4: The product of $1 - 3i$ and $11 + 2i$ can be written in the form of $a + bi$, what is the value of $a - b$?

Solution: Multiply the two complex numbers together and combine like terms.

$$(1 - 3i)(11 + 2i) = 11 + 2i - 33i - 6i^2 = 11 - 31i - 6i^2$$

Now, plug in -1 for i^2.

$$11 - 31i - 6(-1) = 17 - 31i$$

The question tells us that the product is written in the form $a + bi$. We can see that $a = 17$ and $b = -31$ so

$$a - b = 17 - (-31) = 48$$

The answer is 48.

The Complex Conjugate

All complex numbers have a complex conjugate. The complex conjugate is a complex number with an identical real part and an imaginary part with the opposite sign. In algebraic terms,

$$a + bi \text{ and } a - bi \text{ are complex conjugates.}$$

If you prefer numbers,

$$2 + 3i \text{ and } 2 - 3i \text{ are complex conjugates.}$$

To find the complex conjugate of any complex number, switch the sign of the imaginary part.

So why does this matter? The complex conjugate is important because **the product of any complex number and its complex conjugate is a real number**.

$$(a + bi)(a - bi) = a^2 + b^2$$

With numbers, we can see how the imaginary terms cancel out and we just get numbers.

$$(2 + 3i)(2 - 3i) = 4 - 6i + 6i - 9i^2 = 4 - 9i^2 = 4 - 9(-1) = 13$$

Notice that $2^2 + 3^2 = 13$, so we can skip all that math if you memorize the shortcut for the product of complex conjugates.

Complex conjugates are most often used when complex numbers are fractions, and the imaginary part is in the denominator. Fractions are not allowed to have i in the denominator. To get rid of the i in the denominator, we multiply the top and bottom of the fraction by the complex conjugate. For example, if we are given

$$\frac{10}{1-2i}$$

we need to multiply the top and bottom by the complex conjugate, which here is $1 + 2i$.

$$\frac{10}{1-2i} \times \frac{1+2i}{1+2i}$$

We get

$$\frac{10+20i}{(1-2i)(1+2i)} = \frac{10+20i}{5}$$

We can now simplify and get

$$2 + 4i$$

Example 5: Which of the following is equivalent to the equation below?

$$\frac{5}{3-4i}$$

A) $\frac{3}{5} + \frac{4}{5}i$ B) $\frac{5}{3} - \frac{5}{4}i$ C) $\frac{15}{7} - \frac{20}{7}i$ D) $\frac{4}{5} - \frac{4}{25}i$

Solution: To simplify, multiply by the complex conjugate of $3 + 4i$.

$$\frac{5}{3-4i} \times \frac{3+4i}{3+4i}$$

We get

$$\frac{15+20i}{(3-4i)(3+4i)} = \frac{15+20i}{25}$$

We can now simplify to get

$$\frac{3}{5} + \frac{4}{5}i$$

The answer is A.

Complex Numbers Practice: **A calculator may NOT be used on the following questions.** Answers on page 275.

1. Which of the following gives the correct answer when you subtract x from z?

$$x = -3 + 2i$$
$$z = 5 + 4i$$

    A) $2 + 6i$
    B) $8 + 2i$
    C) $8 + 6i$
    D) $2 - 6i$

2. What is the sum of the complex numbers $8 + 2i$ and $3 + 3i$ where $i = \sqrt{-1}$?

    A) 16
    B) $16i$
    C) $11 + 5i$
    D) $24 + 6i$

3. What is the sum of the complex numbers $2 + 7i$ and $6 + 5i$ where $i = \sqrt{-1}$?

    A) $8 + 12i$
    B) $20i$
    C) $9 + 11i$
    D) $12 + 35i$

4. Which of the following complex numbers is equal to $(3 + 6i) - (3i - 5)$, where $i = \sqrt{-1}$?

    A) $-2 + 3i$
    B) $-2 + 9i$
    C) $8 + 3i$
    D) $8 + 9i$

5. What is the product of the complex numbers $4 + 5i$ and $-3 + 3i$?

    A) $27 + 3i$
    B) $-27 - 3i$
    C) $2 + 11i$
    D) $-27 + 11i$

6. What is the product of the complex numbers $3 + 4i$ and $3 - 4i$?

    A) 25
    B) 7
    C) $9 - 16i$
    D) $9 + 16i$

7. Simplify the following set of imaginary numbers: $(-4 + 6i) - (1 + 3i)$

    A) $5 + 3i$
    B) $-5 + 3i$
    C) $-3 + 91$
    D) $3 + 3i$

8. What is the value of $\frac{i^7}{i^3}$?

    A) i
    B) $-i$
    C) -1
    D) 1

9. In the complex number system, which of the following is equivalent to the expression below? (Note $i = \sqrt{-1}$)

$$(6 + 5i) - (2i + 3)$$

A) $8 + 2i$
B) $3 + 3i$
C) $3 + 7i$
D) $9 + 3i$

13. Which of the following is equivalent to the equation below?

$$\frac{4}{1-3i}$$

A) $-\frac{1}{2} - \frac{3}{2}i$
B) $\frac{2}{5} + \frac{6}{5}i$
C) $\frac{2}{5} - \frac{6}{5}i$
D) $\frac{4}{5} - \frac{12}{5}i$

10. Which of the following is equivalent to the following equation?

$$4(3 + 2i) - 0.5(-8 + 6i)$$

A) $8 + 5i$
B) $16 + 5i$
C) $12 + 8i$
D) $16 + 8i$

14. What is the value of i^{37}?

A) i
B) $-i$
C) -1
D) 1

11. What is the value of $(i^5)(i^3)$?

A) i
B) $-i$
C) -1
D) 1

15. What is the product of the complex numbers $6 + 3i$ and $2 + i$?

A) $15 + 12i$
B) $9 + 12i$
C) $12 + 9i$
D) $9 + 6i$

12. Which of the following complex numbers is equal to $(5 + 4i) - (8i^2 - 8i)$, where $i = \sqrt{-1}$?

A) $-13 - 4i$
B) $-3 - 4i$
C) $13 - 4i$
D) $13 + 12i$

16. What is the value of $\frac{i^{12}}{i^6}$?

A) i
B) $-i$
C) -1
D) 1

17. If $i = \sqrt{-1}$, what is the value of the expression $12i^4 + 8i^2 + 12$?

18. In the equation below, a and b are real numbers, what is the value of $b - a$?

$$(8 + 4i)(6i - 3) = a + bi$$

19. Which of the following is equivalent to the equation below?

$$\frac{5}{2-4i}$$

A) $\frac{1}{2} + i$

B) $-\frac{5}{6} - \frac{10}{6}i$

C) $\frac{5}{2} - \frac{5}{4}i$

D) $\frac{5}{9} + \frac{10}{9}i$

20. Which of the following is equivalent to the equation below?

$$\frac{3}{3-3i}$$

A) $\frac{1}{6} + \frac{1}{2}i$

B) $\frac{1}{4} + \frac{3}{4}i$

C) $\frac{1}{2} + \frac{1}{2}i$

D) $1 + i$

21. If $i = \sqrt{-1}$, what is the value of the expression below?

$$8i^4 - 20i^2 + 6$$

22. In the equation below, a and b are real numbers, what is the value of $a + b$?

$$(5 + 3i)(4 + 2i) = a + bi$$

Chapter 29: Unit Conversion

For unit conversion questions, you need to know dimensional analysis, which uses conversion factors to convert from one unit to another. To do dimensional analysis, complete the following steps:

1. **Start with the value given in the question**

2. **Use the conversion factor(s) to switch the units**

3. **Multiply and divide the numbers to find the answer.**

If the conversion factor(s) are setup correctly, the answer will have the correct unit and all other units will cancel! An example of how to do this is shown below:

> **Example 1:** The top speed of Andrew's toy car is 30 meters per second. What is the speed of the toy car in kilometers per hour? (Round your answer the to the nearest whole number) (1 km = 1000 m)

Solution: To solve this question, we need to convert meters to kilometers and seconds to hours.

Whenever you are given a rate that includes two units, set it up as a fraction. In this question, we are given the speed in meters per second, so we can set up 30 meters per second as:

$$\frac{30 \ meters}{1 \ second}$$

From here, we just need to convert the units.

$$\frac{30 \ m}{1 \ s} \times \frac{1 \ km}{1000 \ m} = \frac{30 \ km}{1000 \ s} \qquad \text{1. Convert meters to kilometers.}$$

$$\frac{30 \ km}{1000 \ s} \times \frac{60 \ s}{1 \ min} = \frac{1800 \ km}{1000 \ min} \qquad \text{2. Convert seconds to minutes.}$$

$$\frac{1800 \ km}{1000 \ min} \times \frac{60 \ min}{1 \ hr} = \frac{108000 \ km}{1000 \ hr} \qquad \text{3. Convert minutes to hours.}$$

$$\frac{108000 \ km}{1000 \ hr} = \frac{108 \ km}{1 \ hr} = 108 \ km/hr \qquad \text{4. Simplify the answer.}$$

You can also solve this question in one big step as shown below:

$$\frac{30 \ m}{1 \ s} \times \frac{1 \ km}{1000 \ m} \times \frac{60 \ s}{1 \ min} \times \frac{60 \ min}{1 \ hr} = \frac{108000 \ km}{1000 \ hr} = 108 \ km/hr$$

The answer is 108.

The most difficult part of unit conversion questions is setting up the conversion factors correctly, so pay close attention to the units. If the units cancel and you finish with the units the question is asking for, the equation is up properly, and you will have the correct answer.

TIP – How to Spot Unit Conversion Questions

Many unit conversion questions on the SAT will have a conversion factor in parentheses at the end of the question. The SAT often underlines the changes in units as well. If you spot either of these, you will need to use the given conversion factor and dimensional analysis to find the answer. Unit conversion questions will commonly look like this:

A train is traveling at a speed of 25,600 inches per minute. What is the train's speed in <u>feet per second</u>? (12 inches = 1 foot)

Example 2: Erica bikes at an average speed of 24 miles per hour for 40 minutes. If Rosie bikes at an average speed of 18 miles per hour, how many minutes does it take Rosie to bike the same distance that Erica biked in 40 minutes? (Round your answer to the nearest whole number).

Solution: We first need to find out how far Erica bikes in 40 minutes:

$$40 \text{ minutes} \times \frac{1 \text{ hour}}{60 \text{ minutes}} \times \frac{24 \text{ miles}}{1 \text{ hour}} = 16 \text{ miles}$$

To bike 16 miles, Rosie will take:

$$16 \text{ miles} \times \frac{1 \text{ hour}}{18 \text{ miles}} \times \frac{60 \text{ minutes}}{1 \text{ hour}} = 53.3 \text{ minutes}$$

The answer is 53. On test day, if you bubble in 53.3, your answer will be marked as incorrect. The question tells us to round to the nearest whole number.

> **Test Day Tip*** – **When answering grid-in questions, make sure that you read the questions carefully and follow any directions for rounding.**

Example 3: A metal pipe that is p feet long will be cut into n pieces that are each x inches long. Which of the following expressions correctly describes length, in inches, of each of the n pieces of pipe?

A) $x = \frac{12p}{n}$ B) $x = \frac{p}{nx}$ C) $x = \frac{px}{12n}$ D) $x = \frac{12n}{px}$

Solution #1 - "Math Teacher Way": We first need to convert the length of the metal pipe from feet to inches:

$$p \text{ feet} \times \frac{12 \text{ inches}}{1 \text{ foot}} = 12p \text{ inches}$$

Then, we need to cut it into n pieces, so we will divide the metal pipe by n:

$$\frac{12p \text{ inches}}{n \text{ pieces of pipe}} = x \text{ inches per piece of pipe}$$

The answer is A.

Method #2 – Substitution: If solving algebraically seems tricky, we can just pick numbers to make this question easier. Let's say that the metal pipe is 2 feet long ($p = 2$) and that we will cut it into 3 pieces ($n = 3$). From here, we can easily solve for x, the length of each piece in inches:

$$2 \text{ feet} \times \frac{12 \text{ inches}}{1 \text{ foot}} = 24 \text{ inches}$$

$$\frac{24 \text{ inches}}{3} = 8 \text{ inches per piece}$$

With the numbers we picked, we found that $x = 8$. From here, we plug our values of p, n, and x into the answer choices to find out which equation is correct. Let's confirm this works by plugging in our values to answer choice A.

$$8 = \frac{12(2)}{3}$$

$$8 = 8$$

The equation works with our numbers, so we know that **the answer is A.**

Unit Conversion Practice: A calculator may be used on the following questions. Answers on page 276.

1. A laboratory receives a compound in 4-decagram vials. How many 1-centigram doses are contained in one 4-decagram vial?
(1 decagram = 10 grams)
(100 centigrams = 1 gram)

   A) 0.04
   B) 4
   C) 400
   D) 4,000

2. If a 6-foot giant sub is cut in half and each half is cut into quarters, how many <u>inches</u> long are the resulting pieces of the sub?
(1 foot = 12 inches)

   A) 9
   B) 18
   C) 36
   D) 72

3. The weight limit of a certain elevator is 1,800 pounds. What is the approximate weight limit of the elevator in kilograms?
(1 kilogram = 2.2046 pounds)

   A) 816
   B) 1494
   C) 2168
   D) 3968

4. A bakery purchases flour in 50-gallon bags. The flour is mixed with water to make loaves of bread. Each loaf of bread is made by mixing 3 quarts of flour with 2 quarts of water. What is the maximum number of loaves of bread that can be made from two 50-gallon bags of flour?
(1 gallon = 4 quarts)

   A) 66
   B) 133
   C) 150
   D) 200

5. A 25-foot plank of wood and a 12-foot plank of wood will be cut into 10-inch pieces. How many 10-inch pieces can be cut from the two planks? (1 foot = 12 inches)

   A) 10
   B) 30
   C) 40
   D) 44

6. A category 3 hurricane rains 3 inches per hour for 36 hours. Which of the following is closest to the total <u>feet</u> of rain over the 36 hours?
(1 foot = 12 inches)

   A) 9
   B) 12
   C) 108
   D) 1296

7. James is walking at a speed of 5 miles per hour through downtown Manhattan. If James walks for two hours, how many city blocks has he walked?   (1 city block = $\frac{1}{20}$ of a mile)

   A) 10
   B) 50
   C) 100
   D) 200

8. A set of 4 tires weighs 120 pounds. What is the approximate weight of the set of 4 tires in kilograms? (1 kilogram = 2.2046 pounds)

   A) 22
   B) 54
   C) 122
   D) 265

9. The diameter of Pluto is 1,477 miles. Which of the following best approximates the circumference of Pluto in kilometers?
    (1 kilometer = 0.6214 miles)

    A) 2,883
    B) 5,766
    C) 7,467
    D) 14,935

10. During the first 24 hours of a tropical storm, rain fell at a constant rate of 3 inches per hour. Which of the following is closest to the total amount of rain that fell during the first 7 hours of the storm in <u>millimeters</u>?
    (5 inches = 127 millimeters)

    A) 0.12
    B) 21
    C) 76
    D) 533

11. How many cups, each with a capacity of 6 fluid ounces, can be filled with lemonade from a cooler that holds 9 gallons of lemonade?
    (1 gallon = 128 ounces)

12. The abyssopelagic zone is the zone from the depth of 4,000 yards to 6,000 yards in the ocean. If an object is sinking at a rate of 2 miles per hour, to the nearest minute how many <u>minutes</u> would it take the object to pass from the beginning to the end of the abyssopelagic zone? (1 yard = 3 feet) (1 mile = 5,280 feet)

13. An Olympic bicyclist broke a record during a race in the French hills. He biked 13 miles in 17 minutes. What was his average speed, to the nearest integer, in miles per hour?

14. A racecar has tires with a radius of 1 foot. The racecar completes one lap of a race in 53 seconds, and the tires rotate at an average rate of 2,876 times per minute. To the closest hundredth of a mile, what is the length of the racetrack? (1 mile = 5280 feet)

Chapter 30: Word Problems

One of the challenges of the SAT Math Test is dealing with everyone's least favorite questions: word problems. These questions are often written in a way that makes it difficult to figure out exactly what is happening in the question. Word problems can include a wide variety of math topics that we have already learned in this book, so we will not cover any particular type of word problem in this chapter. Instead, we will focus on the tips that can help you solve all types of word problems more effectively and efficiently.

Tip #1 – Do Not Be Intimidated

Word problems look scary. Many students see a big paragraph and say, "no way, I can't solve that." They feel intimidated before even trying to solve the question. Do not let this be you! Word problems at their core are no more difficult than any other SAT Math questions. When you see a big paragraph on test day, take a deep breath and solve it one step at a time.

Tip #2 – Turn Words into Equations

When approaching a word problem, take it one sentence at a time. As you read through the question, identify each piece of key information and write it down in an equation. If you can convert the question from a word problem into an equation or equation(s), the question will be much easier to solve.

Often, word problems are actually just systems of equations questions. For questions like these, which we covered in Chapter 12, you will need to write down two equations. Once you have converted the word problem into two equations, you will be able to solve the question with the methods we learned in Chapter 12.

Tip #3 – Backsolve with the Answer Choices

For some word problems, writing your own equation(s) is very difficult. If you cannot write out the equation(s) or are not sure if the equation(s) that you wrote are correct, see if you can use the backsolving method. Sometimes it is easier to backsolve by taking the answer choices, going through the steps of the word problem, and seeing if you have the correct answer. Even if you cannot tell which answer is correct, backsolving can often help you eliminate some answer choices and make a better guess. If you need to review how to backsolve, go back to Chapter 1.

Tip #4 – Guess and Move on (If You Have To)

If you get to a word problem, try using the tips above, and still have no idea how to solve it, bubble in your best guess and move on! It is easy to waste a lot of time reading and re-reading long, confusing word problems. Students who do this often end up running out of time. Save those precious minutes to answer more questions that you know how to solve. We know it sounds backwards but giving up quickly on a word problem that you have no idea how to solve may help you actually get a better score.

If you complete the rest of the questions in the section and have time remaining, you can always come back to any questions that you guessed on. Sometimes when re-reading the question, you will realize how to solve it. It is easier to think more clearly when you are no longer worried about finishing the rest of the questions in the section.

Word Problems Practice: A calculator may NOT be used on the following questions. Answers on page 276.

1. Last weekend, Jenny made x cookies per hour for 2 hours, and Cara made y cookies per hour for 3 hours. Which of the following represents the total number of cookies made by Jenny and Cara?

   A) $6xy$
   B) $3x + 2y$
   C) $2x + 3y$
   D) $5xy$

2. Jimmy is a lawyer. Every week, Jimmy has new clients who need their Wills drafted. The number of Wills that Jimmy needs to finish each week is estimated by the equation $W = 42 - 7d$, where W represents the number of Wills left and d is the number of days he has worked. What is the meaning of the number 42 in this equation?

   A) Jimmy will finish the Wills in 42 days.
   B) Jimmy finishes 42 Wills per day.
   C) Jimmy finishes 6 Wills per hour.
   D) Jimmy starts each week with an estimated 42 Wills to complete.

3. John and Matt each ordered food at their favorite restaurant in Italy. The price of John's meal was y dollars and the price of Matt's meal was $6 more than John's meal. Since John is nice, they split the cost of the meal evenly. There was no tip or sales tax. Which of the following expressions represents the amount, in dollars, each of them paid?

   A) y
   B) $y + 6$
   C) $y + 3$
   D) $2y + 6$

4. The equation below relates the number of avocados, x, John buys each week and the number of bananas, y, John buys each week. If each avocado costs $2.25 and each banana costs $0.75, what does the number 35 represent?

   $$2.25x + 0.75y = 35$$

   A) The number of avocados purchased each week.
   B) The amount of money spent purchasing avocadoes and bananas each week.
   C) The total number of avocados and bananas purchased each week.
   D) The difference between the number of the avocados and the number of bananas purchased each week.

5. The yarn store sells blue yard and red yarn. Julie wants to buy 90 feet of red yarn and 45 feet of blue yarn. If red yarn sells for $2 per yard and blue yarn sells for $3 per yard, which of the following is how much Julie will pay for 90 feet of red yarn and 45 feet of blue yarn? (1 yard = 3 feet)

   A) 45
   B) 60
   C) 105
   D) 315

6. The product of 2 positive integers is 84. The smaller integer is one more than one half of the greater integer. What is the smaller integer?

   A) 5
   B) 6
   C) 7
   D) 12

Word Problems Practice: **A calculator may be used on the following questions.**

7. James, Danny, and John all own stock in an oil company. James owns 40 shares, Danny owns 35 shares, and John owns 28 shares. If the value of one share is $7, what is the value of all of their shares combined?

   A) $441
   B) $476
   C) $721
   D) $796

8. Debbie's Cupcake Company serves an average of 146 people each day in 2020. This is 12 less than half the average number of customers the company served each day last year. How many customers did Debbie's Cupcake Company serve on average every day last year?

   A) 79
   B) 292
   C) 304
   D) 316

9. Jamie makes pies and cookies. It takes her 20 minutes to make a pie and 30 minutes to make a tray of cookies. This weekend Jamie is going to spend 8 hours making pies and cookies. She will make twice as many trays of cookies as pies. How many trays of cookies will she make?

   A) 6
   B) 8
   C) 10
   D) 12

10. Jason bought five burgers for a total of $30.97 including a $0.22 sales tax. What would be the cost without sales tax if Jason bought four burgers?

    A) $18.00
    B) $20.25
    C) $24.60
    D) $28.00

11. Danny earns $8.50 per hour for the first 40 hours each week and 1.5 times as much for every additional hour he works. If Danny made $505.75 last week, how many total hours did he work?

    A) 53
    B) 56
    C) 59
    D) 63

12. Chris was skateboarding at 8 feet per second when he came to the top of a hill. After riding down the hill for 3.5 seconds, he was moving at 43 feet per second. Assuming the acceleration was constant, what was his acceleration in feet per second?

    A) 8
    B) 10
    C) 12
    D) 14

13. Julia is wrapping packages for Christmas. If each package requires 20 centimeters of wrapping paper, what is the maximum number of packages that can be wrapped with 4 meters of wrapping paper? (1 meter = 100 centimeters)

    A) 20
    B) 30
    C) 40
    D) 50

14. Jamie spends 20% of his 7-day spring break sleeping. In minutes, how long does Jamie sleep during his spring break?

    A) 140
    B) 336
    C) 2,016
    D) 10,040

Chapter 30: Word Problems

15. Acme Company manufactures sticks of dynamite. This week, Acme Company manufactured 63 more sticks of dynamite on Monday than on Tuesday. If a total of 873 sticks of dynamite were manufactured on Monday and Tuesday, how many sticks did Acme Company manufacture on Tuesday?

    A) 400
    B) 405
    C) 468
    D) 810

16. The German worldwide highway research committee came to the United States to learn more about the highway systems. They found that highways in the United States are on average 934 kilometers long. How long on average are the United States highways in miles?
    (1 kilometer = 0.62 miles)

    A) 540
    B) 579
    C) 934
    D) 1506

17. A professional soccer field is 110 yards long and 70 yards wide. What is the area in square feet of a professional soccer field?
    (1 yard = 3 feet)

    A) 7,700
    B) 23,100
    C) 30,800
    D) 69,300

18. Dave is making his grandmother's famous cornbread recipe. Dave's grandmother's recipe is in tablespoons. The recipe calls for 40 tablespoons of cornmeal, 24 tablespoons of butter, and 12 tablespoons of heavy cream. If 16 tablespoons are in one cup, what is the total number of cups of ingredients that Dave will need?

    A) $2\frac{1}{4}$
    B) $3\frac{1}{4}$
    C) $3\frac{3}{4}$
    D) $4\frac{3}{4}$

19. Woody the woodchuck can chuck at least 13 logs a day and at most 19 logs a day. Willy the woodchuck can chuck at least 7 logs a day and at most 16 logs a day. Based on this, what is a possible number of days it would take Woody and Willy to chuck 175 logs?

20. Johnny's transport company has a ferry with a weight limit of 35,000 pounds. The ferry is already carrying 13,050 pounds in shipments when it arrives at the dock. If each additional crate weighs 750 pounds, what is the maximum number of new crates that the ferry can transport?

21. The Jones family is throwing a huge surprise party for their grandfather's 80th birthday. The birthday party costs $18,000. All of the family members agree to split the cost of the party equally. When 3 members of the family later refused to pay for the event, the remaining members of the family each had to pay an additional $1,000. How many family members were initially going to split the costs for the party?

22. To build a new field, a certain number of companies are going to donate a total of $250,000. Each company will donate the same amount of money. Right at the deadline, 5 more companies decide to donate, and, as a result of the additional companies, each company will pay $2,500 less. How many companies were initially going to donate to pay for the field?

Chapter 31: Absolute Value

Absolute value is defined as a number's distance from zero. Since a distance can never be negative, the absolute value is always positive.

$$|3| = 3 \quad \text{(3 is three units from zero)}$$

$$|-3| = 3 \quad \text{(-3 is three units from zero)}$$

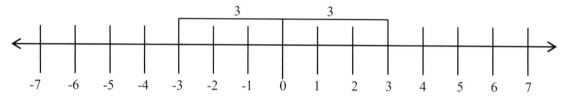

For equations with absolute value bars, **complete any math inside the absolute value bars first**. Then, solve the rest of the equation. For example, to solve

$$|3 - 7| + 2$$

Start by working inside the absolute value bars to get

$$|-4| + 2$$

$|-4| = 4$, so the equation becomes

$$4 + 2 = 6$$

Example 1: $\qquad\qquad a = |2 + 11| - 2|3 - 5|$

For the equation above, what is the value of a?

Solution: We start by working inside the absolute value bars. The equation becomes

$$a = |13| - 2|-2|$$

$|13| = 13$ and $|-2| = 2$, so we get

$$a = 13 - 2(2)$$
$$a = 9$$

The answer is 9.

Absolute Value and Unknown Variables

What if there is an unknown variable inside the absolute value bars? Let's consider the equation below.

$$|x - 3| = 5$$

For any equation like this, there will be two answers. Since $|5| = 5$ and $|-5| = 5$, we need to solve for the values of x when $x - 3 = 5$ and $x - 3 = -5$.

$$x - 3 = 5 \qquad\qquad x - 3 = -5$$
$$x = 8 \qquad\qquad x = -2$$

Both $x = -2$ and $x = 8$ are correct answers.

For any question with an unknown variable inside the absolute value bars, there will be multiple solutions. There are three steps to solve these questions.

1. **Move all terms outside of the absolute value bars to the right side of the equation.**

2. **Set the term inside the absolute value bars equal to the positive value (1ˢᵗ equation) and negative value (2ⁿᵈ equation) of the term(s) on the right side.**

3. **Solve the equations to get the values of the unknown variable.**

Example 2: For the equation $|2x + 1| - 6 = 11$, what is a positive value of x that solves the equation?

Solution: First, we need to move terms outside of the absolute value bars to the right side, so we add 6 to both sides to get

$$|2x + 1| = 17$$

Next, we set the term inside the absolute value bars equal to 17 and -17 and solve.

$$2x + 1 = 17 \qquad\qquad 2z + 1 = -17$$
$$2x = 16 \qquad\qquad 2x = -18$$
$$x = 8 \qquad\qquad x = -9$$

The question asks for a positive value of x, so **the answer is 8**.

Absolute Value Practice: A calculator may NOT be used on the following questions. Answers on page 278.

1. $|8 - 5| - |4 - 8| =$

    A) -1
    B) 0
    C) 3
    D) 7

2. $|5(-3) + 4| =$

    A) -11
    B) 4
    C) 11
    D) 19

3. What is the value of $|3x - 4| + 5$ when $x = -7$?

    A) -30
    B) -20
    C) 25
    D) 30

4. What is a solution to $|3x + 6| = 24$ where $x > 0$?

5. What is the solution set to $|x + 4| = 8$?

    A) $x = 4$
    B) $x = -4$
    C) $x = -12$
    D) $x = 4, -12$

6. The value of one solution to the equation below is 3. What is the value of the other solution?

$$|9 - x| = 6$$

7. If $x = 4$, what is $|3x - 6| + |-4x + 8|$ equal?

A) -18
B) 14
C) 24
D) 28

8. $$|36 - 3x| = 18$$

The value of one solution to the equation above is 6. What is the value of the other solution?

9. $$|4a + 4| - 4 = 12$$

If x and y are the solutions to the equation above, what is $|xy|$?

10. If $|4x - 3| + 2 = 15$ and $|5y + 3| = 17$ what is the smallest possible value of xy?

A) -20
B) -16
C) -11
D) -4

Chapter 32: Ratios and Proportions

We use ratios to make comparisons between two things. Ratios do not give the exact number of items but instead allow you to concisely compare the relationship between two things at the same time.

As an example, if we have oranges and apples in a basket in the ratio of $2:3$, it does not necessarily mean that we have 2 oranges and 3 apples. Instead, the ratio tells us that for every 2 oranges, there are 3 apples. As a result, **you can think of this ratio as $2x:3x$** because we must multiply 2 and 3 by the same value to keep the 2:3 ratio. Using this "x" trick can help you on many ratio questions where you are given a ratio but not any exact numbers.

On the SAT, you will need to solve ratio questions in four different ways. We will review the four types below along with the method(s) to solve them:

#1 - Ratio and a Total

Example 1: The ratio of red marbles to green marbles in a bag is $4:6$. If there are a total of 80 marbles in the bag and all of the marbles in the bag are red or green, how many of the marbles are red?

Solution: Method #1: The "x" trick. We can think of the ratio $4:6$ as $4x:6x$, where the $4x$ represents the red marbles and the $6x$ represents the green marbles.

$$Red\ Marbles + Green\ Marbles = 80$$

$$4x + 6x = 80$$

$$10x = 80$$

$$x = 8$$

To solve for the red marbles, we need to plug the x value back in to the $4x$.

$$Red\ Marbles = 4x = 4(8) = 32$$

The answer is 32.

Method #2: Set up a Proportion. We can set up a proportion from the ratio. Since the ratio of red marbles to green marbles is $4:6$, we know that there are 4 red marbles for every 10 total marbles.

$$\frac{red\ marbles}{total\ marbles} = \frac{4}{10}$$

Since there are 80 total marbles, we can set up an equation to solve for the unknown number of red marbles.

$$\frac{x}{80} = \frac{4}{10}$$

$$10x = 320$$

$$x = 32$$

The answer is 32.

#2 – Ratios as Proportions

Example 2: Beth is baking her famous chocolate cupcakes for her mother's birthday party. For every 3 cupcakes, Beth uses 10 pieces of chocolate. If Beth needs to make 42 cupcakes for the party, how many pieces of chocolate will she need to buy?

Solution: Set up the values from the ratio as a proportion. Here, we set up the proportion as

$$\frac{cupcakes}{pieces\ of\ choclate} = \frac{cupcakes}{pieces\ of\ choclate}$$

Now, we can plug in the values from the question and solve.

$$\frac{3\ cupcakes}{10\ pieces\ of\ chocolate} = \frac{42\ cupcakes}{x\ pieces\ of\ chocolate}$$

$$3x = 420$$

$$x = \frac{420}{3} = 140$$

The answer is 140.

#3 – Comparing Across Ratios

Example 3: The ratio of x to y is 3:4. The ratio of y to z is 2:10. What is the ratio of $x:z$?

   A) 3:10   B) 3:20   C) 15:4   D) 4:15

Solution: We need to make the variable that appears in both ratios, y, have the same numerical value. To do that, we multiply the second ratio by 2, so

$$\begin{array}{cc} x:y & y:z \\ 3:4 & 2:10 \end{array}$$

becomes

$$\begin{array}{cc} x:y & y:z \\ 3:4 & 4:20 \end{array}$$

Now that the y-values are the same, we can compare across the ratios to find $x:z$.

$$x:z = 3:20$$

The answer is B.

#4 – Ratios and Geometry

Example 4: In rectangle ABCD, the ratio of the lengths of side AB to side BC is 8:5. If the total perimeter of the rectangle is 156 feet, what is the length of the longer side of the rectangle?

Solution: To start, sketch out rectangle ABCD. We can think of the ratio as $8x:5x$ instead of just $8:5$. We can label the sides of our rectangle using $8x$ and $5x$ as the side lengths.

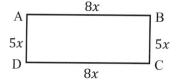

The perimeter of the rectangle is

$$8x + 8x + 5x + 5x = 156$$

$$26x = 156$$

$$x = \frac{156}{26} = 6$$

Now that we have solved for x, we can solve for the longer sides of the rectangle.

$$Longer\ Sides = 8x = 8(6) = 48$$

The answer is 48.

Ratios and Proportions Practice: A calculator may **NOT** be used on the following questions.
Answers on page 278.

1. If a dodgeball team has 6 girls and 11 total team members, what is the ratio of boys to girls?

    A) 5:6
    B) 6:5
    C) 12:10
    D) 15:6

2. There are 35 goldfish and 42 tetras in a fish tank. What is the ratio of goldfish to tetras?

    A) 1:5
    B) 5:6
    C) 5:11
    D) 6:5

3. On a map, $\frac{1}{2}$ inch represents 15 miles. How many miles apart are two gas stations that are $3\frac{1}{2}$ inches apart on the map?

    A) 25
    B) 55
    C) 105
    D) 120

4. There are 38 people at a party. If there are 16 boys, what is the ratio of girls to boys?

    A) 16:38
    B) 16:22
    C) 22:16
    D) 22:38

5. On a map, $\frac{1}{5}$ inch represents 10 miles. How many inches represent 350 miles?

Ratios and Proportions Practice: A calculator may be used on the following questions.

6. A factory that produces fidget spinners can make 2,000 fidget spinners each hour. Of those 2,000 fidget spinners, 17 are randomly selected and inspected. If the factory produces 30,000 fidget spinners this week, how many will be selected for inspection?

    A) 170
    B) 205
    C) 225
    D) 255

7. Eliza is throwing a party. She needs 8 liters of soda for every 6 guests. If Eliza will have 42 guests, how many liters of soda does she need?

    A) 8
    B) 24
    C) 48
    D) 56

8. Atrazine, a weed killer commonly used by farmers, is such a concentrated substance that only $1L$ can be used to spray up to 4 hectares of farm fields. If one hectare is equal to approximately $2\frac{1}{2}$ acres, how many acres of farm fields could 25 L of atrazine be used to spray?

A) 100
B) 150
C) 250
D) 1,750

9. Samantha rows 30 meters in 6.8 seconds. If she rows at the same rate for 2 minutes, which of the following is the closest to the number of meters she will row?

A) 200
B) 410
C) 530
D) 850

10. If $x:y = 7:2$ and $y:z = 3:2$, what is the ratio of $x:z$?

A) $2:7$
B) $7:2$
C) $14:4$
D) $21:4$

11. Four friends buy a winning lottery ticket worth $25,000. They agree to give four times as much to charity as they will spend for fun. How much do they give to charity?

A) $5,000
B) $12,500
C) $18,000
D) $20,000

12. A model of the library that will be built next year is currently on display in principal's office. The model is 36 inches tall and 65 inches wide. The model is $\frac{1}{25}$ the size of the actual building. What will be the height, in feet, of the library?

13. Bailey is baking bread, and the recipe calls for $\frac{3}{4}$ of a teaspoon of yeast and $3\frac{1}{2}$ cups of flour. She decides to use an entire 3 teaspoon pack of yeast and will keep the same yeast to flour ratio. How many cups of flour will she need?

A) $3\frac{1}{2}$
B) 7
C) $10\frac{1}{2}$
D) 14

14. In a drawer full of whole buttons, the ratio of tan to silver to gold buttons is 2:3:4. How many buttons could be in the drawer?

A) 30
B) 27
C) 24
D) 14

15. Julie knows that 30 miles per hour is 44 feet per second. If a cheetah is running 70 miles per hour, approximately how fast is it running in feet per second?

A) 36
B) 48
C) 86
D) 103

16. The weight of an object on Mars is approximately $\frac{6}{10}$ of its weight on Earth. The weight of an object on Saturn is approximately $\frac{21}{10}$ of its weight on Earth. If an object weights 150kg on Earth, approximately how many more kilograms does it weight on Saturn than on Mars?

    A) 60
    B) 150
    C) 210
    D) 225

17. In a certain rectangle, the ratio of the lengths of the 2 sides is 7:4. If the area of the rectangle is 252 square inches, what is the length, in inches, of the shorter side?

    A) 12
    B) 14
    C) 18
    D) 24

18. A box contains a combination of different colored balls. $\frac{1}{4}$ are black, $\frac{1}{8}$ are red, $\frac{1}{2}$ are yellow, and the remaining 20 balls are blue. How many black balls are in the box?

    A) 10
    B) 20
    C) 40
    D) 60

19. The high school football team is raising money to upgrade the turf on the field. The team has only sophomore, junior, and senior members. The ratio of sophomores to juniors to seniors on the football team is 2:4:5. Sophomores on average raised $40 per person, juniors on average raised $55 per person, and seniors on average raised $72 per person. What is the average amount raised per team member?

    A) 57
    B) 59
    C) 60
    D) 62

Chapter 33: Shifting and Transforming Functions

On the SAT, you will need to know how lines, parabolas, cubics, and other functions shift and transform in the xy-plane.

Rules for Shifting and Transforming Functions

1. **Numbers inside the parentheses shift a function horizontally.** Adding a number shifts a function that many units to the left and subtracting a number shifts a function that many units to the right.

2. **Numbers outside the parentheses shift a function vertically.** Adding a number shifts a function that many units up and subtracting a number shifts a function that many units down.

3. **A negative sign in front of a function flips the function vertically.**

4. **A coefficient in front of the function causes a vertical transformation.** If the coefficient is greater than 1, it causes a vertical stretch. If the coefficient is less than 1, it causes a vertical compression.

All functions follow the same rules. As long as you memorize the rules above, you will be able to solve questions with shifts and transformations of lines, parabolas, cubics, or any other type of function.

Parabolas

We will start by reviewing the shifts and transformations using the parabola function $f(x) = x^2$.

	Horizontal Shift	**Vertical Shift**
$f(x) = x^2$	$f(x) = (x - 2)^2$	$f(x) = x^2 - 3$
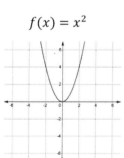	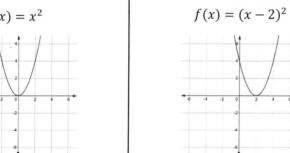	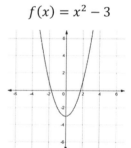
	Numbers in the parentheses cause a shift right with subtraction (as shown above) and a shift left with addition.	Numbers outside the parentheses cause a shift down with subtraction (as shown above) and a shift up with addition.

Vertical Stretch	**Vertical Compression**	**Vertical Flip**
$f(x) = 4x^2$	$f(x) = \dfrac{1}{2}x^2$	$f(x) = -x^2$
	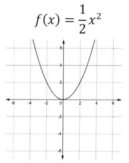	
A coefficient that is greater than 1 causes a vertical stretch.	A coefficient that is less than 1 causes a vertical compression.	A negative sign in the front causes the function to reflect over the x-axis.

Cubics

Below, you can see how the cubic functions follow the same rules for shifts and transformations.

	Horizontal Shift	**Vertical Shift**
$f(x) = x^3$ 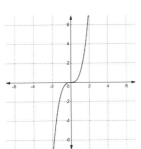	$f(x) = (x + 2)^3$ 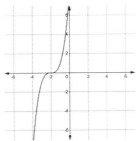 Numbers in the parentheses cause a shift left with addition (as shown above) and a shift right with subtraction.	$f(x) = x^3 + 1$ 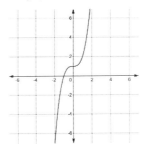 Numbers outside the parentheses cause a shift down with subtraction and a shift up with addition (as shown above).
Vertical Stretch	**Vertical Compression**	**Vertical Flip**
$f(x) = 4x^3$ 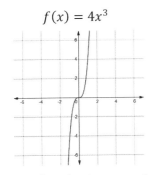 A coefficient that is greater than 1 causes a vertical stretch.	$f(x) = \dfrac{1}{2}x^3$ 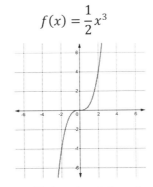 A coefficient that is less than 1 causes a vertical compression.	$f(x) = -x^3$ 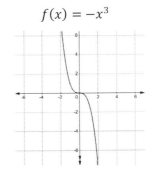 A negative sign in the front causes the function to reflect over the x-axis.

All Other Functions

All functions follow the same basic rules for shifting. At times, the SAT will ask you questions about very weird looking functions. Remember that these functions still follow the same rules for shifts and transformations as the parabolas and cubics that we just reviewed.

$$y = f(x)$$

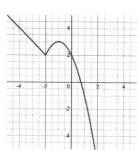

Horizontal Shift	**Vertical Shift**
$$y = f(x + 2)$$	$$y = f(x) - 3$$

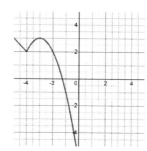
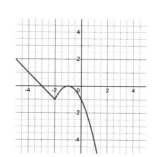

Numbers in the parentheses cause a shift left with addition (as shown above) and a shift right with subtraction.

Numbers outside the parentheses cause a shift down with subtraction (as shown above) and a shift up with addition.

Vertical Stretch	**Vertical Compression**	**Vertical Flip**
$$y = 3f(x)$$	$$y = \frac{1}{3}f(x)$$	$$y = -f(x)$$

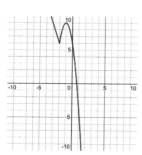
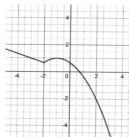
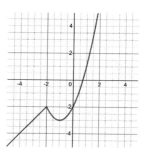

A coefficient that is greater than 1 causes a vertical stretch.

A coefficient that is less than 1 causes a vertical compression.

A negative sign in the front causes the function to reflect over the x-axis.

Shifting and Transforming Functions Practice: A calculator may NOT be used on the following questions. Answers on page 279.

1.
$$h(x) = x^2 - 5$$
$$g(x) = (x - 2)^2 - 1$$

Which of the following correctly describes the shift required to transform $h(x)$ into $g(x)$?

A) Shift $h(x)$ right 2 units and down 4 units.
B) Shift $h(x)$ right 2 units and up 4 units.
C) Shift $h(x)$ left 2 units and down 4 units.
D) Shift $h(x)$ left 2 units and up 4 units.

2.
$$f(x) = (x + 1)^3 + 2$$

Which of the following functions $g(x)$ shifts $f(x)$ up by 4 units and left by 1 unit?

A) $g(x) = x^3 + 6$
B) $g(x) = (x + 5)^3 + 3$
C) $g(x) = (x + 2)^3 - 2$
D) $g(x) = (x + 2)^3 + 6$

3.

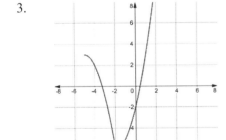

The function $y = f(x + 2) + 1$ is show above. What is the y-intercept of $f(x)$?

A) -4
B) -5
C) -6
D) -7

4.

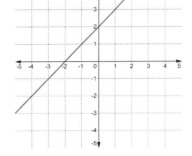

The graph of $f(x)$ is displayed above. Which of the following is the graph of $y = f(x) - 3$?

A)

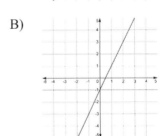

B)

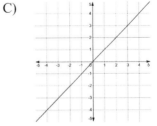

C)

D)

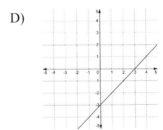

5. The quadratic function f is defined as $f(x) = -3(x+2)^2 - 1$. In the xy-plane, which of the following could be the graph of $f(x)$ shifted 4 units up?

A)

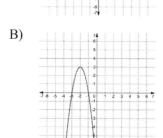

B)

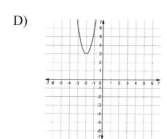

C)

D)

6. The graphs of the following quadratic equations in the xy-plane each have x-intercepts at -1 and 5. The graph of which equation has its vertex furthest from the x-axis?

A) $y = 2(x+1)(x-5)$
B) $y = -9(x+1)(x-5)$
C) $y = \frac{1}{2}(x+1)(x-5)$
D) $y = -\frac{1}{6}(x+1)(x-5)$

7.

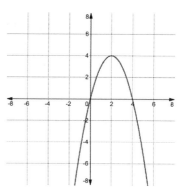

The graph above displays the function for the height of a soccer pass in meters after the referee blew the whistle to restart the game. Which of the graphs below properly model the height of the soccer ball if the player had waited 3 seconds after the referee blew the whistle to make the same pass?

A)

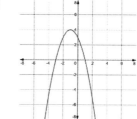

B)

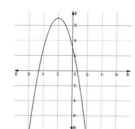

C)

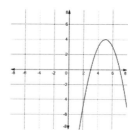

D)

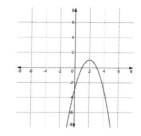

8. Which of the following functions is a downward facing parabola with a vertex that is located above the x-axis?

   A) $y + 3 = (x - 2)^2$
   B) $-2x^2 - y = -5$
   C) $y = (x + 11)^2 - 6$
   D) $y = -(x - 3)^2 - 4$

9.
$$g(x) = -(x - 2)^2 + 9$$
$$h(x) = -(x + 2)^2 + 11$$

   Which of the following transformation are required to turn $h(x)$ into $g(x)$?

   A) Shift 2 units left and reflect over the x-axis.
   B) Shift 4 units left and 2 units up.
   C) Shift 4 units right and reflect over the x-axis.
   D) Shift 4 units right and 2 units down.

10.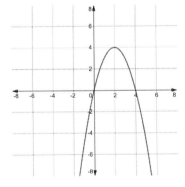

The graph above displays the function $f(x - 4) + 1$. Which of the following is the correct equation for $f(x)$?

   A) $f(x) = -(x + 2)^2 + 3$
   B) $f(x) = -(x - 2)^2 + 4$
   C) $f(x) = -x^2 + 5$
   D) $f(x) = -(x - 6)^2 + 5$

11.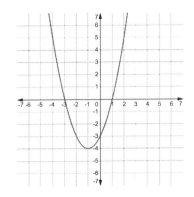

The graph above displays the function $f(x + 2) - 3$. Which of the following correctly displays $f(x)$?

A)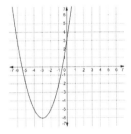

B)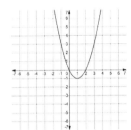

C)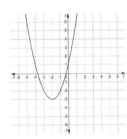

D)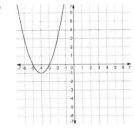

Chapter 34: Interpreting Constants in Linear and Polynomial Functions

The SAT will ask you to interpret constants in linear and polynomial functions. To answer these questions correctly, you will need to be familiar with various forms of linear and polynomial functions and what the constants represent.

Linear Functions

To start, let's look at an easier example with linear functions.

Example 1: The graph of the equation below in the xy-plane is a linear function. Which of the following equivalent forms of the equation includes the y-intercept as a constant?

$$3y = 4x - 6$$

A) $4x = 3y + 6$

B) $3y = 2(x - 3)$

C) $y = \frac{4}{3}x - 2$

D) $x = \frac{3}{4}y + \frac{3}{2}$

Solution - Method #1 – "Math Teacher Way": We want to convert the line from standard form to slope-intercept form. To do so, we need to rewrite the equation in $y = mx + b$ form, since b shows the y-intercept of a line. We divide by 3 to isolate y.

$$3y = 4x - 6$$

$$y = \frac{4}{3}x - 2$$

The y-intercept is at -2. The only answer choice that has -2 as a constant is C. **The answer is C.**

Method #2 – Shortcut Method: That works, but there is an easier and faster way! Rather than do all that work, we can solve this more quickly by using the answer choices. Once we recognize that we want this line in slope-intercept form, you can just look at the answer choices and see that only C is in slope-intercept form. The **answer is C.**

For interpreting constants questions, be sure to **look at the answer choices right away**. These questions almost always have all 4 answer choices as various equivalent forms of the same equation, so you do not need to do any algebra to see if the equations match. You just need to be familiar with what the constants represent in various forms of the same equation.

Make sure you are familiar with various forms of linear equations and what the constants represent.

Linear Equations

Form	Equation	What the Constants Represent
Standard	$ax + by = c$	a, b, and c represent nothing
Slope-Intercept	$y = mx + b$	m is the slope b is the y-intercept
x equals	$x = dy + f$	f is the x-intercept

Finding the x-Intercept and y-Intercept

On many questions involving constants, you will need to be able to locate the x-intercept(s) and y-intercept(s) of various types of functions. Doing so is easy as long as you remember the rules below:

To solve for the x-intercept, set $y = 0$ and solve for x.

To solve for the y-intercept, set $x = 0$ and solve for y.

Be sure to memorize these rules, as they help on a variety of questions throughout the SAT! Now, let's see how these rules can help to solve interpreting constants questions.

Example 2: $\qquad\qquad\qquad 5x - 3y = 20$

The graph of the equation above in the xy-plane is a linear function. Which of the following equivalent forms of the equation includes the x-intercept as a constant?

A) $3y = 5x - 20$

B) $3y = 5(x - 4)$

C) $y = \frac{5}{3}x - \frac{20}{3}$

D) $x = \frac{3}{5}y + 4$

Solution: To solve for the x-intercept, set $y = 0$ and solve for x.

$$5x - 3(0) = 20$$

$$5x = 20$$

$$x = 4$$

Now that we know that the x-intercept is at $x = 4$, we look at the answer choices to see which ones has $+4$ as a constant. **The answer is D**.

Example 3: $\qquad\qquad\qquad x^2 - 2y - 10 = 3x$

For the function above, which of the following equivalent forms of the function includes the y-intercept as a constant?

A. $2y = x^2 - 3x - 10$

B. $y = \frac{x^2}{2} - \frac{3}{2}x - 5$

C. $x(x - 3) = 2y + 10$

D. $y = (x - \frac{5}{2})(x + 2)$

Solution: To solve for the y-intercept, set $x = 0$ and solve for y.

$$(0)^2 - 2y - 10 = 3(0)$$

$$-2y - 10 = 0$$

$$-2y = 10$$

$$y = -5$$

We find that the y-intercept is at $y = -5$, so we need to look at the answer choices to see which one has -5 as a constant. **The answer is B**.

Parabolas

Most commonly, interpreting constants questions will ask you about parabolas. To answer these questions correctly, you will need to know how to identify the x-intercepts, the y-intercepts, and the vertices of vertical and horizontal parabolas.

Make sure you memorize the three forms of a vertical parabola below.

Vertical Parabola

Form	Equation	What the Constants Represent
Standard	$y = ax^2 + bx + c$	c is the y-intercept
Factored	$y = a(x - d)(x - f)$	d and f are the x-intercepts
Vertex	$y = a(x - h)^2 + k$	vertex is at (h, k)

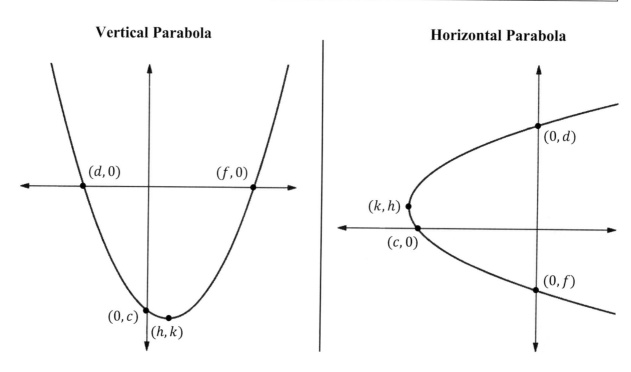

Vertical Parabola   **Horizontal Parabola**

For more difficult questions, you will need to know the three forms for horizontal parabolas. These are far less common on the SAT, but you should memorize these in case you see one on test day.

Horizontal Parabola

Form	Equation	What the Constants Represent
Standard	$x = ay^2 + by + c$	c is the x-intercept
Factored	$x = a(y - d)(y - f)$	d and f are the y-intercepts
Vertex	$x = a(y - h)^2 + k$	vertex is at (k, h)

Now that we have learned the rules for parabolas, let's take a look at a few examples of interpreting constants questions with parabolas.

Example 4:
$$y = x^2 - 10x + 16$$

The equation for parabola P is written above. Which of the following equivalent forms of the equation shows the coordinates of the vertex of parabola P as constants?

 A) $y = (x - 5)^2 - 9$
 B) $y = (x - 8)(x - 2)$
 C) $y - 5 = x^2 - 10x + 11$
 D) $16 = y - x(x - 10)$

Solution: The question asks us to find the constants for the coordinates of the vertex, so we are looking for a parabola that is written in vertex form. The only equation that is written in vertex form is A, which shows the vertex for this parabola is at the point $(5, -9)$. **The answer is A.**

Example 5:
$$x^2 - y + 8x + 12 = 0$$

For the parabola above, which of the following equivalent forms of the equation shows the x-intercepts as constants or coefficients?

 A) $x(x + 8) + 12 = y$
 B) $y = (x + 4)^2 - 4$
 C) $y = (x + 6)(x + 2)$
 D) $x^2 + 8x + 12 = y$

Solution: We need to see the x-intercepts as constants, so we are looking for the parabola that is in factored form. The only answer choice that is written in factored form is C, where we can see the x-intercepts of this parabolas are at $x = -2$ and $x = -6$. **The answer is C.**

As you can see from these two examples, these questions are pretty straightforward as long as you have memorized the three forms of vertical parabolas.

Now, let's take a look at some questions with horizontal parabolas. Since you do not use horizontal parabolas nearly as often as vertical parabolas, questions with horizontal parabolas are more difficult. To get the correct answer for these questions, you will need to memorize the three forms of horizontal parabolas and what the constants in each form represent.

Example 6: Parabola Q in the coordinate plane has the equation $y^2 - 10y + x - 2 = 14$. Which of the following equivalent forms of the equation shows the x-intercept(s) of the parabola as constants or coefficients?

 A) $x = -(y - 5)^2 + 41$
 B) $x = 16 + 10y - y^2$
 C) $y = \sqrt{41 - x} + 5$
 D) $y(y - 10) - 2 = 14 - x$

Solution: Here, we have a horizontal parabola. You can spot horizontal parabolas easily by looking for a y^2 term. To find the x-intercept: set $y = 0$ and solve for x.

$$(0)^2 - 10(0) + x - 2 = 14$$
$$x = 16$$

The x-intercept is at $x = 16$, so we need to look for which answer choice has 16 as a constant or coefficient. **The answer is B.**

We also could have solved this question by knowing the three forms for horizontal parabolas. The standard form of a horizontal parabola shows the x-intercept. Since B is the only answer choice written in standard form, **the answer is B.**

Example 7: Parabola Z in the coordinate plane has the equation $y^2 - 6y - x - 91 = 0$. Which of the following equivalent forms of the equation shows the y-intercept(s) of the parabola as constants or coefficients?

A) $x = (y + 7)(y - 13)$

B) $x = y^2 - 6y - 91$

C) $y(y - 6) = x + 91$

D) $y = \sqrt{x + 82} + 3$

Solution: We again see a horizontal parabola in this question. The y-intercepts for a horizontal parabola are constants when the equation is written in factored form. The only answer choice in factored form is A, where we can see that the y-intercepts are at $y = -7$ and $y = 13$. **The answer is A.**

We could have also solved this question using our rule to find the y-intercepts: set $x = 0$ and solve for y.

$$y^2 - 6y - (0) - 91 = 0$$
$$y^2 - 6y - 91 = 0$$
$$(y - 13)(y + 7) = 0$$
$$y = -7, 13$$

We find the y-intercepts are at $y = -7$ and $y = 13$. The only answer choice that shows these as constants or coefficients is A. **The answer is A.**

Interpreting Constants Practice: A calculator may NOT be used on the following questions. Answer on page 280.

1. The graph of the equation below in the xy-plane is a linear function. Which of the following equivalent forms of the equation includes the x-intercept as a constant?

$$y = 2x + 6$$

A) $y - 2x = 6$

B) $\frac{1}{2}y - x = 3$

C) $y = 2(x + 3)$

D) $x = \frac{1}{2}y - 3$

2. The graph of the equation below in the xy-plane is a parabola. Which of the following equivalent forms of the equation includes the x-coordinate of the vertex as a constant?

$$y = x^2 - 8x + 12$$

A) $y = (x - 4)^2 - 4$
B) $y = (x - 6)(x - 2)$
C) $y = x(x - 8) + 12$
D) $y - 12 = x(x - 8)$

3. The graph of the equation below in the xy-plane is a linear function. Which of the following equivalent forms of the equation includes the y-intercept as a constant?

$$2x + 3y = 12$$

A) $x = -\frac{3}{2}y + 6$

B) $3y = -2x + 12$

C) $\frac{2}{3}x - 4 + y = 0$

D) $y = -\frac{2}{3}x + 4$

4. If $f(x) = a(x - b)(x + c)$, where a, b, and c are constants, which of the following lists the x-intercept(s) of $f(x)$?

A) $-ab$ and ac
B) $a, -b,$ and c
C) b and $-c$
D) $-b$ and c

5. The graph of the equation below in the xy-plane is a linear function. Which of the following is a form of the equation that includes the x-intercept as a constant?

$$6x + 4y = 24$$

A) $y = \frac{3}{2}x + 6$

B) $y = -\frac{3}{2}x + 6$

C) $x = -\frac{2}{3}y + 4$

D) $x = -\frac{2}{3}y + 6$

6. The equation below represents a parabola in the xy-plane. Which of the following equations displays the x-intercepts of the parabola as constants or coefficients?

$$y = x^2 - 13x + 36$$

A) $y = (x - 4)(x - 9)$
B) $y = x(x - 13) + 36$
C) $y = x^2 - 13(x + 3) - 3$
D) $y - 36 = x^2 - 13x$

7. Parabola A in the xy-plane has the equation $x - y^2 + 8y + 5 = 2y + 13$. Which of the following is an equivalent form of the equation that shows the y-intercept(s) of the parabola as constants or coefficients?

A) $x = y^2 - 6y + 8$
B) $x = y^2 - 6y + 18$
C) $x = (y - 4)(y - 2)$
D) $x = (y - 3)^2 - 1$

8. The equation below represents a parabola in the xy-plane. Which of the following is an equivalent form that displays the y-intercept of the parabola as a constant or coefficient?

$$y = -3(x + 2)(x + 3)$$

A) $y = -3x^2 - 15x - 18$
B) $y = -3x^2 - 5x - 6$
C) $y = -3x^2 + 15x + 18$
D) $y = -3x - 9x + 6$

9. The equation below represents a parabola in the xy-plane. Which of the following equivalent forms of the equation displays the x-intercepts of the parabola as constants or coefficients?

$$y = x^2 - 6x + 8$$

A) $y - 8 = x^2 - 6x$
B) $y + 1 = (x - 3)^2$
C) $y = (x - 4)(x - 2)$
D) $y = x(x - 6) + 8$

10. Parabola X in the xy-plane has the equation of $y = x^2 - z$. Which of the following is equal to the x-intercept(s) of the parabola as constants or coefficients?

A) $z, -z$
B) $-z$
C) z^2
D) $\sqrt{z}, -\sqrt{z}$

11. Parabola Q in the coordinate plane has the equation $x - 3y^2 - 18y + 13 = 0$. Which equation shows the x-intercept(s) of the parabola as constants or coefficients?

A) $x = 3(y - 3)^2 - 14$
B) $x = 3y^2 + 18y - 13$
C) $x + 14 = 3(y - 3)^2$
D) $y = \sqrt{\dfrac{x+14}{3}} + 3$

12. If $y = 5x^2 - 16x + 3$ is graphed in the xy-plane, which of the following elements of the graph is displayed as a constant?

A) x-intercept
B) y-intercept
C) x-coordinate of the vertex
D) y-coordinate of the vertex

13. If $f(x) - d = a(x - b)^2 + c$, where $a, b, c,$ and d are constants, which of the following is equal to the y-coordinate of the vertex of $f(x)$?

A) b
B) $c + d$
C) $-ab$
D) c

14. If $(y - 3)^2 + 8 - 2x = 0$ is graphed in the xy-plane, which of the following elements of the graph is displayed as a constant?

A) x-intercept
B) y-intercept
C) x-coordinate of the vertex
D) y-coordinate of the vertex

15. Parabola B in the xy-plane has the equation of $y = x^2 - ax - bx + ab$. Which of the following is equivalent to the x-coordinate for the vertex of the parabola?

A) $\dfrac{a+b}{2}$
B) $\dfrac{-a-b}{2}$
C) ab
D) $\dfrac{a}{b}$

Chapter 35: Special Quadratics – Perfect Squares and Difference of Squares

Special quadratics questions require you to know the perfect squares and difference of squares formulas. These questions are difficult until you learn how to spot them and the techniques for solving them. To start, let's review the formulas you will need to know.

Equation	Formula	Example
Perfect Square (Addition)	$(x + y)^2 = x^2 + 2xy + y^2$	$(x + 2)^2 = x^2 + 4x + 4$
Perfect Square (Subtraction)	$(x - y)^2 = x^2 - 2xy + y^2$	$(x - 3)^2 = x^2 - 6x + 9$
Difference of Squares	$(x + y)(x - y) = x^2 - y^2$	$(x + 6)(x - 6) = x^2 - 36$

Difference of Squares

The SAT most commonly asks you special quadratics questions where you need to use the difference of squares formula. To start, let's take a look at how one of these questions might appear on test day.

> **Example 1:** If $x + y = 3$ and $x^2 - y^2 = -15$, what is the value of $x - y$?
>
> A) -45 B) -15 C) -5 D) 5

Solution: To solve this question, we need to use the difference of squares formula.

$$(x + y)(x - y) = x^2 - y^2$$

The question tells us $(x + y) = 3$ and $x^2 - y^2 = -15$, so we can plug those values in for $x + y$ and $x^2 - y^2$ and solve for $x - y$.

$$(3)(x - y) = -15$$

$$x - y = -\frac{15}{3} = -5$$

The answer is C.

> **Example 2:** If $a - b = 10$ and $a + b = 3$, what is the value of $(a^2 - b^2)(a + b)$?

Solution: We need to spot that this is a difference of squares question. Since $(a^2 - b^2) = (a + b)(a - b)$, we can substitute in $(a + b)(a - b)$ for $(a^2 - b^2)$ and the equation becomes

$$(a + b)(a - b)(a + b)$$

The question tells us $a - b = 10$ and $a + b = 3$, so we can just plug in the values for $(a + b)$ and $(a - b)$ to solve.

$$(3)(10)(3) = 90$$

The answer is 90.

> **Example 3:** If $x^4 - y^4 = 120$ and $x^2 - y^2 = 20$, what is $x^2 + y^2$ equal to?
>
> A) 100   B) 40   C) 12   D) 6

Solution: While this question may look more complicated at first, we can solve it exactly like the previous examples. We need to notice this is still a difference of squares question, only with higher powers now.

$$(x^2 + y^2)(x^2 - y^2) = x^4 - y^4$$

The questions tells us $x^4 - y^4 = 120$ and $x^2 - y^2 = 20$, we just need to plug in the values for $x^4 - y^4$ and $x^2 - y^2$ to solve.

$$(x^2 + y^2)(20) = 120$$

$$x^2 + y^2 = \frac{120}{20} = 6$$

The answer is D.

Example 4: If $x - y = q$ and $\sqrt{x} + \sqrt{y} = 15$, which of the following expressions is equal to $\sqrt{x} - \sqrt{y}$?

A) $\frac{q}{15}$ B) $\frac{15}{q}$ C) $15q$ D) $15 - q$

Solution: To solve, we need to recognize that

$$\left(\sqrt{x} + \sqrt{y}\right)\left(\sqrt{x} - \sqrt{y}\right) = x - y$$

Once we spot this unusual difference of squares, we can substitute in the values of $x - y$ and $\sqrt{x} + \sqrt{y}$ from the question to solve.

$$(15)\left(\sqrt{x} - \sqrt{y}\right) = q$$

$$\sqrt{x} - \sqrt{y} = \frac{q}{15}$$

The answer is A.

Questions with unusual difference of squares are difficult to recognize on test day. Just remember that if you ever see a term that looks anything like $x^2 - y^2$, $x^5 - y^5$ or any other variation, you are dealing with a difference of squares question.

TIP – Difference of Squares with Other Powers

The SAT can make difference of squares questions more difficult by using powers other than simple squares as we just saw in examples 3 and 4. Remember that the factors (terms in parentheses) are always half the power of the other terms. Below are some examples:

$$(x^2 + y^2)(x^2 - y^2) = x^4 - y^4$$

$$\left(\sqrt{x} + \sqrt{y}\right)\left(\sqrt{x} - \sqrt{y}\right) = x - y$$

Perfect Squares

The SAT also asks questions involving perfect squares. If a question gives you a value for a $(x + y)$, $(x - y)$, or $(x^2 + y^2)$ and for xy, you are most likely dealing with a perfect squares question.

Let's see how this might appear on the SAT below:

Example 5: If $x^2 + y^2 = 30$ and $xy = 3$, what is the value of $x + y$?

A) 90   B) 15   C) 10   D) 6

Solution: Here, we need to use the perfect square (addition) formula.

$$(x + y)^2 = x^2 + 2xy + y^2$$

We can reorder the terms to make the equation look like this:

$$(x + y)^2 = (x^2 + y^2) + 2xy$$

The question tells us $x^2 + y^2 = 30$ and $xy = 3$, so we can plug in the given values for $x^2 + y^2$ and xy and solve for $x + y$.

$$(x + y)^2 = (30) + 2(3)$$

$$(x + y)^2 = 36$$

$$x + y = 6$$

We see that $x + y = 6$, so **the answer is D**.

Example 6: If $4x^2 - 4xy + y^2 = 9z^2$, which of the following expresses the value of $2x - y$?

A) $9z$ B) $3z$ C) $81z^4$ D) $\frac{9z}{2}$

Solution: This is a more advanced example of a perfect square question. To solve, we need to recognize that

$$(2x - y)^2 = 4x^2 - 4xy + y^2$$

We know that $4x^2 - 4xy + y^2 = 9z^2$, so we can substitute in the $9z^2$.

$$(2x - y)^2 = 9z^2$$

To solve, we now take the square root of both sides and get

$$\sqrt{(2x - y)^2} = \sqrt{9z^2}$$

$$2x - y = 3z$$

The answer is B.

TIP – How to Spot Special Quadratics Questions

All special quadratics questions give you values for terms that include two variables. The five terms you should keep an eye out for are:

$$x^2 - y^2 \qquad x^2 + y^2 \qquad x + y \qquad x - y \qquad xy$$

The SAT can make these questions more difficult by using different variables or using unusual powers (as discussed in the TIP box on the previous page). Below are some examples of how these might appear:

$$m^4 - n^4 \qquad a^2 - b^2 \qquad p + q \qquad \sqrt[3]{c} - \sqrt[3]{d} \qquad ab$$

If you spot anything that looks like these terms, you are most likely dealing with a special quadratics question and will need to use the difference of squares or perfect squares formulas.

Special Quadratics Practice: A calculator should NOT be used on the following questions. Answers on page 280.

1. If $a + b = 7$ and $a - b = 3$, what is the value of $a^2 + 2ab + b^2$?

   A) 9
   B) 40
   C) 49
   D) 58

2. If $l + k = 9$ and $l - k = 3$, what is the value of $l^2 - 2lk + k^2$?

   A) 9
   B) 18
   C) 36
   D) 81

3. If $x + y = 11$ and $x - y = 5$, what is the value of $x^2 - y^2$?

   A) 25
   B) 55
   C) 96
   D) 121

4. If $a^2 + 2ab + b^2 = 36$ and $a - b = 9$, what is the value of $a + b$?

   A. 2
   B. 4
   C. 6
   D. 12

5. If $a + b = 12$ and $a - b = 4$, what is the value of $a^2 - b^2$?

   A) 16
   B) 48
   C) 128
   D) 144

6. If $x - y = 5$ and $x^2 - y^2 = 75$, what is the value of $x + y$?

   A) 5
   B) 10
   C) 15
   D) 25

7. If $\frac{3^{x^2}}{3^{y^2}} = 3^{12}$ and $x + y = 6$, what is the value of $x - y$?

8. If $m + l = 10$ and $m - l = 4$, what is the value of $(m + l)(m^2 - l^2)$?

9. If $a^2 + b^2 = 12$ and $ab = -6$, what is the value of $a - b$?

   A) -2
   B) 0
   C) $2\sqrt{6}$
   D) 6

10. If $a^2 - b^2 = 6$ and $a^2 + b^2 = 12$, what is the value of $a^4 - b^4$?

    A) 36
    B) 72
    C) 108
    D) 144

11. If $\left(2^{x^2}\right)\left(2^{-y^2}\right) = 4^9$ and $x - y = 2$, what is the value of $x + y$?

13. If $\frac{3^{a^2}}{3^{b^2}} = 9^4$ and $a + b = 2$, what is the value of $a - b$?

12. If $\sqrt{x} - \sqrt{y} = 9$ and $x - y = 45$, what is the value of $3\sqrt{x} + 3\sqrt{y}$?

A) 5
B) 15
C) $3\sqrt{5}$
D) 36

14. If $x > 1$, $\frac{x^{a^2-ab}}{x^{ab-b^2}} = x^{16}$, and $a + b = 8$, what is the value of $a - b$?

Answer Explanations

Chapter 1 – Backsolving (Page 2)

1. **C** Method 1: Backsolve. $3.25(8) + 6 = 5(8) - 8 \;\rightarrow\; 32 = 32$
   Method 2: Algebra. $3.25x + 6 = 5x - 8 \;\rightarrow\; 14 = 1.75x \;\rightarrow\; x = 8$

2. **B** Method 1: Backsolve. Take each answer choice, which is the width, add 8 to it to find the length, and then multiply both values by 2 to find the perimeter. $9 + 8 = 17 \;\rightarrow\; 9(2) + 17(2) = 52$
   Method 2: Algebra: $2l + 2w = 52$ and $w + 8 = l \;\rightarrow\; 2(w + 8) + 2w = 52 \;\rightarrow\; 4w + 16 = 52 \;\rightarrow\;$
   $4w = 36 \;\rightarrow\; w = 9$

3. **C** Method 1: Backsolve. $20 \times \frac{4}{5} = 16$
   Method 2: Algebra. $20w = 16 \;\rightarrow\; w = \frac{4}{5}$

4. **C** Method 1: Backsolve. $\sqrt{3(27)} = 9 \;\rightarrow\; \sqrt{81} = 9 \;\rightarrow\; 9 = 9$
   Method 2: Algebra. $(\sqrt{3x})^2 = 9^2 \;\rightarrow\; 3x = 81 \;\rightarrow\; x = 27$

5. **B** Method 1: Backsolve. $30 + 2(30) + 3(30) = 180$
   Method 2: Algebra. $x + y + z = 180 \;\rightarrow\; x + 2x + 3x = 180 \;\rightarrow\; 6x = 180 \;\rightarrow\; x = 30$

6. **C** Method 1: Backsolve. $250 - \left(\frac{1}{5} \times 250\right) = 200 \;\rightarrow\; 200 - \left(\frac{1}{4} \times 200\right) = 150$
   Method 2: Algebra. $x\left(\frac{4}{5}\right)\left(\frac{3}{4}\right) = 150 \;\rightarrow\; x = 250$

7. **D** Method 1: Backsolve. For $x = -28$, $\left|\frac{1}{2}(-28) + 6\right| = 8 \;\rightarrow\; |-8| = 8 \;\rightarrow\; 8 = 8$
   For $x = 4$, $\left|\frac{1}{2}(4) + 6\right| = 8 \;\rightarrow\; |8| = 8 \;\rightarrow\; 8 = 8$
   Method 2: Algebra. $\left|\frac{1}{2}x + 6\right| = 8 \;\rightarrow\; \frac{1}{2}x + 6 = 8$ and $\frac{1}{2}x + 6 = -8 \;\rightarrow\; \frac{1}{2}x = 2$ and $\frac{1}{2}x = -14 \;\rightarrow\;$
   $x = 4, -28$

8. **A** Method 1: Backsolve. For $x = 4$, $\sqrt{4} = 4 - 2 \;\rightarrow\; 2 = 2$
   Method 2: Algebra. Step 1: $\left(\sqrt{x}\right)^2 = (x - 2)^2 \;\rightarrow\; x = x^2 - 4x + 4 \;\rightarrow\; 0 = x^2 - 3x + 4 \;\rightarrow\;$
   $0 = (x - 4)(x + 1) \;\rightarrow\; x = -1, 4$
   Step 2: Check for extraneous solutions. We see from method 1 in this solution that $x = 4$ works. For
   $x = -1$, $\sqrt{-1} = 1 - 2 \;\rightarrow\; \sqrt{-1} \neq -1$, so $x = -1$ does not work.

Chapter 2 – Substitution (Pages 4 – 5)

1. **C** Replace the variables with values and test which answer choice is smallest. $0 < a < b < c \;\rightarrow\;$
   $0 < 1 < 2 < 3 \;\rightarrow\; \frac{a}{c} = \frac{1}{3}$. Conceptually, C is the correct answer because it gives the smallest value divided by the largest value, which will result in the smallest possible value.

2. **D** Method 1: Substitution. Step 1: Pick a value for the starting side length of the square. We will use 3.
   Step 2: Find the area of our new square after increasing the side length by 4. $3 + 4 = 7 \;\rightarrow\; 7^2 = 49$
   Step 3: Plug $s = 3$ into the answer choices and find which answer choice is equivalent to 49. $(3 + 4)^2 = 49$
   Method 2: Algebra. $A = s^2 \;\rightarrow\;$ After increasing the side length by 4, $A = (s + 4)^2$

3. **A** Method 1: Substitution. Step 1: Pick any values of x and y that make the equation true. $x + y = 11$. We will use $x = 5$ and $y = 6$.
   Step 2: Plug the values into the equation. $\frac{x - 11}{3y} \;\rightarrow\; \frac{5 - 11}{3(6)} \;\rightarrow\; \frac{-6}{18} = -\frac{1}{3}$
   Method 2: Algebra: Plug in $11 - y$ for $x \;\rightarrow\; \frac{11 - y - 11}{3y} = \frac{-y}{3y} = -\frac{1}{3}$

4. **B** Method 1: Substitution. Step 1: Pick values of x and y that make the original equation true. We will use
   $x = 5$ and $y = 2$. $\frac{x}{5} = \frac{y}{2} \;\rightarrow\; \frac{5}{5} = \frac{2}{2} \;\rightarrow\; 1 = 1$
   Step 2: Plug in the value for y for $\frac{y}{3}$. $\frac{y}{3} = \frac{2}{3}$
   Step 3: Plug in $x = 5$ to the answer choices until you find the answer choice that equals $\frac{2}{3}$. $\frac{2(5)}{15} = \frac{10}{15} = \frac{2}{3}$
   Method 2: Algebra. Plug in $\frac{2x}{5}$ for $y \;\rightarrow\; \frac{\frac{2x}{5}}{3} = \frac{2x}{15}$

5. **C** Method 1: Substitution. Step 1: Pick values for the variables. We will use $m = 4, n = 10, p = 5$.
Step 2: Solve the question using the numbers we picked. $10 \times 5 = 50$ (This gives the total amount of money given) $\rightarrow \frac{50}{4} = 8$. This tells us that each club receives \$8 with the numbers we picked.
Step 3: Plug in the values for the variables to find which answer equal $8 \rightarrow \frac{np}{m} = \frac{(10)(5)}{4} = 8$
Method 2: Algebra. np gives the total amount raised. $\frac{np}{m}$ gives the amount each club will receive.

6. **B** Method 1: Substitution. Step 1: Pick an odd integer for x. $x = 3$. Pick an even integer for y. $y = 2$.
Step 2: Plug the values into the answer choices to find which one must be odd. $3(3) + 2 = 11$
Method 2: Alternative method: You must know the following. $even \times even = even$, $odd \times even = even$
$odd \times odd = odd$, $odd + even = odd$, $even + even = even$, $odd + odd = even$.

7. **A** Method 1: Substitution. Step 1: Pick values for the variables. x can be any value. We will use $x = 3 \rightarrow$
$z = 5x \rightarrow z = 15$
Step 2: Solve for $z + 3$. $z + 3 = 15 + 3 = 18$
Step 3: Plug $x = 3$ into the answer choices to find which answer choice equals $18 \rightarrow 5(3) + 3 = 18$
Method 2: Algebra. $z = 5x \rightarrow z + 3 = 5x + 3$

8. **A** Method 1: Substitution. Step 1: Pick values for the variables that meet the question's requirements.
$3x = 4y = 6z \rightarrow 3(4) = 4(3) = 6(2) \rightarrow x = 4, y = 3, z = 2$
Step 2: Find the average of x and y. $\frac{4+3}{2} = 3.5$
Step 3: Find the answer choice that equals 3.5 when $z = 2$. $\frac{7z}{4} \rightarrow \frac{7(2)}{4} \rightarrow \frac{14}{4} = 3.5$
Method 2: Algebra. Step 1: Put x and y in terms of z. $3x = 6z \rightarrow x = 2z$. $4y = 6z \rightarrow y = \frac{3}{2}z$
Step 2: Plug in for x and y and solve. $\frac{x+y}{2} = \frac{2z + \frac{3}{2}z}{2} = \frac{7z}{4}$

9. **D** Method 1: Substitution. Step 1: Pick values for the base and height. We will use $b = 2$ and $h = 3$. The original triangle's area is $\frac{1}{2}(2)(3) = 3$
Step 2: Quadruple the original base and height. Now $b = 8$ and $h = 12$. The new triangle's area is $\frac{1}{2}(8)(12) = 48$
Step 3: Find out how many times larger the new area is. $\frac{48}{3} = 16$
Method 2: Algebra. $A = \frac{1}{2}bh \rightarrow \frac{1}{2}(4b)(4h) = 8bh \rightarrow \frac{8bh}{\frac{1}{2}bh} = 16$

10. **C** Method 1: Substitution. Step 1: Pick values for d and c. We will use $d = 4$ and $c = 2$.
Step 2: It will take two hours to run 4 miles while running 2 miles per hour. 2 hours = 120 minutes.
Step 3: Plug in $d = 4$ and $c = 2$ to the answer choices to find which answer choice equals 120.
$\frac{60d}{c} = \frac{60(4)}{2} = 120$
Method 2: Algebra. $\frac{d}{c}$ will give how long in hours it will take to the end of driveway. $\frac{60d}{c}$ converts from hours to minutes.

Chapter 3 – Equivalent Questions in the No-Calculator Section (Page 7)

1. **A** Method 1: Step 1: Plug in $x = 1$. $x^2 - 5x - 18 \rightarrow 1^2 - 5(1) - 18 = 1 - 5 - 18 = -22$
Step 2: Plug $x = 1$ into the answer choices to find which answer choice equals -22.
$(x + 3)(x - 6) - 2x \rightarrow (1 + 3)(1 - 6) - 2(1) = (4)(-5) - 2 = -22$
Method 2: Algebra. $(x + 3)(x - 6) - 2x = x^2 - 3x - 18 - 2x = x^2 - 5x - 18$

2. **C** Method 1: Step 1: Plug in $x = 1$. $(2x + 2)^2 + (2x + 2) \rightarrow (2(1) + 2)^2 + (2(1) + 2) = 4^2 + 4 = 20$
Step 2: Plug $x = 1$ into the answer choices to find which answer choice equals 20.
$(2x + 2)(2x + 3) \rightarrow (2(1) + 2)(2(1) + 3) = (4)(5) = 20$
Method 1: Algebra. $(2x + 2)^2 + (2x + 2) = 4x^2 + 8x + 4 + 2x + 2 = 4x^2 + 10x + 6 = (2x + 3)(2x + 2)$

3. **A** Method 1: Step 1: Plug in $x = 1$. $\frac{2}{x+7} + \frac{1}{2} \rightarrow \frac{2}{1+7} + \frac{1}{2} = \frac{2}{8} + \frac{1}{2} = \frac{2}{8} + \frac{4}{8} = \frac{6}{8} = \frac{3}{4}$

   Step 2: Plug $x = 1$ into the answer choices to find which answer choice equals $\frac{3}{4}$.

   $\frac{x+11}{2x+14} \rightarrow \frac{1+11}{2(1)+14} = \frac{12}{16} = \frac{3}{4}$

   Method 2: Algebra. Create a common denominator and simplify. $\frac{2}{x+7} + \frac{1}{2} = \frac{4}{2x+14} + \frac{x+7}{2x+14} = \frac{x+11}{2x+14}$

4. **C** Method 1: Step 1: Plug in $x = 1$. $(-3x + 4)^2 - 9x^2 \rightarrow (-3(1) + 4)^2 - 9(1)^2 = 1 - 9 = -8$

   Step 2: Plug $x = 1$ into the answer choices to find which answer choice equals -8.

   $-8(3x - 2) \rightarrow -8(3(1) - 2) = -8(1) = -8$

   Method 2: Algebra. $(-3x + 4)^2 - 9x^2 = 9x^2 - 24x + 16 - 9x^2 = -24x + 16 = -8(3x - 2)$

5. **C** Step 1: Plug in $a = 1$. $\frac{6a^2 - 3a}{2a+1} \rightarrow \frac{6(1)^2 - 3(1)}{2(1)+1} = \frac{6-3}{3} = \frac{3}{3} = 1$

   Step 2: Plug $a = 1$ into the answer choices to find which answer choice equals 1.

   $3a - 3 + \frac{3}{2a+1} \rightarrow 3(1) - 3 + \frac{3}{2(1)+1} = 3 - 3 + 1 = 1$

6. **B** Method 1: Step 1: Plug in $x = 1$. $x + 2 + \frac{3}{x+1} \rightarrow 1 + 2 + \frac{3}{1+1} = 3 + \frac{3}{2} = \frac{9}{2}$

   Step 2: Plug $x = 1$ into the answer choices to find which answer choice equals $\frac{9}{2}$.

   $\frac{x^2 + 3x + 5}{x+1} \rightarrow \frac{1^2 + 3(1) + 5}{1+1} = \frac{1+3+5}{2} = \frac{9}{2}$

   Method 2: Create common denominators and simplify. $x + 2 + \frac{3}{x+1} = \frac{x^2+x}{x+1} + \frac{2x+2}{x+1} + \frac{3}{x+1} = \frac{x^2+3x+5}{x+1}$

7. **B** Method 1: Step 1: Plug in $x = 1$. $16x^4 + 8x^3 - 24x^2 - 12x \rightarrow 16(1)^4 + 8(1)^3 - 24(1)^2 - 12(1) = 16 + 8 - 24 - 12 = -12$

   Step 2: Plug $x = 1$ into the answer choices to find which answer choice equals -12.

   $x(4x + 2)(4x^2 - 6) \rightarrow 1(4(1) + 2)(4(1)^2 - 6) = 1(6)(-2) = -12$

   Method 2: Factor and simplify. $16x^4 + 8x^3 - 24x^2 - 12x = x(16x^3 + 8x^2 - 24x - 12) = x(4x^2(4x + 2) - 6(4x + 2)) = x(4x + 2)(4x^2 - 6)$

8. **A** Method 1: Step 1: Plug in $x = 1$. $x^2 + 10x + 20 \rightarrow 1^2 + 10(1) + 20 = 31$

   Step 2: Plug $x = 1$ into the answer choices to find which answer choice equals 31.

   $(x + 4)(x + 6) - 4 \rightarrow (1 + 4)(1 + 6) - 4 = (5)(7) - 4 = 35 - 4 = 31$

   Method 2: Algebra. $(x + 4)(x + 6) - 4 = x^2 + 10x + 24 - 4 = x^2 + 10x + 20$

Chapter 4 - Algebra Skills (Pages 11 – 14)

1. **C** $(x^4 + x) + (x^3 - x) = x^4 + x + x^3 - x = x^4 + x^3$

2. **A** $3(x + 5) = 16 \rightarrow 3x + 15 = 16 \rightarrow 3x = 1 \rightarrow x = \frac{1}{3}$

3. **C** $4x - 18 = 14 \rightarrow 4x = 32 \rightarrow x = 8$

4. **B** $x^2 + 4 = 40 \rightarrow x^2 = 36$. We know x^2, so we can solve: $x^2 - 8 = 36 - 8 = 28$

5. **D** $(3x^2 - 2x + 5) - (-2x^2 + 3x - 2) = 3x^2 - 2x + 5 + 2x^2 - 3x + 2 = 5x^2 - 5x + 7$

6. **C** $3x + 4 = 4x - 1 \rightarrow x = 5 \rightarrow 2x + 3 = 2(5) + 3 = 13$

7. **D** $3x = 36 \rightarrow x = 12 \rightarrow 4x - 6 = 4(12) - 6 = 42$

8. **D** $(x^2 + 5) - (-2x^2 - 2) = x^2 + 5 + 2x^2 + 2 = 3x^2 + 7$

9. **A** $\frac{2x}{3} = \frac{5}{6} \rightarrow 12x = 15 \rightarrow x = \frac{15}{12} = \frac{5}{4}$

10. **B** $\frac{x+4}{4} = k$ and $k = 2 \rightarrow \frac{x+4}{4} = 2 \rightarrow x + 4 = 8 \rightarrow x = 4$

11. **C** $(x^2y^2 - 4x^3 + 2xy^2) - (2x^2y^2 + 2x^3 - 3xy^2) = x^2y^2 - 4x^3 + 2xy^2 - 2x^2y^2 - 2x^3 + 3xy^2 = -x^2y^2 - 6x^3 + 5xy^2$

12. **D** Method 1: Step 1: Solve for x. $x - 3 = \sqrt{x + 17} \rightarrow x^2 - 6x + 9 = x + 17 \rightarrow x^2 - 7x - 8 = 0 \rightarrow (x - 8)(x + 1) = 0 \rightarrow x = 8, -1$

    Step 2: Plug values back in to check for extraneous solutions.

    For $x = 8$: $8 - 3 = \sqrt{8 + 17} \rightarrow 5 = 5$ ⠀⠀⠀⠀ For $x = -1$: $-1 - 3 = \sqrt{-1 + 17} \rightarrow -4 \neq 4$

    Therefore, 8 is the only solution.

    Method 2: Backsolve to see which answer choice works. Only 8 works.

13. **C** $5(3x - 3) - 2(2x - 4) = 5(2x + 2) \rightarrow 15x - 15 - 4x + 8 = 10x + 10 \rightarrow 11x - 7 = 10x + 10 \rightarrow x = 17$

14. **D** Method 1: Step 1: Solve equation. $\sqrt{x-3} = x - 3 \rightarrow (\sqrt{x-3})^2 = (x-3)^2 \rightarrow$
$x - 3 = x^2 - 6x + 9 \rightarrow 0 = x^2 - 7x + 12 \rightarrow 0 = (x-4)(x-3) \rightarrow x = 4, 3$
Step 2: Plug values back into the original equation to check for extraneous solutions.
For $x = 4$: $\sqrt{4-3} = 4 - 3 \rightarrow \sqrt{1} = 1 \rightarrow 1 = 1$ For $x = 3$: $\sqrt{3-3} = 3 - 3 \rightarrow \sqrt{0} = 0 \rightarrow 0 = 0$
Therefore, 3 and 4 are both solutions.
Method 2: Backsolve to see which answer choice(s) work. 3 and 4 work.

15. **A** Step 1: Solve for b. $\frac{b}{4} = 2 \rightarrow b = 8$
Step 2: Solve for a. $ab = 24 \rightarrow a(8) = 24 \rightarrow a = 3$
Step 3: Solve for $a - b$. $3 - 8 = -5$

16. **C** Method 1: Step 1: Solve equation. $x - 4 = \sqrt{x+2} \rightarrow (x-4)^2 = (\sqrt{x+2})^2 \rightarrow$
$x^2 - 8x + 16 = x + 2 \rightarrow x^2 - 9x + 14 = 0 \rightarrow (x-7)(x-2) = 0 \rightarrow x = 7, 2$
Step 2: Plug values back into the equation to check for extraneous solutions.
For $x = 7$: $7 - 4 = \sqrt{7+2} \rightarrow 3 = \sqrt{9} \rightarrow 3 = 3$ For $x = 2$: $2 - 4 = \sqrt{2+2} \rightarrow -2 = \sqrt{4} \rightarrow -2 \neq 2$
Therefore, 7 is the only solution.
Method 2: Backsolve to see which answer choice(s) work. Only 7 works.

17. **16** $\sqrt{4x} = 8 \rightarrow (\sqrt{4x})^2 = (8)^2 \rightarrow 4x = 64 \rightarrow x = 16$

18. **C** $5ax - 5b - 7 = 28 \rightarrow 5ax - 5b = 35 \rightarrow 5(ax - b) = 35 \rightarrow ax - b = 7$

19. **8** $\frac{8x+24}{x+3} = x \rightarrow \frac{8(x+3)}{x+3} = x \rightarrow 8 = x$

20. **B** $(x + \frac{y}{4})^2 = (x + \frac{y}{4})(x + \frac{y}{4}) = x^2 + \frac{2xy}{4} + \frac{y^2}{16} = x^2 + \frac{xy}{2} + \frac{y^2}{16}$

21. **A** Method 1: Use the answer choices to see which answer choice matches the given expression.
$(x + 4)^2 - 5 = x^2 + 8x + 16 - 5 = x^2 + 8x + 11$
Method 2 – Substitution: Step 1: Plug $x = 1$ into the initial equation and solve. $1^2 + 8(1) + 11 = 20$
Step 2: Plug $x = 1$ into the answer choices to see which one equals 20. $(1 + 4)^2 - 5 = 25 - 5 = 20$

22. **A** $y = \frac{xz - z^2}{x-1} \rightarrow xy - y = xz - z^2 \rightarrow xy - xz = -z^2 + y \rightarrow x(y - z) = -z^2 + y \rightarrow x = \frac{-z^2 + y}{y - z}$. If we
factor a -1 out of the top and bottom, we get $\frac{-1(z^2 - y)}{-1(-y+z)}$. -1 cancels and we can reorder the terms on the bottom
to get $\frac{z^2 - y}{z - y}$.

23. **4** $x^3 - 4x^2 + 3x - 12 = 0 \rightarrow x^2(x - 4) + 3(x - 4) = 0 \rightarrow (x^2 + 3)(x - 4) \rightarrow x = 4$

24. **B** $x - 2 = \frac{3^2}{x-2} \rightarrow (x-2)^2 = 9 \rightarrow x - 2 = 3 \rightarrow x = 5$

25. **A** Step 1: Solve for x. $\frac{2}{x} = 10 \rightarrow 2 = 10x \rightarrow x = \frac{1}{5}$
Step 2: Solve for y. $\frac{\frac{1}{5}}{y} = 8 \rightarrow \frac{1}{5} = 8y \rightarrow \frac{1}{40} = y$

26. **16** $x + \frac{1}{4}b = 2 \rightarrow -2 + \frac{1}{4}b = 2 \rightarrow \frac{1}{4}b = 4 \rightarrow b = 16$

27. **D** $2(3x + 1)(2x + 2) = 2(6x^2 + 8x + 2) = 12x^2 + 16x + 4$

28. **5** $x - \frac{15}{b} = 0 \rightarrow 3 - \frac{15}{b} = 0 \rightarrow -\frac{15}{b} = -3 \rightarrow -15 = -3b \rightarrow b = 5$

29. **D** Step 1: Solve for y. $\frac{y}{3} = 12 \rightarrow y = 36$
Step 2: Solve for x. $x - 36 = 14 \rightarrow x = 50$

30. **8** $3(5x - 20) - (5x - 60) = 80 \rightarrow 15x - 60 - 5x + 60 = 80 \rightarrow 10x = 80 \rightarrow x = 8$

31. **D** $12x^3 + 4x^2 - 3x - 1 = 0 \rightarrow 4x^2(3x + 1) - 1(3x + 1) = 0 \rightarrow (4x^2 - 1)(3x + 1) = 0 \rightarrow$
For $4x^2 - 1 = 0 \rightarrow 4x^2 = 1 \rightarrow x^2 = \frac{1}{4} \rightarrow x = -\frac{1}{2}, \frac{1}{2}$. For $3x + 1 = 0 \rightarrow x = -\frac{1}{3}$

32. **B** $ab = \frac{a + bc + 6c}{3} \rightarrow 3ab = a + bc + 6c \rightarrow 3ab - a = bc + 6c \rightarrow a(3b - 1) = bc + 6c \rightarrow a = \frac{bc+6c}{3b-1}$

33. **6** $\frac{11x-22}{x-2} = x + 5 \rightarrow \frac{11(x-2)}{x-2} = x + 5 \rightarrow 11 = x + 5 \rightarrow x = 6$

Chapter 5 – Fractions (Pages 19 – 22)

1. $\frac{17}{6}$ $\frac{4}{3} + \frac{3}{2} = \frac{8}{6} + \frac{9}{6} = \frac{17}{6}$

2. $\frac{7}{20}$ $\frac{3}{5} - \frac{1}{4} = \frac{12}{20} - \frac{5}{20} = \frac{7}{20}$

3. $\frac{11}{8}$ $\quad \frac{7}{8} + \frac{1}{2} = \frac{7}{8} + \frac{4}{8} = \frac{11}{8}$

4. $-\frac{11}{6}$ $\quad \frac{2}{3} - \frac{5}{2} = \frac{4}{6} - \frac{15}{6} = -\frac{11}{6}$

5. $\frac{11}{21}$ $\quad \frac{6}{7} - \frac{1}{3} = \frac{18}{21} - \frac{7}{21} = \frac{11}{21}$

6. $\frac{57}{10}$ $\quad \frac{21}{5} + \frac{3}{2} = \frac{42}{10} + \frac{15}{10} = \frac{57}{10}$

7. $\frac{11}{6}$ $\quad \frac{16}{3} - \frac{7}{2} = \frac{32}{6} - \frac{21}{6} = \frac{11}{6}$

8. $\frac{9}{20}$ $\quad \frac{\frac{3}{5}}{\frac{4}{3}} = \frac{3}{5} \times \frac{3}{4} = \frac{9}{20}$

9. $\frac{3}{2}$ $\quad \frac{\frac{1}{2}}{\frac{1}{3}} = \frac{1}{2} \times \frac{3}{1} = \frac{3}{2}$

10. $\frac{4}{15}$ $\quad \frac{\frac{2}{5}}{\frac{3}{2}} = \frac{2}{5} \times \frac{2}{3} = \frac{4}{15}$

11. **4** $\quad \frac{\frac{4}{3}}{\frac{1}{3}} = \frac{4}{3} \times \frac{3}{1} = \frac{12}{3} = 4$

12. $\frac{9}{2}$ **or 4.5** $\quad 3 - \frac{2}{3}b = 0 \ \rightarrow \ -\frac{2}{3}b = -3 \ \rightarrow \ b = -3 \times -\frac{3}{2} = \frac{9}{2}$

13. **C** $\quad \frac{2}{x} + \frac{1}{3} = \frac{6}{3x} + \frac{x}{3x} = \frac{6+x}{3x}$

14. **C** $\quad \frac{3+9x}{15} \div \frac{3}{3} = \frac{1+3x}{5}$

15. **D** $\quad x = \frac{2}{5}(10) \ \rightarrow \ x = 4 \ \rightarrow \ 3x + 3 = 3(4) + 3 = 15$

16. **A** $\quad \frac{2}{x-1} + \frac{3}{x} = \frac{2x}{x^2-x} + \frac{3x-3}{x^2-x} = \frac{5x-3}{x^2-x}$

17. **B** $\quad \frac{x}{y} = 3 \ \rightarrow \ x = 3y.$ Plug in $3y$ for $x \rightarrow \ \frac{3y}{x} \ \rightarrow \ \frac{3y}{3y} = 1$

18. **A** $\quad \frac{x}{x+1} - \frac{3}{x-1} = \frac{x^2-x}{x^2-1} - \frac{3x+3}{x^2-1} = \frac{x^2-4x-3}{x^2-1}$

19. **C** $\quad \frac{x^2+5x}{x} = \frac{x(x+5)}{x} = x + 5$

20. **A** $\quad \frac{4}{x-2} + \frac{6}{3(x-2)} = \frac{4}{x-2} + \frac{2}{x-2} = \frac{6}{x-2}$

21. $\frac{6}{5}$ **or 1.2** Step 1: Make denominators the same. $\frac{1}{3}x + \frac{2}{7} = \frac{4}{7}x \ \rightarrow \ \frac{7}{21}x + \frac{6}{21} = \frac{12}{21}x$

 Step 2: Solve the equation in the numerator. $7x + 6 = 12x \ \rightarrow \ 6 = 5x \ \rightarrow \ x = \frac{6}{5}$

22. $\frac{3}{5}$ **or 0.6** Step 1: Make denominators the same. $\frac{4}{3}x - \frac{1}{2} = \frac{3}{6}x \ \rightarrow \ \frac{8}{6}x - \frac{3}{6} = \frac{3}{6}x$

 Step 2: Solve equation in the numerator. $8x - 3 = 3x \ \rightarrow \ 5x = 3 \ \rightarrow \ x = \frac{3}{5}$

23. **C** $\quad \frac{m+3}{m+5} = 8 \ \rightarrow \ m + 3 = 8m + 40 \ \rightarrow \ -37 = 7m \ \rightarrow \ m = -\frac{37}{7}$

24. $\frac{21}{5}$ **or 4.2** Step 1: Make denominators the same. $x - \frac{4}{5} = 2 + \frac{1}{3}x \ \rightarrow \ \frac{15}{15}x - \frac{12}{15} = \frac{30}{15} + \frac{5}{15}x$

 Step 2: Solve equation in the numerator. $15x - 12 = 30 + 5x \ \rightarrow \ 10x = 42 \ \rightarrow \ x = \frac{42}{10} = \frac{21}{5}$

25. $\frac{1}{4}$ **or 0.25** $\quad \frac{8}{3}x = \frac{2}{3} \ \rightarrow \ x = \frac{\frac{2}{3}}{\frac{8}{3}} \ \rightarrow \ x = \frac{2}{3} \times \frac{3}{8} = \frac{6}{24} = \frac{1}{4}$

26. **1** Denominators are the same, so set numerators equal and solve. $2x + 8 = 10 \ \rightarrow \ 2x = 2 \ \rightarrow \ x = 1$

27. **C** Denominators are the same, so set numerators equal and solve. $2a = 4 \ \rightarrow \ a = 2$

28. **A** $y\left(\frac{2}{x+3}\right) = \left(\frac{x+1}{x}\right)$ To isolate y, divide by $\left(\frac{2}{x+3}\right)$ so multiply by the reciprocal. $y = \left(\frac{x+1}{x}\right) \times \left(\frac{x+3}{2}\right) = \frac{x^2+4x+3}{2x}$

29. **D** $y\left(\frac{x-2}{x+3}\right) = \left(\frac{x+2}{x+1}\right).$ To isolate y, divide by $\frac{x-2}{x+3}$ so multiply by the reciprocal. $y = \left(\frac{x+2}{x+1}\right) \times \left(\frac{x+3}{x-2}\right) = \frac{x^2+5x+6}{x^2-x-2}$

30. **D** $\frac{8k}{4b} = \frac{1}{3} \rightarrow 24k = 4b \rightarrow 6k = b \rightarrow 6 = \frac{b}{k}$

31. **5** $\frac{x}{x-3} + \frac{2}{3} = \frac{ax-6}{3x-9} \rightarrow \frac{3x}{3x-9} + \frac{2x-6}{3x-9} = \frac{ax-6}{3x-9} \rightarrow \frac{5x-6}{3x-9} = \frac{ax-6}{3x-9} \rightarrow 5x-6 = ax-6 \rightarrow a = 5$

32. **7** $\frac{x}{x-3} + \frac{4}{x+2} = \frac{ax^2+bx-12}{x^2-x-6} \rightarrow \frac{x^2+2x}{x^2-x-6} + \frac{4x-12}{x^2-x-6} = \frac{ax^2+bx-12}{x^2-x-6} \rightarrow \frac{x^2+6x-12}{x^2-x-6} = \frac{ax^2+bx-12}{x^2-x-6} \rightarrow$
$x^2 + 6x - 12 = ax^2 + bx - 12 \rightarrow a = 1, b = 6 \rightarrow a + b = 7$

33. **11** $\frac{x+2}{x-3} + \frac{5}{x+3} = \frac{ax^2+bx-9}{x^2-9} \rightarrow \frac{x^2+5x+6}{x^2-9} + \frac{5x-15}{x^2-9} = \frac{ax^2+bx-9}{x^2-9} \rightarrow \frac{x^2+10x-9}{x^2-9} = \frac{ax^2+bx-9}{x^2-9} \rightarrow$
$x^2 + 10x - 9 = ax^2 + bx - 9 \rightarrow a = 1, b = 10 \rightarrow a + b = 11$

34. **C** Step 1: Solve for x. $\frac{5x^2+2x}{x^2-4} - \frac{3x}{x-2} = \frac{3}{x+2} \rightarrow \frac{5x^2+2x}{x^2-4} - \frac{3x^2+6x}{x^2-4} = \frac{3x-6}{x^2-4} \rightarrow \frac{2x^2-4x}{x^2-4} = \frac{3x-6}{x^2-4} \rightarrow$
$2x^2 - 4x = 3x - 6 \rightarrow 2x^2 - 7x + 6 = 0 \rightarrow (2x-3)(x-2) = 0 \rightarrow x = \frac{3}{2}, x = 2$

Step 2: Check for extraneous solutions. You must plug $x = \frac{3}{2}$ and $x = 2$ back into the original equation to check to make sure neither answer gives an undefined value. $x = 2$ will be an extraneous solution since the denominator will equal 0. Therefore, $x = \frac{3}{2}$ is the only correct answer.

35. **C** $\frac{7}{5}x = \frac{9}{8} \rightarrow x = \frac{\frac{9}{8}}{\frac{7}{5}} \rightarrow x = \frac{9}{8} \times \frac{5}{7} = \frac{45}{56}$

36. **B** $\frac{4x+y}{2x+y} = \frac{8}{5} \rightarrow 20x + 5y = 16x + 8y \rightarrow 4x = 3y \rightarrow \frac{4}{3}x = y \rightarrow \frac{4}{3} = \frac{y}{x}$

Chapter 6 – Extraneous Solutions (Page 26)

Although you should be backsolving, the algebraic method is also shown. The answer explanations only show backsolving using the value(s) from the correct answer.

1. **B** Method 1 – Backsolve: $x - 6 = \sqrt{3x} \rightarrow 12 - 6 = \sqrt{3(12)} \rightarrow 6 = \sqrt{36} \rightarrow 6 = 6$
   Method 2 – Algebraic Method: Step 1: Solve for x. $x - 6 = \sqrt{3x} \rightarrow x^2 - 12x + 36 = 3x \rightarrow$
   $x^2 - 15x + 36 = 0 \rightarrow (x-12)(x-3) = 0 \rightarrow x = 12, x = 3$
   Step 2: Plug values back in to test. For $x = 12$: $12 - 6 = \sqrt{3(12)} \rightarrow 6 = \sqrt{36} \rightarrow 6 = 6$
   For $x = 3$: $3 - 6 = \sqrt{3(3)} \rightarrow -3 = \sqrt{9} \rightarrow -3 \neq 3$

2. **A** Method 1 – Backsolve: $-x = \sqrt{6x} \rightarrow -0 = \sqrt{6(0)} \rightarrow 0 = 0$
   Method 2 – Algebraic Method: Step 1: Solve for x. $-x = \sqrt{6x} \rightarrow x^2 = 6x \rightarrow x^2 - 6x = 0 \rightarrow$
   $x(x-6) = 0 \rightarrow x = 0, x = 6$
   Step 2: Plug values back in to test. For $x = 0$: $-0 = \sqrt{6(0)} \rightarrow 0 = 0$ For $x = 6$: $-6 = \sqrt{6(6)} \rightarrow$
   $-6 = \sqrt{36} \rightarrow -6 \neq 6$

3. **B** Method 1 – Backsolve: $x - 10 = \sqrt{5x} \rightarrow 20 - 10 = \sqrt{5(20)} \rightarrow 10 = \sqrt{100} \rightarrow 10 = 10$
   Method 2 – Algebraic Method: Step 1: Solve for x. $x - 10 = \sqrt{5x} \rightarrow x^2 - 20x + 100 = 5x \rightarrow$
   $x^2 - 25x + 100 = 0 \rightarrow (x-20)(x-5) = 0 \rightarrow x = 20, x = 5$
   Step 2: Plug values back in to test. For $x = 20$: $20 - 10 = \sqrt{5(20)} \rightarrow 10 = \sqrt{100} \rightarrow 10 = 10$
   For $x = 5$: $5 - 10 = \sqrt{5(5)} \rightarrow -5 = \sqrt{25} \rightarrow -5 \neq 5$

4. **C** Method 1 – Backsolve: $\frac{5}{x+2} = \frac{x-3}{2x+4} \rightarrow \frac{5}{13+2} = \frac{13-3}{2(13)+4} \rightarrow \frac{5}{15} = \frac{10}{30} \rightarrow \frac{1}{3} = \frac{1}{3}$
   Method 2 – Algebraic Method: Step 1: Multiply first fraction by $\frac{2}{2}$ to get common denominator.
   $\frac{2}{2}\left(\frac{5}{x+2}\right) = \frac{x-3}{2x+4} \rightarrow \frac{10}{2x+4} = \frac{x-3}{2x+4}$
   Step 2: Set numerators equal and solve for x. $10 = x - 3 \rightarrow x = 13$
   Step 3: Plug value back in to test. For $x = 13$ $\frac{5}{13+2} = \frac{13-3}{2(13)+4} \rightarrow \frac{5}{15} = \frac{10}{30} \rightarrow \frac{1}{3} = \frac{1}{3}$.

5. **A** Method 1 – Backsolve: $-x = \sqrt{x+6} \rightarrow -(-2) = \sqrt{-2+6} \rightarrow 2 = \sqrt{4} \rightarrow 2 = 2$

Method 2 – Algebraic Method. Step 1: Solve for x. $-x = \sqrt{x+6} \rightarrow x^2 = x+6 \rightarrow x^2 - x - 6 \rightarrow$ $(x-3)(x+2) = 0 \rightarrow x = 3, x = -2$

Step 2: Plug values back in to test. For $x = 3$: $-3 = \sqrt{3+6} \rightarrow -3 = \sqrt{9} \rightarrow -3 \neq 3$

For $x = -2$: $-(-2) = \sqrt{-2+6} \rightarrow 2 = \sqrt{4} \rightarrow 2 = 2$

6. **C** Method 1 – Backsolve: $x - 4 = \sqrt{3x-2} \rightarrow 9 - 4 = \sqrt{3(9)-2} \rightarrow 5 = \sqrt{25} \rightarrow 5 = 5$

Method 2 – Algebraic Method: Step 1: Solve for x. $x - 4 = \sqrt{3x-2} \rightarrow x^2 - 8x + 16 = 3x - 2 \rightarrow$ $x^2 - 11x + 18 = 0 \rightarrow (x-9)(x-2) = 0 \rightarrow x = 9, x = 2$

Step 2: Plug values back in to test. For $x = 9$: $9 - 4 = \sqrt{3(9)-2} \rightarrow 5 = \sqrt{25} \rightarrow 5 = 5$

For $x = 2$: $2 - 4 = \sqrt{3(2)-2} \rightarrow -2 = \sqrt{4} \rightarrow -2 \neq 2$

7. **B** Method 1 – Backsolve: $\sqrt{2x} = x - 4 \rightarrow \sqrt{2(8)} = 8 - 4 \rightarrow \sqrt{16} = 4 \rightarrow 4 = 4$

Method 2 – Algebraic Method: Step 1: Solve for x. $\sqrt{2x} = x - 4 \rightarrow 2x = x^2 - 8x + 16 \rightarrow$ $0 = x^2 - 10x + 16 \rightarrow 0 = (x-8)(x-2) \rightarrow x = 8, x = 2$

Step 2: Plug values back in to test. For $x = 8$: $\sqrt{2(8)} = 8 - 4 \rightarrow \sqrt{16} = 4 \rightarrow 4 = 4$

For $x = 2$: $\sqrt{2(2)} = 2 - 4 \rightarrow \sqrt{4} = -2 \rightarrow 2 \neq -2$

8. **A** Method 1 – Backsolve: $\frac{2x}{x+1} - 3 = \frac{2}{x^2+x} \rightarrow \frac{2(-2)}{-2+1} - 3 = \frac{2}{(-2)^2+(-2)} \rightarrow \frac{-4}{-1} - 3 = \frac{2}{2} \rightarrow 1 = 1$

Method 2 – Algebraic Method: Step 1: Multiply fractions to get common denominator of $x^2 + x$.

$\frac{2x}{x+1} \times \frac{x}{x} - 3 \times \frac{x^2+x}{x^2+x} = \frac{2}{x^2+x} \rightarrow \frac{2x^2}{x^2+x} - \frac{3x^2+3x}{x^2+x} = \frac{2}{x^2+x}$.

Step 2: Set numerators equal and solve for x. $2x^2 - 3x^2 - 3x = 2 \rightarrow -x^2 - 3x - 2 = 0 \rightarrow$ $-(x^2 + 3x + 2) = 0 \rightarrow -(x+2)(x+1) = 0 \rightarrow x = -2, x = -1$

Step 3: Plug values back in to test: For $x = -2$: $\frac{2(-2)}{-2+1} - 3 = \frac{2}{(-2)^2+(-2)} \rightarrow \frac{-4}{-1} - 3 = \frac{2}{2} \rightarrow 1 = 1$

For $x = -1$: $\frac{2(-1)}{-1+1} - 3 = \frac{2}{(-1)^2+(-1)} \rightarrow \frac{-2}{0} - 3 = \frac{2}{0}$. Since denominator cannot equal 0, $x = -1$ does not work.

Chapter 7 – "In Terms of" (Pages 28 – 29)

1. **C** $z = 20hw \rightarrow w = \frac{z}{20h}$

2. **C** $v = \frac{m}{s} \rightarrow sv = m \rightarrow s = \frac{m}{v}$

3. **B** To solve for the average rate we need $\frac{c}{t}$ since units of the rate is c cubic inches per t seconds. $c = 6t\sqrt{t} \rightarrow$ $\frac{c}{t} = \frac{6t\sqrt{t}}{t} = 6\sqrt{t}$

4. **B** $g = \frac{m+3p+5}{q} \rightarrow gq = m + 3p + 5 \rightarrow -3p = m + 5 - gq \rightarrow p = \frac{gq-m-5}{3}$

5. **C** (a, b) is the same as (x, y) so plug a in for x and b in for y. k is the slope, so solve for k. $b = ka - 3 \rightarrow b + 3 = ka \rightarrow k = \frac{b+3}{a}$

6. **C** $3\sqrt{5x} = b \rightarrow \sqrt{5x} = \frac{b}{3} \rightarrow 5x = \frac{b^2}{9}$

7. **C** $1.18p + 40 = n \rightarrow 1.18p = n - 40 \rightarrow p = \frac{n-40}{1.18}$

8. **D** $5x = \sqrt{a} \rightarrow (5x)^2 = (\sqrt{a})^2 \rightarrow 25x^2 = a$

9. **C** $abd - bcd = ed - cd \rightarrow abd - bcd + cd = ed \rightarrow d(ab - bc + c) = ed \rightarrow \frac{d(ab-bc+c)}{d} = e \rightarrow$ $ab - bc + c = e$

10. **D** $2\sqrt[3]{5x} = b \rightarrow \sqrt[3]{5x} = \frac{b}{2} \rightarrow 5x = \frac{b^3}{8} \rightarrow x = \frac{b^3}{40}$

11. **C** $a^2 = 16b^4 \rightarrow \frac{a^2}{16} = b^4 \rightarrow b = \frac{\sqrt{a}}{2}$

12. **A** $E = \sqrt{\frac{s^2+2f}{A}} \rightarrow E^2 = \frac{s^2+2f}{A} \rightarrow E^2A = s^2 + 2f \rightarrow E^2A - 2f = s^2 \rightarrow \sqrt{E^2A - 2f} = s$

Chapter 8 – Inequalities (Pages 34 – 35)

1. **C** $40h$ is number of trees planted per hour. $+200$ is correct because there are 200 trees that have already been planted.
2. **C** Substitute 12 in for $3x$ in the first equation. $y > 3x - 3 \rightarrow y > 12 - 3 \rightarrow y > 9$
3. **A** Divide all terms by 3. $(18x - 12 > 24) \div 3 \rightarrow 6x - 4y > 8$
4. **A** John started with 15 pieces of candy, gave away x, so x is subtracted, gained y, so y is added. John's candy at the end of the day is $15 - x + y$. He has at least 23 therefore ≥ 23.
5. **C** The first equation will be $150d + 120b \leq 3,000$. Each dresser requires 150 square feet of wood and each bed frame requires 120 square feet of wood. The equation uses $\leq 3,000$ because there are only 3,000 square feet of wood. $d \geq 10$ and $b \geq 5$ are correct because James wants to make at least 10 dressers and 5 beds.
6. **B** $13x$ is the money earned from the barista job, and $15y$ is the money earned from the surf instructor job. $x + y \leq 25$ since he can work no more than 25 hours per week. It must be ≥ 340 since he wants to earn at least \$340 per week.
7. **A** The line must be equivalent to $y = x + 1$. Since the equation is $\leq$, we shade below the line.
8. **B** $9p$ is the total pounds of pork and $6f$ is the total pounds of flank steak. The total meat, $9p + 6f$, must be no more than 400 total pounds. $9p + 6f \leq 400$. To have three times as many packages of pork as packages of flank steak, the flank steak quantity needs to be multiplied by 3. $p \geq 3f$.
9. **7** Step 1: Find how many legs and segments of plywood are needed for each group to construct 2 small coffee tables and 1 large coffee table. For legs: $6l + 2(3l) = 12l$ For segments: $4s + 2(2s) = 8s$.   Each group needs 12 legs and 8 segments.
    Step 2: Set up an inequality to solve for the maximum number of groups. $12\ legs\ (x\ groups) \leq 85\ legs \rightarrow l \leq 7.08\ groups$ $8\ segments\ (x\ groups) \leq 79\ segments \rightarrow s \leq 9.875\ groups$
    Step 3: The groups must be whole numbers. Correctly pick the smaller value of the two, which is 7. There are only enough legs for 7 groups, so 7 is the answer. The class run out of legs before segments.
10. **20** Step 1: Set up the equations. $3a + 6b \leq 230$ $a + b \leq 50$ $a \geq 1.5b$. The third equation makes sure there is at least 50% more of car A than car B.
    Step 2: We want to maximize the number of car B, so we only want exactly 50% more of car A. By minimizing the number of car A, we maximize the number of car B. $a = 1.5b$
    Step 3: Solve both inequalities. $3(1.5b) + 6b \leq 230 \rightarrow 10.5b \leq 230 \rightarrow b \leq 21.9$.
    $1.5b + b \leq 50 \rightarrow 2.5b \leq 50 \rightarrow b \leq 20$
    We must satisfy both inequalities, so the maximum value of b possible is 20.
11. **B** Method 1: Since the monthly average in June is $A\ °F$ and the daily temperature is $x\ °F$, the average must be at least 9 °F lower than the daily temperature. $A \leq x - 9$
    Method 2 – Substitution: Picking numbers will make this clearer for many students and is a good trick to use on the test. Here, let's say the average temperature in June is 80 °F, so $A = 80$. For a heatwave, the daily temperature could be 89 °F or higher for there to be a heatwave. It is best to pick a value that is not exactly equal to be able to tell which answer choice is correct. Let's pick $x = 90$. Plug in these values to the answer choices to see which one works. $A \leq x - 9 \rightarrow 80 \leq 90 - 9$.

Chapter 9 – Percentages

Part 1: Simple Percentages (Pages 37 – 39)

1. **B** Method 1 – Proportion: $\frac{x}{50} = \frac{80}{100} \rightarrow x = 40$ Method 2 – Decimal Shortcut: $0.8(50) = 40$
2. **D** Step 1: Find the number of correct answers. $50 - 8 = 42$
    Step 2: Set up proportion and solve: $\frac{42}{50} = \frac{x}{100} \rightarrow x = 84$
3. **B** Set up proportion. We need to find the total acres to find the "of" part of the equation.
    $280 + 420 = 700 \rightarrow \frac{280}{700} = \frac{x}{100} \rightarrow x = 40$
4. **B** $\frac{48}{x} = \frac{150}{100} \rightarrow x = 32$
5. **B** Step 1: Solve for x: $\frac{x}{200} = \frac{40}{100} \rightarrow x = 80$
    Step 2: Solve for 125% of x: $\frac{x}{80} = \frac{125}{100} \rightarrow x = 100$ or $1.25(80) = 100$
6. **C** $\frac{15}{x} = \frac{25}{100} \rightarrow x = 60$

7. **D** Step 1: Convert the hours to minutes: $\frac{10\ hours}{1} \times \frac{60\ minutes}{1\ hour} = 600\ minutes$

   Step 2: Set up the proportion and solve: $\frac{x}{600} = \frac{18}{100} \rightarrow x = 108$

8. **A** Method 1 – Proportion: $\frac{x}{870} = \frac{27}{100} \rightarrow x = 234.90$ Method 2 – Decimal shortcut: $(0.27)870 = 234.90$

9. **B** Find the category that Amanda spent the second most on: $240 on food

   Method 1 – Proportion: $\frac{240}{800} = \frac{x}{100} \rightarrow x = 30$ Method 2 – Turn Decimal into Percentage: $\frac{240}{800} = 0.3 = 30\%$

10. **B** Step 1: Find the entire senior class: $25 + 275 = 300$

    Step 2: Method 1 – Proportion: $\frac{x}{300} = \frac{20}{100} \rightarrow x = 60$ Method 2 – Decimal shortcut: $0.2(300) = 60$

11. **C** Step 1: Add the percentages for those who learned from a friend who attended and social media: $35\% + 12\% = 47\%$

    Step 2: Method 1 – Proportion: $\frac{x}{1,500} = \frac{47}{100} \rightarrow x = 705$ Method 2 – Decimal shortcut: $0.47(1,500) = 705$

12. **B** Step 1: Solve for junior members with golfing membership: $\frac{x}{252} = \frac{12}{100} \rightarrow x = 30.24$. The question says approximately, so we can round this to 30.

    Step 2: Solve for senior members with golfing membership: $\frac{x}{780} = \frac{26}{100} \rightarrow x = 202.8$. We can round this to 203.

    Step 3: Add the two x-values to find the total number of members: $30 + 203 = 233$

13. **A** Method 1 – "Math Teacher Way": Multiply original price by 0.76 for 76% and 1.10 for 110%. $(0.76)(1.10)p = 0.84p$

    Method 2 – Substitution. Pick an original price for the pickup truck and then solve for the final price using the steps we described in method 1. Divide final price by initial price to find the percent.

14. **7.5** Step 1: Set up the equation: $\frac{Total\ chlorine}{Total\ solution} = 0.2 \rightarrow \frac{0.4x + 0.05(10)}{x + 10} = 0.2$

    The numerator solves for the total amount of chlorine, the denominator solves for the total amount of solution, and it is set equal to the percentage of solution that needs to be obtained. The x represent the gallons of unknown solution.

    Step 2: Multiply both sides by $(10 + x)$ and solve for x: $0.4x + 0.5 = 2 + 0.2x \rightarrow 0.2x = 1.5 \rightarrow x = 7.5$

15. **B** Step 1: Find what percentage of students are business majors: $100\% - 30\% - 15\% - 25\% = 30\%$

    Step 2: 24 business students represent 30% of the total. Find the total students: $\frac{24}{x} = \frac{30}{100} \rightarrow x = 80$

    Step 4: Find the number of science and history majors: Science: $\frac{x}{80} = \frac{30}{100} \rightarrow x = 24$

    History: $\frac{x}{80} = \frac{15}{100} \rightarrow x = 12$

    Step 4: Subtract the number of history majors from the science majors. $24 - 12 = 12$

Part 2: Percentage Increase and Decrease (Pages 41 – 44)

1. **D** Method 1 – Proportion: $\frac{x}{50} = \frac{160}{100} \rightarrow x = 80$ Method 2 – Decimal shortcut: $1.6(50) = 80$

2. **B** Method 1 – Proportion: $\frac{x}{30} = \frac{70}{100} \rightarrow x = 21$ Method 2 – Decimal shortcut: $0.7(30) = 21$

3. **B** Method 1 – Proportion: $\frac{x}{600,000} = \frac{80}{100} \rightarrow x = 480,000$

   Method 2 – Decimal shortcut: $0.8(600,000) = 480,000$

4. **B** Method 1 – Proportion: $\frac{x}{700} = \frac{92}{100} \rightarrow x = 644$ Method 2 – Decimal shortcut: $(0.92)700 = 644$

5. **B** $\frac{1,391 - 1,231}{1,231} \times 100 = 12.99\% \approx 13\%$.

6. **30** Step 1: Find her new driving speed: $\frac{x}{50} = \frac{120}{100} \rightarrow x = 60$ or $1.2(50) = 60$

   Step 2: Find how long in minutes it takes for Julie to get to work.

   $distance = speed \times time \rightarrow 30\ miles = \left(\frac{60\ miles}{1\ hour}\right) \times t \rightarrow t = \frac{1}{2}\ hour$

   Step 3: Since the time is currently in hours, convert it to minutes: $\frac{1}{2}\ hour = 30\ minutes$

7. **D** Method 1 – Proportion: $\frac{168}{x} = \frac{70}{100} \rightarrow x = 240$

   Method 2 – Decimal shortcut: $0.7(x) = 168 \rightarrow x = \frac{168}{0.7} = 240$

8. **D** Method 1 – Proportion: $\frac{x}{20} = \frac{108}{100} \rightarrow x = 21.60$ Method 2 – Decimal shortcut: $1.08(20) = 21.60$

9. **C** $\frac{190.56-176.45}{176.45} \times 100 = 7.99\% \approx 8\%$

10. **B** Method 1 – Proportion: $\frac{76}{x} = \frac{108}{100} \rightarrow x = 70.37$

    Method 2 – Decimal shortcut: $1.08(x) = 76 \rightarrow x = \frac{76}{1.08} = 70.37$

11. **D** Method 1: Step 1: Solve for price of 2 tons of wood: $2(2,500) = 5,000$

    Step 2: Apply 15% discount: $\frac{x}{5,000} = \frac{85}{100} \rightarrow x = 4,250$

    Step 3: Apply 10% sales tax: $\frac{x}{4,250} = \frac{110}{100} \rightarrow x = 4,675$

    Method 2: Step 1: Solve for price of 2 tons of wood: $2(2,500) = 5,000$

    Step 2: Calculate final price in one step: $5000(0.85)(1.10) = 4,675$ (Multiply by 0.85 for the 15% discount and 1.10 for the 10% sales tax).

12. **C** Method 1 – Proportion: $\frac{x}{85} = \frac{130}{100} \rightarrow x = 110.50$ Method 2 – Decimal shortcut: $1.3(85) = 110.50$

13. **B** $\frac{325}{x} = \frac{130}{100}$ (Andrew is the new since he is 30% faster than Cole) $\rightarrow x = 250$

14. **B** Method 1 – Proportion: $\frac{118}{x} = \frac{108}{100} \rightarrow x = 109.26$

    Method 2 – Decimal shortcut: $1.08(x) = 118 \rightarrow x = \frac{118}{1.08} = 109.26$

15. **B** Step 1: Find percent increase from September to October: $\frac{1,403-1,200}{1,200} \times 100 = 16.91\%$

    Step 2: Find the number of cookies for August: $\frac{1,200}{x} = \frac{116.91}{100} \rightarrow x = 1,026.43$

    Method 2: Step 1: Find percent increase from September to October: $\frac{1,403-1,200}{1,200} \times 100 = 16.91\%$

    Step 2: Find the number of cookies for August: $1.1691(x) = 1200 \rightarrow x = \frac{1,200}{1.1691} = 1,026.43$

16. **A** Method 1 – Proportion: $\frac{386}{x} = \frac{132}{100} \rightarrow x = 292.43$ Method 2 – Decimal shortcut: $\frac{386}{1.32} = 292.43$

17. **B** Method 1: Step 1: Solve for the remaining total dining dollars: $8(3) = 24 \rightarrow 600 - 24 = 576$

    Step 2: $\frac{8}{576} = \frac{x}{100} \rightarrow x = 1.38$

    Method 2: Step 1: Solve for remaining total dining dollars: $8(3) = 24 \rightarrow 600 - 24 = 576$

    Step 2: $\frac{8}{576} = 0.0138 = 1.38\%$

18. **D** Method 1: The "Math Teacher Way" $A = lw \rightarrow 1.08a = (0.8l)(1+q)(w)$ Here. we use 1.08 since. $1 = 100\%$ and $0.08 = 8\%$ so 1.08 shows an 8% increase. For the same reason, $1 - 0.2 = 0.8$ and we have $1 + q$ since $1 = 100\%$ and there is a q percent increase. $\frac{1.08a}{(0.8l)(w)} = 1+q \rightarrow \frac{1.08a}{0.8lw} = 1+q$. (We can cancel out the a and lw since $A = lw$) $\rightarrow \frac{1.08}{0.8} = 1+q \rightarrow q = 0.35$

    Method 2: Step 1: Plug-in values for length and width and the use the steps of the question to solve. Here, let $l = 5$ and $w = 2$. Step 1: Find original area: $A = (5)(2) = 10$

    Step 2: Find new area: $A = 1.08(10) = 10.8$

    Step 3: Find new length: $l = 0.8(5) = 4$

    Step 4: Find new width: $A = lw \rightarrow 10.8 = 4(w) \rightarrow w = 2.7$

    Step 5: Find percentage increase in width: $\frac{2.7-2}{2} = 0.35 \rightarrow 35\%$

19. **D** Method 1: Proportion: $\frac{34,000}{x} = \frac{87}{100} \rightarrow x = 39,080$, which is closest to 39,000.

    Method 2. Decimal shortcut: $0.87(x) = 34,000 \rightarrow x = \frac{34,000}{0.87} = 39,080$ which is closest to 39,000.

20. **D** $\frac{76.24-85.95}{85.95} \times 100 = -11.3\%$. The negative sign shows the percent decrease is 11.3%.

21. **C** Method 1: Step 1: Find price before sales tax was added: $\frac{850.76}{x} = \frac{108}{100} \rightarrow x = 787.74$

    Step 2: Find the price before the 20% discount: $\frac{787.74}{x} = \frac{80}{100} \rightarrow x = 984.68$

    Method 2: $\frac{850.76}{(1.08)(0.80)} = 984.68$

22. **D** Method 1: Decimal shortcut: $0.025(x) = 275 \rightarrow x = \frac{275}{0.025} = 11,000$. To find the total number, divide by the percentage. This is the most efficient way to solve any questions where you are given a number and told what percent it is of the total.

Method 2: Use the answer choices and whatever answer choice multiplied by 0.025 equals 275 is correct.

Method 3: Proportion: $\frac{275}{x} = \frac{2.5}{100} \rightarrow x = 11,000$

23. **D** Step 1: Convert the time of 2 hours and 20 minutes to minutes. Many students make the mistake of expressing 2 hours and twenty minutes as 2.2 hours, which is incorrect.

$2 \text{ hours and } 20 \text{ minutes} = 2(60) + 20 = 140 \ minutes$

Step 2: Find how many minutes Julie studies each day the last week: $\frac{x}{140} = \frac{130}{100} \rightarrow x = 182$ or $1.3(140) = 182$

Step 3: Convert minutes per day to minutes per week: $182(7) = 1,274$

Step 4: Convert into hours and minutes: $\frac{1,274}{60} = 21.233$ hours. Here, we can already tell the answer is D. To turn minutes into hours and minutes $\rightarrow 21 \ hours \times \frac{60 \ minutes}{1 \ hour} = 1260 \ minutes \rightarrow$ $1274 \ minutes - 1260 \ minutes = 14 \ minutes \rightarrow 21$ hours and 14 minutes.

24. **D** Method 1: Step 1: Find the first 12% increase for week 1: $\frac{x}{250} = \frac{112}{100} \rightarrow x = 280$ or $1.12(250) = 280$

Step 2: Find the second 12% increase for week 2: $\frac{x}{280} = \frac{112}{100} \rightarrow x = 313.60$ or $1.12(280) = 313.60$

Method 2 (faster method): $250(1.12)(1.12) = 250(1.12)^2 = 313.60$

25. **D** Multiply by 2.3 for the 130% increase and by 1.65 for the 6% increase.

26. **B** Multiply by 1.30 for the 30% increase and by 0.94 for the 6% decrease.

Chapter 10 – Exponents and Roots

Exponents Exercise (Page 47)

1. $\boldsymbol{x^6y^3}$ $(x^4y)(x^2y^2) = x^6y^3$
2. $\boldsymbol{3x^5}$ $(3x^3)(2x^4)\left(\frac{1}{2}x^{-2}\right) = 3x^5$
3. $\boldsymbol{24x^3y^7}$ $(8x^{-3}y^4)(3x^6y^3) = 24x^3y^7$
4. $\boldsymbol{4x^2y^6}$ $(2xy^3)^2 = 4x^2y^6$
5. $\boldsymbol{\frac{3y^5}{x^2}}$ $3x^{-2}y^5 = \frac{3y^5}{x^2}$
6. $\boldsymbol{9x^4}$ $\frac{18x^8}{2x^4} = 9x^4$
7. $\boldsymbol{\frac{9y}{x^3z^2}}$ $9x^{-3}yz^{-2} = \frac{9y}{x^3z^2}$
8. $\boldsymbol{\frac{1}{x}}$ $(x^{-2}y^2)(xy^{-2}) = x^{-1} = \frac{1}{x}$
9. $\boldsymbol{\frac{z}{x^4}}$ $\frac{x^{-3}yz^2}{xyz} = x^{-4}z = \frac{z}{x^4}$
10. $\boldsymbol{\frac{9x^{10}z^2}{y^4}}$ $(3x^5y^{-2}z)^2 = 9x^{10}y^{-4}z^2 = \frac{9x^{10}z^2}{y^4}$
11. $\boldsymbol{16xy^3}$ $\frac{(4xy^2)^2}{xy} = \frac{16x^2y^4}{xy} = 16xy^3$
12. $\boldsymbol{\frac{25x^{17}}{8y^7}}$ $\frac{(5x^4y^{-2})^2}{(2x^{-3}y)^3} = \frac{25x^8y^{-4}}{8x^{-9}y^3} = \frac{25x^{17}}{8y^7}$
13. $\boldsymbol{1}$ $12^{-3} \times 12^5 = 144^x \rightarrow 12^2 = 144^x \rightarrow 144 = 144^x \rightarrow x = 1$
14. $\boldsymbol{8}$ $\frac{7^2 \times 7^x}{49} = 7^8 \rightarrow \frac{7^{x+2}}{7^2} = 7^8 \rightarrow 7^x = 7^8 \rightarrow x = 8$
15. $\boldsymbol{5, -5}$ $\frac{x^7}{x^5} = 25 \rightarrow x^2 = 25 \rightarrow x = 5, -5$
16. $\boldsymbol{1}$ Set the exponents equal. $-2x + 3 = 2 - x \rightarrow x = 1$
17. $\boldsymbol{\frac{11}{6}}$ $(2^x)^3 = 2^4 \times 2^{\frac{3}{2}} \rightarrow 2^{3x} = 2^{4+\frac{3}{2}} \rightarrow 2^{3x} = 2^{\frac{11}{2}} \rightarrow 3x = \frac{11}{2} \rightarrow x = \frac{11}{6}$
18. $\boldsymbol{6}$ $9^{\frac{3}{2}} = 3^{\frac{x}{2}} \rightarrow (3^2)^{\frac{3}{2}} = 3^{\frac{x}{2}} \rightarrow 3^3 = 3^{\frac{x}{2}} \rightarrow 3 = \frac{x}{2} \rightarrow x = 6$

19. **6** $16^{\frac{3}{2}} = 2^x \rightarrow (2^4)^{\frac{3}{2}} = 2^x \rightarrow 2^6 = 2^x \rightarrow x = 6$

20. **8** $\frac{8}{8^{-3}} = 2^{2x-4} \rightarrow 8^4 = 2^{2x-4} \rightarrow (2^3)^4 = 2^{2x-4} \rightarrow 2^{12} = 2^{2x-4} \rightarrow 12 = 2x - 4 \rightarrow x = 8$

Roots Exercise (Page 50)

1. **$2\sqrt{15}$** $\sqrt{60} = \sqrt{2 \times 2 \times 15} = 2\sqrt{15}$

2. **$7\sqrt{6}$** $\sqrt{150} + \sqrt{24} = 5\sqrt{6} + 2\sqrt{6} = 7\sqrt{6}$

3. **$2\sqrt{5}$** $6\sqrt{5} - \sqrt{80} = 6\sqrt{5} - 4\sqrt{5} = 2\sqrt{5}$

4. **$7\sqrt{2}$** $\sqrt{32} - \sqrt{18} + \sqrt{72} = 4\sqrt{2} - 3\sqrt{2} + 6\sqrt{2} = 7\sqrt{2}$

5. **$5\sqrt[3]{6}$** $\sqrt[3]{48} + \sqrt[3]{162} = 2\sqrt[3]{6} + 3\sqrt[3]{6} = 5\sqrt[3]{6}$

6. **$\sqrt{3}$** $\frac{\sqrt{45}}{\sqrt{15}} = \sqrt{\frac{45}{15}} = \sqrt{3}$

7. **1** $\frac{5\sqrt{12}}{10\sqrt{3}} = \frac{10\sqrt{3}}{10\sqrt{3}} = 1$

8. **$2b^2\sqrt{2a}$** $\sqrt{8ab^4} = \sqrt{8} \times \sqrt{a} \times \sqrt{b^4} = 2\sqrt{2} \times \sqrt{a} \times b^2 = 2b^2\sqrt{2a}$

9. **$4x\sqrt{y}$** $\sqrt{16x^2y} = \sqrt{16} \times \sqrt{x^2} \times \sqrt{y} = 4 \times x \times \sqrt{y} = 4x\sqrt{y}$

10. **$a^3\sqrt{b}$** $\sqrt[4]{a^{12}b^2} = (a^{12}b^2)^{\frac{1}{4}} = a^3 b^{\frac{1}{2}} = a^3\sqrt{b}$

11. **$(2x^2)\sqrt[3]{3y^4}$** $\sqrt[3]{24x^6y^4} = (24x^6y^4)^{\frac{1}{3}} = 24^{\frac{1}{3}}x^2 y^{\frac{4}{3}} = x^2 \times \sqrt[3]{24} \times \sqrt[3]{y^4} = x^2 \times 2\sqrt[3]{3} \times \sqrt[3]{y^4} = (2x^2)\sqrt[3]{3y^4}$

12. **$4x^5$** $\sqrt{16x^{10}} = (16x^{10})^{\frac{1}{2}} = 4x^5$

13. **$\frac{18}{3}$** Set terms under radicals equal and solve. $3x - 2 = 18 \rightarrow 3x = 20 \rightarrow x = \frac{20}{3}$

14. **45** $\sqrt{15} = \frac{\sqrt{x}}{\sqrt{3}} \rightarrow \sqrt{15} = \sqrt{\frac{x}{3}} \rightarrow 15 = \frac{x}{3} \rightarrow x = 45$

15. **3** $\sqrt{18} \times \sqrt{3} = x\sqrt{6} \rightarrow \sqrt{54} = x\sqrt{6} \rightarrow 3\sqrt{6} = x\sqrt{6} \rightarrow x = 3$

16. **90** $\sqrt{x} - \sqrt{40} = \sqrt{10} \rightarrow \sqrt{x} - 2\sqrt{10} = \sqrt{10} \rightarrow \sqrt{x} = 3\sqrt{10} \rightarrow (\sqrt{x})^2 = (3\sqrt{10})^2 \rightarrow x = 90$

17. **6** $\sqrt{3x} + \sqrt{8} = \sqrt{50} \rightarrow \sqrt{3x} + 2\sqrt{2} = 5\sqrt{2} \rightarrow \sqrt{3x} = 3\sqrt{2} \rightarrow (\sqrt{3x})^2 = (3\sqrt{2})^2 \rightarrow 3x = 18 \rightarrow$
    $x = 6$

18. **$\frac{45}{2}$ or 22.5** $(3\sqrt{5})^2 = 2x \rightarrow 45 = 2x \rightarrow x = \frac{45}{2}$

19. **4** $\sqrt{6x} = 2\sqrt{6} \rightarrow (\sqrt{6x})^2 = (2\sqrt{6})^2 \rightarrow 6x = 24 \rightarrow x = 4$

20. **5** $\sqrt[3]{54} + \sqrt[3]{16} = x\sqrt[3]{2} \rightarrow 3\sqrt[3]{2} + 2\sqrt[3]{2} = x\sqrt[3]{2} \rightarrow 5\sqrt[3]{2} = x\sqrt[3]{2} \rightarrow x = 5$

Exponents and Roots Practice (Pages 50 – 52)

1. **C** Multiply the coefficients and use power rule for exponents. $(2x^4)(9x^9) = 18x^{13}$

2. **C** $\frac{Distance}{Speed} = Time$. Divide the coefficients and subtract the exponents. $\frac{10 \times 10^{13}}{2.5 \times 10^6} = \frac{10}{2.5} \times \frac{10^{13}}{10^6} = 4 \times 10^7$

3. **A** Divide the coefficients and use quotient rule for exponents. $\frac{12 \times 10^{14}}{3 \times 10^2} = \frac{12}{3} \times \frac{10^{14}}{10^2} = 4 \times 10^{12}$

4. **C** Use fraction power rule. $x^{\frac{3}{4}} \rightarrow \sqrt[4]{x^3}$

5. **A** Distribute the square root to all values underneath the square root. $\sqrt{16x^2} = \sqrt{16} \times \sqrt{x^2} = 4(x^2)^{\frac{1}{2}} = 4|x|$.
   Since $(x^2)^{\frac{1}{2}} = \pm x$, we write this as $|x|$.

6. **C** Step 1: Simplify the numerator using quotient rule. $\frac{x^{17}}{x^6} = x^{11}$

   Step 2: Use negative exponent rule on denominator so we can then apply our exponent rules. $\frac{1}{x^4} = x^{-4}$

   Step 3: Use the quotient rule. $\frac{x^{11}}{x^{-4}} = x^{15}$

7. **A** Use fraction power rule. $\sqrt[y]{x^z} = x^{\frac{z}{y}}$

8. **$\frac{1}{8}$** Distribute the power and apply the quotient rule. $\frac{(2x)^3}{(4x)^3} = \frac{2^3x^3}{4^3x^3} = \frac{8x^3}{64x^3} = \frac{1}{8}$

9. $\frac{26}{3}$ Step 1: Use power rule. $(x^{\frac{1}{3}})^6(x^{\frac{4}{3}})^5 = x^z \rightarrow x^2 x^{\frac{20}{3}}$

   Step 2: Add the exponents and solve for z. $x^{\frac{26}{3}} = x^z \rightarrow z = \frac{26}{3}$

10. **D** Figure out what exponent rule we can use to get from $x^{5y} \rightarrow x^{10y}$. To change from $x^{5y} \rightarrow x^{10y}$, we must square the x^{5y}. $(x^{5y})^2 = x^{10y}$. We must do the same thing to 10. $(x^{5y})^2 = (10)^2 \rightarrow x^{10y} = 100$

11. **1** Use the power rule and simplify. $\frac{(4x^4)^2}{(2x^2)^4} = \frac{4^2 x^8}{2^4 x^8} = \frac{16 x^8}{16 x^8} = 1$

12. **C** Figure out what exponent rule we can use to get from $x^4 \rightarrow x^8$. To change from $x^4 \rightarrow x^8$, we must square x^4. Therefore, we must do the same thing to 4. $(x^4)^2 = (4)^2 \rightarrow x^8 = 16$

13. **B** Convert the root to an exponent and then use power rule and fraction power rule. $\sqrt[4]{g^8 m^2} = (g^8 m^2)^{\frac{1}{4}} = g^{8(\frac{1}{4})} m^{2(\frac{1}{4})} = g^2 m^{\frac{1}{2}} = g^2 \sqrt{m}$

14. **B** Move the terms with negative exponents from the top to the bottom to make it positive and the negative exponent from the bottom to the top to make it positive. Then add the exponents. $\frac{x^{-3} y^{\frac{1}{3}}}{x^2 y^{-2}} = \frac{y^2 y^{\frac{1}{3}}}{x^2 x^3} = \frac{y^{\frac{6}{3}} y^{\frac{1}{3}}}{x^2 x^3} = \frac{y^{\frac{7}{3}}}{x^5}$

15. **D** Convert the root to an exponent and then use power rule. $\sqrt[2]{16 a^2 b^6 c} \rightarrow (16 a^2 b^6 c)^{\frac{1}{2}} \rightarrow 4 a b^3 c^{\frac{1}{2}} \rightarrow 4 a b^3 \sqrt{c}$

16. **A** Figure out what exponent rule we can use to get from $y^{20} \rightarrow y^5$. To change from $y^{20} \rightarrow y^5$, we must raise $(y^{20})^{\frac{1}{4}}$. Therefore, we must do the same thing to 16. $(y^{20})^{\frac{1}{4}} = (16)^{\frac{1}{4}} \rightarrow y^5 = \sqrt[4]{16} \rightarrow y^5 = 2$

17. **D** Step 1: Reduce 8 and 16 to have the same base of 2. $(8^x)(16^y) = (2^3)^x (2^4)^y = (2^{3x})(2^{4y})$
    Step 2: Add the exponents. $(2^{3x})(2^{4y}) = 2^{3x+4y}$
    Step 3: Substitute the value of $3x + 4y = 16$. $2^{3x+4y} = 2^{16}$

18. **9** $g(5) = 9g(4) \rightarrow g(5) = c^5$ and $g(4) = c^4$ so plug in c^5 for $g(5)$ and c^4 for $g(4) \rightarrow c^5 = 9c^4 \rightarrow \frac{c^5}{c^4} = 9 \rightarrow c = 9$

19. **A** Distribute the $\frac{1}{3}$ power. $(27x^3)^{\frac{1}{3}} \rightarrow (27^{\frac{1}{3}})(x^3)^{\frac{1}{3}} \rightarrow 3x$

20. **D** Step 1: Reduce 9 to a base of 3. $\frac{3^x}{9^y} = \frac{3^x}{(3^2)^y} = \frac{3^x}{3^{2y}}$

    Step 2: Subtract the exponents. $\frac{3^x}{3^{2y}} = 3^{x-2y}$
    Step 3: Substitute the value of $x - 2y = 9$. $3^{x-2y} = 3^9$

21. **5** $f(9) = 25f(7) \rightarrow f(9) = a^9$ $f(7) = a^7$ so plug in a^9 for $f(9)$ and a^7 for $f(7) \rightarrow 25a^7 \rightarrow \frac{a^9}{a^7} = 25 \rightarrow a^2 = 25 \rightarrow a = 5$

22. **D** Convert the root to an exponent then use power rule and simplify. $\sqrt[3]{16x^5 y} \rightarrow (16x^5 y)^{\frac{1}{3}} \rightarrow 2\sqrt[3]{2} x^{\frac{5}{3}} y^{\frac{1}{3}} \rightarrow 2x \sqrt[3]{2x^2 y}$

23. **C** Convert the root to an exponent then use power rule and simplify. $\sqrt[3]{24 x^4 y^2 z^3} \rightarrow (24 x^4 y^2 z^3)^{\frac{1}{3}} \rightarrow 2\sqrt[3]{3} x^{\frac{4}{3}} y^{\frac{2}{3}} z \rightarrow 2xz \sqrt[3]{3xy^2}$

24. **3** $h(5) = 9h(3) \rightarrow h(5) = b^5$ $h(3) = b^3$ so plug in b^5 for $h(5)$ and b^3 for $h(3) \rightarrow b^5 = 9 \times b^3 \rightarrow \frac{b^5}{b^3} = 9 \rightarrow b^2 = 9 \rightarrow b = 3$

25. **B** Step 1: Reduce 9 and 27 to a base of 3. $\frac{9^x}{27^y} = \frac{(3^2)^x}{(3^3)^y} = \frac{3^{2x}}{3^{3y}}$

    Step 2: Subtract the exponents. $\frac{3^{2x}}{3^{3y}} = 3^{2x-3y}$
    Step 3: Substitute the value of $2x - 3y = 7$. $3^{2x-3y} = 3^7$

Chapter 11 – Quadratics (Pages 62 – 68)

1. **A** Combine like terms. $x^2 + 3x^2 = 4x^2$. $4x + 3x = 7x$. $3 + 6 + 1 - 1 = 9 \rightarrow 4x^2 + 7x + 9$
2. **C** Step 1: FOIL and combine like terms. $(3x - 5)(-x + 7) = -3x^2 + 26x - 35$
   Step 2: Check each answer choice to see which is the same.
   Alternative method: Plug in $x = 1$ to the initial equation and the answer choices and see which one is the same.
   Original equation: $(3(1) - 5)(-1 + 7) = -12$. Correct answer: $(-3(1) + 5)(1 - 7) = -12$

3. **D** Method 1: Step 1: Factor and solve for the solutions. $x^2 - 7x + 12 = 0 \rightarrow (x-4)(x-3) = 0 \rightarrow$
   $x = 4, 3$
   Step 2: Add the solutions. $3 + 4 = 7$
   Method 2: Use $-\frac{b}{a}$ to find sum of the solutions. $-\frac{-7}{1} = 7$

4. **D** Factor and solve for solutions. $3x^2 + 9x - 12 = 0 \rightarrow (3x-3)(x+4) = 0 \rightarrow 3x - 3 = 0$ and
   $x + 4 = 0 \rightarrow x = 1$ and $x = -4$

5. **A** Step 1: Set equal. $x^2 + 6x + 6 = 2x + 2$
   Step 2: Move all of the values to one side to set equal to 0 and factor. $x^2 + 4x + 4 = 0 \rightarrow$
   $(x+2)(x+2) = 0 \rightarrow x = -2$

6. **D** Method 1: Step 1: Factor and solve for solutions. $x^2 - 4x - 21 = (x-7)(x+3) \rightarrow x = 7, -3$
   Step 2: Add the solutions. $7 + (-3) = 4$
   Method 2: Use $-\frac{b}{a}$ to find sum of the solutions. $-\frac{-4}{1} = 4$

7. **C** Step 1: Identify the solutions or x-intercepts on the graph are at $x = 0, 3$
   Step 2: To identify whether the factors should be $x(x-3)$ or $x^2(x-3)$, look at the behavior of the graph at
   the intercept. Since the graph bounces at $x = 0$ and passes straight through at $x = 3$, the factors must be
   $x^2(x-3)$.

8. **A** Step 1: Set equal. $20 = (x+3)(x+4)$
   Step 2: FOIL the right side of the equation. $20 = x^2 + 7x + 12$
   Step 3: Move all of the values to one side to set equal to 0 and factor. $0 = x^2 + 7x - 8 \rightarrow$
   $0 = (x+8)(x-1) \rightarrow x = -8, 1$

9. **A** Step 1: FOIL the right side of the equation. $9x^2 - 16 = (ax-b)(ax+b) \rightarrow 9x^2 - 16 = a^2x^2 - b^2$
   Step 2: Solve for a by using the x-terms. $9x^2 = a^2x^2 \rightarrow 9 = a^2 \rightarrow 3 = a$

10. **A** Step 1: For these types of question, FOIL out the answer choices and then combine like terms.
    $(x+4)^2 - 8 = x^2 + 8x + 16 - 8 = x^2 + 8x + 8$
    Alternative method: Plug in $x = 1$ to the initial equation and the answer choices and see which one is the same.
    Original equation: $1^2 + 8(1) + 8 = 17$. Correct answer: $(1+4)^2 - 8 = 17$

11. **B** Step 1: Solve for the solutions by setting each factor equal to 0. $x - 1.2 = 0$ and $x + 5 = 0 \rightarrow$
    $x = 1.2, -5$
    Step 2: Find the sum of the two solutions. $-5 + 1.2 = -3.8$

12. **D** Step 1: Identify the solutions or x-intercepts of the graph are at $x = -3, 0, 1$
    Step 2: Use the zeros to find the appropriate factors. $x(x+3)(x-1)$

13. **C** Step 1: To find the root of a quadratic, set the factors equal to zero and solve for x. Here, we want to do the
    reverse. To find the factors, set x equal to the root and solve by setting equal to zero.
    For $x = -4 \rightarrow x + 4 = 0$
    For $x = 3 \rightarrow x - 3 = 0$
    For $x = -5 \rightarrow x + 5 = 0$
    $x - 3$ is the only factor that is an answer choice.

14. **B** Step 1: Find the three x-intercepts of $x = 0$, $x = 1$, and $x = 4$. The factors are $x(x-1)(x-4)$.
    Step 2: Find the multiplicity. Since the function go straight through each x-intercept, each solution has a
    multiplicity of 1.

15. **A** Use the quadratic formula and simplify the square root. $x = \frac{-6 \pm \sqrt{6^2 - 4(1)(3)}}{2(1)} = \frac{-6 \pm \sqrt{24}}{2} = \frac{-6 \pm 2\sqrt{6}}{2} = -3 \pm \sqrt{6}$

16. **D** Method 1: Step 1: Set equation equal to zero and solve for the solutions. $x^2 - 13x + 40 = 6x - 8 \rightarrow$
    $x^2 - 19x + 48 = 0 \rightarrow (x-16)(x-3) = 0 \rightarrow x = 16, 3$
    Step 2: Add the solutions. $16 + 3 = 19$
    Method 2: Step 1: Move all terms to left side. $x^2 - 13x + 40 = 6x - 8 \rightarrow x^2 - 19x + 48 = 0$
    Step 2: Use $-\frac{b}{a}$ to find sum of the solutions. $-\frac{-19}{1} = 19$

17. **A** Step 1: Set equal and then move all terms to one side. $2x + 3 = x^2 + 8x + 9 \rightarrow 0 = x^2 + 6x + 6$
    Step 2: Since this is not factorable, use the quadratic formula to solve.
    $x = \frac{-6 \pm \sqrt{6^2 - 4(1)(6)}}{2(1)} \rightarrow \frac{-6 \pm \sqrt{12}}{2} \rightarrow \frac{-6 \pm 2\sqrt{3}}{2} \rightarrow -3 \pm \sqrt{3}$

18. **C** Step 1: Identify the solutions or x-intercepts of the graph are at $x = -4, x = 2$, and $x = 6$.

Step 2: Use the zeros to find the appropriate factors. $(x + 4)(x - 2)(x - 6)$

Step 3: You don't need to solve for the $\frac{1}{5}$. Based on the shape of the graph, we can tell this will be positive.

Since the cubic function starts in the bottom left and finishes in the top right, the coefficient must be positive.

19. **A** Step 1: Identify this is an upward-facing parabola, so the answer must be A or B.

Step 2: $\frac{-b}{2a}$ identifies the x-coordinate of the vertex of the graph. $-\frac{3}{2(1)} = -1.5$

20. **B** Step 1: Set the quadratic and the factors equal and FOIL the left side.

$(2x + 3)(x - 4) = 2x^2 + (z - 1)x + 2z - 4 \rightarrow 2x^2 - 5x - 12 = 2x^2 + (z - 1)x + 2z - 4$

Step 2: The easiest way to solve this question is to plug in the answer choices to see which one makes both sides equal.

Alternatively, solve for z. $2x^2 - 5x - 12 = 2x^2 + (z - 1)x + 2z - 4 \rightarrow -5x - 12 = zx - x + 2z - 4 \rightarrow -4x - 8 = zx + 2z \rightarrow z = -4$

21. **D** Step 1: Factor out $(x^2 - 4)$. $(x^2 - 4) = (x + 2)(x - 2)$ so the equation becomes $(x + 1)(x + 7)(x + 2)(x - 2) = 0$

Step 2: To find the roots, set the factors equal to zero and solve for x. $x + 1 = 0 \rightarrow x = -1$

$x + 7 = 0 \rightarrow x = -7 \qquad x + 2 = 0 \rightarrow x = -2 \qquad x - 2 = 0 \rightarrow x = 2$

22. **D** Step 1: Identify this is a downwards facing parabola therefore it must be $-x^2$.

Step 2: $\frac{-b}{2a}$ will identify the x-coordinate of the vertex of the graph. D gives the correct vertex location.

$x = -\frac{-3}{2(-1)} = -\frac{3}{2} = -1.5$

23. **A** Method 1: Step 1: Set equal. $x^2 + 2x + 1 = -3x - 3$

Step 2: Move all of the values to one side to set equal to 0 and factor. $x^2 + 5x + 4 = 0 \rightarrow (x + 4)(x + 1) = 0 \rightarrow x = -4, -1$

Step 3: Add the solutions. $-1 + -4 = -5$

Method 2: Complete the same steps 1 and the first part of 2 to get $x^2 + 5x + 4 = 0$

Step 3: Use $-\frac{b}{a}$ to find sum of the solutions. $-\frac{5}{1} = -5$

24. **A** $\frac{-b}{2a}$ will identify the x-coordinate of the vertex of the graph. $x = -\frac{-2}{2(1)} = 1$

Answer choice A has the only graph with an x-coordinate of the vertex at $x = 1$.

25. **0** Step 1: Set equal. $x^2 + 5x + 8 = 8 - 2x$

Step 2: Move all of the values to one side to set equal to 0 and factor. $x^2 + 7x = 0 \rightarrow x(x + 7) = 0 \rightarrow x = 0 \quad x + 7 = 0 \rightarrow x = 0, -7$. You cannot grid in a negative number on the SAT, so the answer is 0.

26. **A** Step 1: Identify this is a downward-facing parabola, so the answer must be A or B.

Step 2: $\frac{-b}{2a}$ will identify the x-coordinate of the vertex of the graph. $x = -\frac{4}{2(-1)} = 2$

27. **C** Use the quadratic formula. $x = \frac{4 \pm \sqrt{(-4)^2 - 4(1)(1)}}{2(1)} \rightarrow x = \frac{4 \pm \sqrt{12}}{2} \rightarrow x = \frac{4 \pm 2\sqrt{3}}{2} \rightarrow x = 2 \pm \sqrt{3}$

28. **D** Identify the y-intercept is 1. Plug in $x = 0$ to the answer choices to solve for which one gives the correct y-intercept. $f(0) = \frac{1}{2}(0 - 2)(0 + 2) + 3 \rightarrow f(0) = -2 + 3 \rightarrow f(0) = 1$

29. **A** Step 1: Set the quadratic equal to zero. $zx^2 + 6x - 3 = 0$

Step 2: To find when a quadratic will have one real value, set the discriminant equal to zero.

$b^2 - 4ac = 0 \rightarrow 6^2 - 4(z)(-3) = 0 \rightarrow 36 + 12z = 0 \rightarrow 12z = -36 \rightarrow z = -3$

30. **C** Step 1: Factor out the quadratic. $(x + a)(x + b) = 0$

Step 2: Solve for the factors. $x + a = 0 \rightarrow x = -a \qquad x + b = 0 \rightarrow x = -b$

Since a and b are positive constants and do not equal each other, there are two distinct x-intercepts.

Alternative method: Pick different positive values for a and b and solve.

31. **D** Move all of the values to one side to set equal to 0 and factor. $5x^2 + 6x - 8 = 0 \rightarrow (5x - 4)(x + 2) = 0 \rightarrow x = \frac{4}{5}, -2$

32. **C** Step 1: Set equal. $x^2 + 9x + 8 = 11x + 7$

Step 2: Move all of the values to one side to equal 0 and factor. $x^2 - 2x + 1 = 0 \rightarrow (x - 1)^2 = 0 \rightarrow x = 1$

Step 3: Plug $x = 1$ into either equation to solve for y. $y = 11x + 7 \rightarrow y = 11(1) + 7 \rightarrow y = 18$

Step 4: Solve for $y - x$. $18 - 1 = 17$

33. **A** Method 1: Step 1: Move all values to one side and set equal to 0.
Step 2: Factor. $x^2 - 14x + 24 = 0 \rightarrow (x - 12)(x - 2) = 0 \rightarrow x = 2, 12$
Step 2: Add the solutions. $12 + 2 = 14$
Method 2: Use same step 1 as above. Step 2: Use $-\frac{b}{a}$ to find sum of the solutions. $-\frac{-14}{1} = 14$

34. **B** Step 1: Set equal. $x^2 + 11x + 4 = 5x - 5$
Step 2: Move all of the values to one side to set equal to 0 and factor. $x^2 + 6x + 9 = 0 \rightarrow$
$(x + 3)^2 = 0 \rightarrow x = -3$
Alternatively, use the discriminate to find the number of solutions. $b^2 - 4ac = 6^2 - 4(1)(9) = 0$, which means there is 1 solution.

35. **1026** FOIL the two factors on the left side. $(80x - 42)(15x + 12) = ax^2 + bx + c \rightarrow$
$1200x^2 + 330x - 504 = ax^2 + bx + c$ so $a = 1200$, $b = 330$, and $c = -504$
$a + b + c = 1200 + 330 - 504 = 1026$

36. **D** Step 1: FOIL out the left side of the equation. $(kx + 3)(4x^2 - mx - 3) = 20x^3 - 3x^2 - 24x - 9 \rightarrow$
$4kx^3 + 12x^2 - kmx^2 - 3kx - 3mx - 9 = 20x^3 - 3x^2 - 24x - 9$
Step 2: Solve for k using the x^3 terms. $4kx^3 = 20x^3 \rightarrow k = 5$
Step 3: Solve for m using the x^2. Use the $k = 5$. $12x^2 - kmx^2 = -3x^2 \rightarrow 12x^2 - 5mx^2 = -3x^2 \rightarrow$
$-5mx^2 = -15x^2 \rightarrow m = 3$
Step 4: Solve for km. $(3)(5) = 15$

37. **B** To find the solution to a quadratic, set the factors equal to zero and solve for x. We want to do the reverse. To find the factors, set x equal to the root and solve. $x = -3 \rightarrow x + 3 = 0 \quad x = 6 \rightarrow x - 6 = 0$
$x = 8 \rightarrow x - 8 = 0 \quad (x + 3)$ is the only factor that is an answer choice.

38. **C** Factor and solve for x. $(x^2 - 9)(x + 1)^2 \rightarrow (x + 3)(x - 3)(x + 1)(x + 1) \rightarrow x = -3, 3, -1$

39. **C** Solve for the solutions. $x + a = 0 \rightarrow x = -a \quad x - a = 0 \rightarrow x = a \quad x + b = 0 \rightarrow x = -b$
Three different solutions which are the same as three distinct x-intercepts.
Alternatively, you can pick values for a and b and then solve.

40. **C** The ball will hit the ground at the x-intercept. Solve for the positive x-intercept.
$0 = -x^2 + 10x + 56 \rightarrow 0 = x^2 - 10x - 56 \rightarrow 0 = (x - 14)(x + 4) \rightarrow x = 14, -4$

41. **A** Use the quadratic formula. $x = \frac{-4 \pm \sqrt{4^2 - 4(2)(1)}}{2(2)} = \frac{-4 \pm \sqrt{8}}{4} = \frac{-4 \pm 2\sqrt{2}}{4} = \frac{-2 \pm \sqrt{2}}{2}$

42. **D** Step 1: When looking for a maximum or minimum, find the vertex of the parabola. Use $\frac{-b}{2a}$ to solve for the x-coordinate of the vertex. $x = -\frac{30}{-2} = 15$
Step 2: Plug in $x = 15$ to solve for the height. $H(15) = -(15^2) + 30(15) = 225$

43. **B** Find the x-coordinate of the vertex using $x = -\frac{b}{2a}$. Plug in answer choices to find which gives the correct x-coordinate of -1.5. $x = -\frac{3}{2} = -1.5$
Alternatively, pick a point on the graph and plug in the values to solve for b. We will use point $(-3, 3)$.
$3 = -3^2 - 3b + 3 \rightarrow 3 = 9 - 3b + 3 \rightarrow -9 = -3b \rightarrow 3 = b$

44. **D** To solve for x-intercepts, set $y = 0$. B will have an x-intercept of $x = 4.5$. C is factorable and will have x-intercepts of $x = -1, -7$. A is also factorable and will have an x-intercept of $x = 3$. D is not factorable and the discriminant $\sqrt{b^2 - 4ac} < 0$. $\sqrt{16 - 4(1)(6)} = \sqrt{-8}$. Therefore, there is no real solution which means there is no x-intercept.

45. **B** Step 1: Move all of the values to one side to set equal to 0. $5x^2 - 2x - 2 = 0$
Step 2: Use the quadratic formula. $x = \frac{2 \pm \sqrt{(-2)^2 - 4(5)(-2)}}{2(5)} = \frac{2 \pm \sqrt{44}}{10} = \frac{2 \pm 2\sqrt{11}}{10} = \frac{1 \pm \sqrt{11}}{5}$

46. **C** Step 1: To find points of intersection, set the equations equal and solve for x.
$-3x + 50 = -x^2 + 6x + 30 \rightarrow x^2 - 9x + 20 = 0 \rightarrow (x - 4)(x - 5) = 0 \rightarrow x = 4, 5$
Step 2: Correctly interpret there being two possible points of intersection since both values are positive. The baseball and Dave on the zip line will intersect at 4 and 5 seconds.
Alternatively, if you have a graphing calculator, graph the equations to see where they intercept.

47. **A** Step 1: Rewrite first equation in terms of x. $y = x - 18 \rightarrow x = y + 18$

Step 2: Substitute into the second equation and solve for y. $y^2 + (x - 14)^2 - 12 = 0 \rightarrow$ $y^2 + (y + 18 - 14)^2 - 12 = 0 \rightarrow y^2 + (y + 4)^2 - 12 = 0 \rightarrow y^2 + y^2 + 8y + 16 - 12 = 0 \rightarrow$ $2y^2 + 8y + 4 = 0$

Step 3: Use the quadratic formula to solve for y. $y = \frac{-8 \pm \sqrt{8^2 - 4(2)(4)}}{2(2)} = \frac{-8 \pm \sqrt{32}}{4} = \frac{-8 \pm 4\sqrt{2}}{4} = -2 \pm \sqrt{2}$

48. **C** Step 1: Set equal and then set equal to 0. $6x + 2 = ax^2 + b \rightarrow ax^2 - 6x + b - 2 = 0$

Step 2: Notice that you need to use the discriminant. When the discriminant equals 0, there is one solution. At this point, you can backsolve using the answer choices. The correct answer of C is shown. $ax^2 - 6x + b - 2 = 0 \rightarrow 9x^2 - 6x + 3 - 2 = 0 \rightarrow 9x^2 - 6x + 1$

Step 3: Use discriminant. $(-6)^2 - 4(9)(1) = 0$ so there is only one solution.

Chapter 12 – Systems of Equations (Pages 73 – 77)

1. **D** Use elimination. Step 1: Multiply the bottom equation by 3 to cancel out the y-terms.
   Step 2: Add the two equations and solve for x.
   $$x - 3y = 3$$
   $$+\ 3x + 3y = 21$$
   $$4x = 24 \rightarrow x = 6$$

2. **B** Use substitution. Step 1: Substitute the second equation in for y. $x - (3 - 2x) = 3$ Make sure to distribute the negative to both the 3 and the $-2x$.
   Step 2: Solve for x. $x - 3 + 2x = 3 \rightarrow x + 2x = 6 \rightarrow 3x = 6 \rightarrow x = 2$

3. **2** Use elimination. Step 1: Multiply the top equation by -4 to cancel out the x-terms.
   Step 2: Add the two equations and solve for y.
   $$-x + 8y = 16$$
   $$+\ \ x + y = 2$$
   $$9y = 18 \rightarrow y = 2$$

4. **D** Use elimination. Step 1: Multiply the top equation by 2 and the bottom equation by 3 to cancel out the y-terms.
   Step 2: Add the two equations and solve for x.
   $$4x - 6y = -12$$
   $$+\ 9x + 6y = 12$$
   $$13x = 0 \rightarrow x = 0$$
   Step 3: Plug $x = 0$ into either equation and solve for y. $3(0) + 2y = 4 \rightarrow 2y = 4 \rightarrow y = 2$
   Step 4: $x + y = 0 + 2 = 2$

5. **D** Set equal. Step 1: Divide the second equation by two. $\frac{2y = -8 + 3x}{2} \rightarrow y = -4 + 1.5x$
   Step 2: Set the two equations equal and solve for x. $-1.5x - 1 = -4 + 1.5x \rightarrow 3x = 3 \rightarrow x = 1$
   Step 3: Plug $x = 1$ in for x in either equation and solve for y. $y = -1.5(1) - 1 = -2.5$
   Step 4: Solve for $2y - x$. $2(-2.5) - 1 = -6$

6. **C** Set equal. Step 1: Divide the second equation by two. $\frac{2y = 4 - 6x}{2} \rightarrow y = 2 - 3x$
   Step 2: Set the two equations equal. $2 - 3x = x^2 - 11x + 14$
   Step 3: Move all of the values to one side and factor. $0 = x^2 - 8x + 12 \rightarrow 0 = (x - 6)(x - 2) \rightarrow x = 6, 2$

7. **A** Step 1: Set the two equations equal. $x^2 = 7x + 8$
   Step 2: Move all of the values to one side and factor. $x^2 - 7x - 8 = 0 \rightarrow (x - 8)(x + 1) = 0 \rightarrow x = 8, -1$
   Step 3: Since $x < 0$, plug $x = -1$ into either equation. $y = 7(-1) + 8 \rightarrow y = 1$

8. **A** Step 1: FOIL the top equation. $y = x^2 - 3x - 10$
   Step 2: Set the two equations equal and solve for x. $-6x - 12 = x^2 - 3x - 10$
   Step 3: Move all of the values to one side and factor. $0 = x^2 + 3x + 2 \rightarrow 0 = (x + 1)(x + 2) \rightarrow x = -1, -2$
   Step 4: Plug $x = -1$ into either equation and solve for y. No answer choices have $x = -2$, so do not plug it in. $y = -6(-1) - 12 \rightarrow y = 6 - 12 \rightarrow y = -6$

9. **A** The first equation $C + B = 20$ gives the total number of boxes of cookies and brownies that will be ordered. The second equation $6C + 8B = 150$ gives the prices of each of the cookies and brownies set equal to the total amount Max will spend.

10. $\frac{26}{3}$ Use elimination. Step 1: Multiply the top equation by 2 to cancel out the y-terms.
    Step 2: Add the equations and solve for x.
    $2x - 2y = 42$
    $\underline{+ \ x + 2y = -16}$
    $\qquad 3x = 26 \ \rightarrow \ x = \dfrac{26}{3}$

11. **B** Set equal. Step 1: Rearrange the second equation. $y = 5x - 8$
    Step 2: Set equations equal. $5x - 8 = x^2 + 9x - 4$
    Step 3: Move all of the values to one side and factor. $0 = x^2 + 4x + 4 \ \rightarrow \ 0 = (x+2)(x+2) \ \rightarrow \ x = -2$

12. **D** Set equal. Step 1: Rewrite the second equation as $x = -2y + 24$
    Step 2: Set equations equal. $-2y + 24 = y^2 + 8y$
    Step 3: Move all of the values to one side and factor. $0 = y^2 + 10y - 24 \ \rightarrow \ 0 = (y+12)(y-2) \ \rightarrow$
    $y = -12, 2$

13. **C** Use substitution. Step 1: Substitute the second equation in for x in the first equation. This is easier than
    reworking the second equation and substituting in for the y-value because to substitute in for the y-value the
    second equation would need to be rewritten as $y = \frac{1}{2}x + 1$. This would be much more difficult to FOIL.
    $(2y + 2 - 1)^2 + (y - 2)^2 = 35$
    Step 2: FOIL the expressions and combine like terms. $(2y + 1)^2 + (y - 2)^2 = 35 \ \rightarrow$
    $4y^2 + 4y + 1 + y^2 - 4y + 4 = 35 \ \rightarrow \ 5y^2 + 5 = 35$
    Step 3: Solve for y. $5y^2 = 30 \ \rightarrow \ y^2 = 6 \ \rightarrow \ y = \sqrt{6}$
    Step 4: Plug in for y in the second equation to solve for x. $x = 2\left(\sqrt{6}\right) + 2 \ \rightarrow \ x = 2\sqrt{6} + 2$

14. **C** Use elimination. Step 1: Multiply the second equation by -5 to cancel out the y-terms.
    Step 2: Add the two equations and solve for x.
    $3x + 5y = 26$
    $\underline{+ \ -5x - 5y = -170}$
    $\qquad -2x = -144 \ \rightarrow \ x = 72$

15. **A** Use substitution. Step 1: Substitute the second equation in for y in the first equation. $6x = (96 - 7x) + 8$
    Step 2: Solve for x. $13x = 104 \ \rightarrow \ x = 8$
    Step 3: Plug $x = 8$ into either equation to solve for y. $6(8) = y + 8 \ \rightarrow \ 48 = y + 8 \ \rightarrow \ y = 40$
    Step 4: Solve for $x - y$. $8 - 40 = -32$

16. **B** Use elimination. Step 1: Multiply the second equation by 4 to cancel out the x-terms.
    Step 2: Add the two equations and solve for y.
    $-4x - 15y = 78$
    $\underline{+ \ 4x + 12y = -120}$
    $\qquad -3y = -42 \ \rightarrow \ y = 14$. At this point, only one answer has 14 for the y-value, so the answer is B.
    To finish the algebraically, we also show step 3 below.
    Step 3: Plug $y = 14$ into either equation and solve for x. $3(14) + x = -30 \ \rightarrow \ 42 + x = -30 \ \rightarrow \ x = -72$

17. **A** Use elimination. Step 1: Multiply the second equation by -2 to cancel out the x-terms
    Step 2: Add the two equations and solve for y.
    $4x + 3y = 10$
    $\underline{+ \ -4x - 12y = 8}$
    $\qquad -9y = 18 \ \rightarrow \ y = -2$

18. **D** Use substitution. Step 1: Rewrite the first equation as $y = 3x$.
    Step 2: Substitute in for y in the second equation and solve for x. $2(3x + 12) = 8x \ \rightarrow \ 6x + 24 = 8x \ \rightarrow$
    $24 = 2x \ \rightarrow \ x = 12$

19. **B** Use elimination. Step 1: Multiply the top equation by 2 and the bottom equation by 3 to cancel out the
    y-terms.
    Step 2: Add the two equations and solve for x.
    $4x - 6y = -18$
    $\underline{+ \ 9x + 6y = 57}$
    $\qquad 13x = 39 \ \rightarrow \ x = 3$
    Step 3: Plug $x = 3$ into either equation to solve for y. $3(3) + 2y = 19 \rightarrow 9 + 2y = 19 \rightarrow 2y = 10 \rightarrow y = 5$
    Step 4: Solve for $y - x$. $5 - 3 = 2u$

20. **C** Method 1: Subtract the equations to get straight to the answer.

$$4x + 3y = 22$$
$$- \quad 3x + 2y = 16$$
$$x + y \ = 6$$

Method 2: Use elimination. Step 1: Multiply the top equation by 2 and the bottom equation by -3 to cancel out the y-terms.

Step 2: Add the two equations and solve for x.

$$8x + 6y = 44$$
$$+ - \ 9x - 6y = -48$$
$$-x = -4 \ \rightarrow \ x = 4$$

Step 3: Plug $x = 4$ into either equation to solve for y. $3(4) + 2y = 16 \ \rightarrow \ 12 + 2y = 16 \ \rightarrow \ y = 2$

Step 4: Solve for $x + y$. $4 + 2 = 6$

21. **360** Step 1: Create a system of equations by using the points given to solve for a and b. $850 = 15a + b$ $1{,}305 = 28a + b$

Step 2: Solve the system of equations using substitution or elimination. Here we will use elimination. Multiply the entire top equation by -1 to cancel out the b-terms.

$$-850 = -15a - b$$
$$+ \ 1{,}305 = 28a + b$$
$$455 = 13a \ \rightarrow \ a = 35$$

Step 3: Plug $a = 35$ into either equation to solve for b. $1{,}305 = 28(35) + b \ \rightarrow \ 1{,}305 = 980 + b \rightarrow$ $b = 325$

Step 4: Solve for $a + b$. $35 + 325 = 360$

22. **A** Set equal. Step 1: Rewrite both equations in $y =$ form. $y = -9x + 22$. $y = -x^2 + 4$

Step 2: Set the two equations equal to each other. $-x^2 + 4 = -9x + 22$

Step 3: Move all of the values to one side and factor. $0 = x^2 - 9x + 18 \ \rightarrow$ $0 = (x - 6)(x - 3) \ \rightarrow \ x = 6, 3$

Step 4: Plug in either $x = 3$ and $x = 6$ to either of the equations to solve for y.

For $x = 6$: $9(6) + y = 22 \ \rightarrow \ 54 + y = 22 \ \rightarrow \ y = -32$
For $x = 3$: $9(3) + y = 22 \ \rightarrow \ 27 + y = 22 \ \rightarrow \ y = -5$

23. **C** Step 1: Write the two equations. Let r represent Reubens and b represent brisket. $r + b = 99$ $8.1b + 7.35r = 759.90$

Step 2: Solve using substitution or elimination. Substitution is easier, so we will use that. Rewrite the first equation as $b = 99 - r$

Step 3: Substitute into the second equation and solve for r. $8.1(99 - r) + 7.35r = 759.90 \ \rightarrow$ $801.9 - 8.1r + 7.35r = 759.90 \ \rightarrow \ -0.75r = -42 \ \rightarrow \ r = 56$

24. **B** Step 1: Write the two equations. Let d represent dimes and n represent nickels. $d + n = 25$ $0.1d + 0.05n = 2.25$

Step 2: Solve using substitution or elimination. Substitution is easier, so we will use that. Rewrite the first equation as $d = 25 - n$

Step 3: Substitute into the second equation and solve for n. $0.1(25 - n) + 0.05n = 2.25 \ \rightarrow$ $2.5 - 0.1n + 0.05n = 2.25 \ \rightarrow \ -0.05n = -0.25 \ \rightarrow \ n = 5$

25. **D** Step 1: Write the two equations. Let x represent 8-person rafts and y represent 6-person rafts. $x + y = 20 \qquad 8x + 6y = 150$

Step 2: Solve via substitution or elimination. We will use substitution. Rewrite the first equation as $y = 20 - x$

Step 3: Substitute into the second equation and solve for x. $8x + 6(20 - x) = 150 \ \rightarrow$ $8x + 120 - 6x = 150 \ \rightarrow \ 2x = 30 \ \rightarrow \ x = 15$

26. **3** Use elimination. Step 1: Multiply the top equation by 2 to cancel out the y-terms.

Step 2: Add the two equations and solve for x.

$$6x - 4y = -2$$
$$+ \ 10x + 4y = 50$$
$$16x = 48 \ \rightarrow \ x = 3$$

27. **100** Step 1: Write the two equations. Let c represent the calories in a carnitas taco and f represent the calories in a fish taco. $c = f + 50$ $\quad$ $3c + 2f = 650$
Step 2: Solve via substitution or elimination. We will use substitution.
Step 3: Substitute into the second equation to solve for f. $3(f + 50) + 2f = 650$ $\rightarrow$
$3f + 150 + 2f = 650$ $\rightarrow$ $5f = 500$ $\rightarrow$ $f = 100$

28. **B** Use substitution. Step 1: Plug in y^2 for x in the second equation. $-14y + y^2 = 32$
Step 2: Move all of the values to one side and factor. $y^2 - 14y - 32 = 0$ $\rightarrow$ $(y - 16)(y + 2) = 0$ $\rightarrow$
$y = 16, -2$
Step 3: Plug $y = -2$ in either equation for y since $y < 0$ and solve for x. $x = (-2)^2$ $\rightarrow$ $x = 4$

29. **D** Step 1: Write the two equations. Let x represent the hours traveling by car and y represent the hours traveling by train. $x + y = 7$ $\quad$ $40x + 60y = 400$
Step 2: Solve the system of equations using substitution or elimination. Here, we will use substitution to solve for y by rewriting the original equation as $x = 7 - y$
Step 3: Substitute into the second equation and solve for y. $40(7 - y) + 60y = 400$ $\rightarrow$
$280 - 40y + 60y = 400$ $\rightarrow$ $20y = 120$ $\rightarrow$ $y = 6$
Step 4: Multiply the speed by the time to find out how far was traveled by train. $6 \times 60 = 360$

30. **2.5 or $\frac{5}{2}$** Step 1: Rewrite both equations in the form of $ax + by = c$. $\frac{1}{4}x - 4y = -4$
$-\frac{3}{4}x + 5y = -\frac{55}{10}$
Step 2: Use elimination. Multiply the top equation by 3 to cancel the x-terms.
Step 3: Add the two equations and solve for y.

$$\frac{3}{4}x - 12y = -12$$
$$+ \ -\frac{3}{4}x + 5y = -\frac{55}{10}$$
$$-7y = -\frac{175}{10} \ \rightarrow \ y = \frac{5}{2}, 2.5$$

31. **5** Use substitution. Plug in $2x$ for y in the first equation and solve for x.
$(2x)^2 + 4x^2 = 200$ $\rightarrow$ $4x^2 + 4x^2 = 200$ $\rightarrow$ $8x^2 = 200$ $\rightarrow$ $x^2 = 25$ $\rightarrow$ $x = 5, -5$. Since the questions tells us that $x > 0$, the answer is $x = 5$.

32. **175** Step 1: Create a system of equations using the points given to solve for a and b.
$71 = a(3)^2 + b(3) + 35$ $\rightarrow$ $9a + 3b = 36$
$251 = a(9)^2 + b(9) + 35$ $\rightarrow$ $81a + 9b = 216$
Step 2: Solve the system of equations using substitution or elimination. Here, we will use elimination. Multiply the top equation by -3 to cancel out the b-terms.

$$-27a - 9b = -108$$
$$+ \ \ 81a + 9b = 216$$
$$54a = 108 \ \rightarrow \ a = 2$$

Step 3: Plug $a = 2$ into either equation to solve for b. $9(2) + 3b = 36$ $\rightarrow$ $3b = 18$ $\rightarrow$ $b = 6$
Step 4: Solve for $f(7)$. $f(7) = 2(7)^2 + 6(7) + 35 = 98 + 42 + 35 = 175$

33. **338** Step 1: Understand the standard form of a quadratic equation is $y = ax^2 + bx + c$. Since the point $(0, 0)$ is on the graph of the function, $c = 0$.
Step 2: Create a system of equations to solve for a and b.
$50 = a(10)^2 + 10b$ $\rightarrow$ $100a + 10b = 50$
$450 = a(30)^2 + 30b$ $\rightarrow$ $900a + 30b = 450$
Step 3: Solve the system of equations using substitution or elimination. We will use elimination. Multiply the entire top equation by -3 to cancel out the b-terms and solve for a.

$$-300a - 30b = -150$$
$$+ \ \ 900a + 30b = 450$$
$$600a = 300 \ \rightarrow \ a = \frac{1}{2}$$

Step 4: Plug $a = \frac{1}{2}$ into either equation to solve for b. $50 = 100\left(\frac{1}{2}\right) + 10b$ $\rightarrow$ $50 = 50 + 10b$ $\rightarrow$ $b = 0$
Step 5: Solve for $p(26)$. $p(26) = \frac{1}{2}(26^2) = 338$

34. **B** Step 1: Rewrite the second equation as $y = 2x + 3$.
Step 2: Plug in for y in the first equation and then solve for x. $(2x + 3)^2 = 3x^2 - 6x - 72 \rightarrow$
$4x^2 + 12x + 9 = 3x^2 - 6x - 72$
Step 3: Move all of the values to one side and factor. $x^2 + 18x + 81 = 0 \rightarrow (x + 9)(x + 9) = 0 \rightarrow$
$x = -9 \rightarrow$ One real solution.

Chapter 13 – Systems of Equations with Infinite Solutions or No Solution (Pages 80 – 81)

1. **D** For no solution, set up a proportion to make the slopes equal. $\frac{5}{-4} = \frac{b}{-12} \rightarrow -60 = -4b \rightarrow b = 15$

2. **C** For no solution, set up a proportion to make the slopes equal. $\frac{3}{4} = \frac{5}{a} \rightarrow 3a = 20 \rightarrow a = \frac{20}{3}$

3. **D** For a system of equations to have infinitely many solutions, the lines must be identical. Both the slope and the intercept must be the same. For questions like this, you are looking for the equations to be multiples of each other. $-2(2x + 5y + 12) = -4x - 10y - 24$

4. **B** For no solution, set up a proportion to make the slopes the same. $\frac{a}{b} = \frac{6}{3} \rightarrow \frac{a}{b} = 2$

5. **A** For no solution, set up a proportion to make the slopes the same. $\frac{4}{8} = \frac{3}{6} \rightarrow 8a = 24 \rightarrow a = 3$

6. **D** For infinite solutions, set up a proportion so the lines will be identical. $\frac{3}{5} = \frac{b}{50}$. This could also be set up as $\frac{-6}{-10} = \frac{b}{50}$. We will continue using the first way it was set up. $\frac{3}{5} = \frac{b}{50} \rightarrow 150 = 5b \rightarrow b = 30$

7. **2** For infinite solutions, set up a proportion so the lines will be identical. $\frac{a}{b} = \frac{12}{6} \rightarrow \frac{a}{b} = 2$. The proportion is set up this way since the constants must be in the same ratio as the for the x-terms.

8. **D** Step 1: Rewrite the second equation into $y = mx + b$ form. $gx + 5y = 20 \rightarrow y = -\frac{g}{5}x + 4$
Step 2: Set the slopes of both lines equal and solve for g. $-\frac{g}{5} = 4 \rightarrow g = -20$
Step 3: Since there is no solution, solve for k to make sure the y-intercepts will not be equal. $4 \neq 5k \rightarrow$
$\frac{4}{5} \neq k$

9. **A** For a system of equations to have infinitely many solutions, the lines must be identical. The slope and the intercept must be the same.
Step 1: Set up a proportion to solve for a. $\frac{-a}{3} = \frac{20}{30} \rightarrow -30a = 60a \rightarrow a = -2$
Step 2: Set up a proportion to solve for b. $\frac{4}{-b} = \frac{20}{30} \rightarrow 120 = -20b \rightarrow b = -6$
Step 3: Solve for $a + b$. $(-2) + (-6) = -8$

10. **B** Step 1: Rewrite the second equation into $y = mx + b$ form. $gx + 9y = z \rightarrow y = -\frac{g}{9}x + \frac{z}{9}$
Step 2: Set up a proportion to solve for g by setting the slopes equal to each other. $-\frac{g}{9} = 2 \rightarrow g = -18$
Step 3: Set up a proportion to solve for k by setting the y-intercepts equal. $\frac{z}{9} = k$

Chapter 14 – Solving for Constants (Pages 87 – 89)

1. **D** Step 1: Distribute. $2x^2 - 2x + 2x + 8 = ax^2 + bx + c \rightarrow 2x^2 + 8 = ax^2 + bx + c$. We see that $b = 0$ since there are no x-values.
Step 2: Solve for a and c. For a: $2x^2 = ax^2 \rightarrow a = 2$. For c: $c = 8$
Step 3: $a - b + c = 2 - 0 + 8 = 10$

2. **A** Step 1: Distribute the a. $8x + 6 = a(-3x + 2) - x \rightarrow 8x + 6 = -3ax + 2a - x$
Step 2: Solve for a. Use the x-values. For no solution, the coefficients for the variables on both sides of the equation must be the same but the numbers must be different. $8x = -3ax - x \rightarrow 9x = -3ax \rightarrow -3 = a$

3. **C** Step 1: Distribute the 3. $ax + 3(3x - 2) = 5x + b \rightarrow ax + 9x - 6 = 5x + b$
Step 2: Solve for b. Use the numbers and b. For infinite solutions, the two equations must be completely identical. $b = -6$
Step 3: Solve for a. Use the x-values. $ax + 9x = 5x \rightarrow ax = -4x \rightarrow a = -4$
Step 4: $a + b = -4 + -6 = -10$

4. **B** Step 1: Distribute the 6 and the a. $6(2x - 17) = a(5x + 1) \rightarrow 12x - 102 = 5ax + a$
Step 2: For no solution, the coefficients of the variables must be the same, but the numbers must be different. Set the x-terms equal and solve for a. $12x = 5ax \rightarrow a = \frac{12}{5} = 2.4$

5. **D** Step 1: FOIL the left side of the equation. $(3x - b)(x + 2) = 3x^2 + 4x - 4$ →
$3x^2 - bx + 6x - 2b = 3x^2 + 4x - 4$
Step 2: Use either the x-terms or the numbers to solve for b. The numbers are easier, so we will set the numbers equal to solve for b. $-2b = -4$ → $b = 2$

6. **D** Step 1: Use the -5 is a zero statement. If -5 is a zero, that means when $x = -5$, $F(-5) = 0$.
Step 2: Plug in $x = -5$ and $F(x) = 0$ and solve for a. $0 = (-5)^2 - a(-5) + 15$ → $0 = 25 + 5a + 15$ →
$-5a = 40$ → $a = -8$

7. **A** Step 1: FOIL the left side of the equation. $(ax - 6)(bx + 3) = -2.75x^2 - 14.25x - 18$ →
$abx^2 - 6bx + 3ax - 18 = -2.75x^2 - 14.25x - 18$
Step 2: Use the x^2 terms of the equation to solve for ab. $abx^2 = -2.75x^2$ → $ab = -2.75$

8. **B** Step 1: Distribute the 4. $ax^2 + 4(3x^2 + 2b) = 15x^2 + 24$ → $ax^2 + 12x^2 + 8b = 15x^2 + 24$
Step 2: Use the x^2 terms to solve for a. $ax^2 + 12ax^2 = 15x^2$ → $ax^2 = 3x^2$ → $a = 3$

9. **A** Step 1: Distribute the $4x$. $-7x^4 + 4x(ax^3 + b) = 13x^4 + 24x$ → $-7x^4 + 4ax^4 + 4bx = 13x^4 + 24x$
Step 2: Solve for b by setting the x-terms equal. $4bx = 24x$ → $b = 6$
Step 3: Solve for a by setting x^4 terms equal. $-7x^4 + 4ax^4 = 13x^4$ → $4ax^4 = 20x^4$ → $a = 5$
Step 4: $a + b = 5 + 6 = 11$

10. **D** For no real solution, the variables must have the same coefficients but numbers must be different. Since the numbers are already different, the coefficients of the variables must be the same. $3x^2 = ax^2$ → $a = 3$

11. **C** Set the two equations equal to each other to solve for b. $\frac{1}{3}a^2 - 5 = \frac{1}{3}(a - b)(a + b)$ →
$\frac{1}{3}a^2 - 5 = \frac{1}{3}(a^2 - b^2)$ → $\frac{1}{3}a^2 - 5 = \frac{1}{3}a^2 - \frac{1}{3}b^2$ → $-5 = -\frac{1}{3}b^2$ → $15 = b^2$ → $b = \sqrt{15}$

12. **D** Step 1: Add like terms. $(x^3 + ax^2 + 5ax - 4) + (2x^3 + bx^2 - bx - 3) = 3x^3 + 8x^2 + 10x - 7$ →
$3x^3 + ax^2 + bx^2 + 5ax - bx - 7 = 3x^3 + 8x^2 + 10x - 7$
Step 2: Set up a system of equations to solve for a and b. When setting up the system of equations, use the like terms for each equation. The first equation will use the x^2 terms and the second will use the x-terms.
First equation: $ax^2 + bx^2 = 8x^2$ → $a + b = 8$
Second equation: $5ax - bx = 10x$ → $5a - b = 10$
Step 3: Solve the system of equations.
$a + b = 8$
$+ 5a - b = 10$
$\overline{6a = 18}$ → $a = 3$
Step 4: Plug $a = 3$ into either equation to solve for b. $3 + b = 8$ → $b = 5$

13. **C** Step 1: Distribute the $-5x$. $23x - 5x(a + 2) = 4x$ → $23x - 5ax - 10x = 4x$
Step 2: For infinite solutions, the coefficients for the x-terms need to be the same. Solve for a.
$23x - 5ax - 10x = 4x$ → $23x - 5ax = 14x$ → $-5ax = -9x$ → $a = \frac{9}{5}$

14. **A** Step 1: Distribute the 3. $5x - 3(ax + b) = -31x + 30$ → $5x - 3ax - 3b = -31x + 30$
Step 2: Solve for b by setting the numbers equal. $-3b = 30$ → $b = -10$
Step 3: Solve for a by setting the x-terms equal. $5x - 3ax = -31x$ → $-3ax = -36x$ → $a = 12$
Step 4: $b - a = -10 - 12 = -22$

15. **3** Plug in $x = 5$. $ax^2 + 5x = 115 - 5a$ → $a(25) + 5(5) = 115 - 5a$ →
$25a + 25 = 115 - 5a$ → $30a = 90$ → $a = 3$

16. **D** Step 1: Recognize what to look for. If no value of x satisfies the equation, this equation has no real solution. The coefficients for the variables must be the same but the numbers must be different for the two sides of the equation.
Step 2: Distribute the values. $\frac{1}{3}ax - 12 = 3(x + 4) - 3(1 - 3x)$ →
$\frac{1}{3}ax - 12 = 3x + 12 - 3 + 9x$ → $\frac{1}{3}ax - 12 = 12x + 9$
Step 3: Since the coefficients for the variables must be the same, set the x-terms equal and solve for a.
$\frac{1}{3}ax = 12x$ → $a = 36$

Chapter 15 – Functions (Pages 93 – 96)

1. **25** $f(4) = 2(4^2) - 7 = 32 - 7 = 25$
2. **103** $g(-31) = -3(-31) + 10 = 103$
3. **193** $f(-10) = 2(-10)^2 - 7 = 193$

4. **−22** $h(-19) = -19 - 3 = -22$

5. **$18x^2 - 7$** $f(3x) = 2(3x)^2 - 7 = 18x^2 - 7$

6. **$-3x + 19$** $g(x - 3) = -3(x - 3) + 10 = -3x + 9 + 10 = -3x + 19$

7. **−2** $-5 = x - 3 \to x = -2$

8. **−7** $31 = -3x + 10 \to 21 = -3x \to x = -7$

9. **5, −5** $43 = 2x^2 - 7 \to 2x^2 = 50 \to x^2 = 25 \to x = 5, -5$

10. **7** $-11 = -3x + 10 \to -21 = -3x \to x = 7$

11. **52** $g(h(-11)) = -3(-11 - 3) + 10 = -3(-14) + 10 = 52$

12. **$8x^2 - 24x + 11$** Step 1: Find $f(h(x))$. $f(h(x)) = 2(x - 3)^2 - 7 = 2(x^2 - 6x + 9) - 7 = 2x^2 - 12x + 18 - 7 = 2x^2 - 12x + 11$

    Step 2: Find $f(h(2x))$. $f(h(2x)) = 2(2x)^2 - 12(2x) + 11 = 8x^2 - 24x + 11$

13. **91** $f(h(-4)) = 2((-4 - 3)^2) - 7 = 2((-7)^2) - 7 = 2(49) - 7 = 91$

14. **$\frac{1}{3}$** Step 1: Find $g(h(x))$. $g(h(x)) = -3(x - 3) + 10 = -3x + 9 + 10 = -3x + 19$

    Step 2: Solve for $g(h(x)) = 18$. $18 = -3x + 19 \to -3x = -1 \to x = \frac{1}{3}$

15. **$-54x^2 + 31$** Step 1: Find $g(f(x))$. $g(f(x)) = -3(2x^2 - 7) + 10 = -6x^2 + 21 + 10 = -6x^2 + 31$

    Step 2: Solve for $g(f(3x))$. $g(f(2x)) = -6(3x)^2 + 31 = -6(9x^2) + 31 = -54x^2 + 31$

16. **B** $f(2) = 2^2 - 4(2) = -4$

17. **C** $g(f(2)) = 2(2(2^2) + 2) - 1 = 2(10) - 1 = 19$

18. **B** $y = \frac{x+1}{3}$ $f(x)$ is the same as y. Rewrite the equation this way so it will be easier to work through when we switch the places of x and y. $x = \frac{y+1}{3} \to 3x = y + 1 \to 3x - 1 = y$

19. **C** $f(g(5)) = 3(2(5) - 3) + 7 = 3(7) + 7 = 28$

20. **A** $\frac{x^2+10x-24}{x^2-4} = \frac{(x+12)(x-2)}{(x+2)(x-2)} = \frac{x+12}{x+2}$

21. **D** $g(3) = 10 - f(3) = 10 - (-5(3) + 2) = 10 - (-13) = 23$

22. **A** $h(-2x) = 4(-2x) - 7 = -8x - 7$

23. **B** The minimum of the graph is where $x = 3$ so $k = 3$. $g(3) = 2(3) - 7 = -1$

24. **D** $g(h(6)) = g(5) = 11$. Since $h(6) = 5$ so we can rewrite $g(h(6))$ as $g(5)$. We know that $g(5) = 11$

25. **D** Plug in the values from the table. $t(4) = 9$ and $p(4) = -7 \to 9 + (-7) = 2$

26. **B** Step 1: Solve for b using $p(2) = 5$. $5 = 2^2 + 2(2) - b \to 5 = 4 + 4 - b \to 5 = 8 - b \to -3 = -b \to 3 = b$

    Step 2: Solve for $p(-3)$. $p(-3) = (-3)^2 + 2(-3) - 3 = 9 - 6 - 3 = 0$

27. **C** $f(-3) = 3(-3^2) + 3(-3) + 10 = 27 - 9 + 10 = 28$

28. **D** $f(-3) = -6(-3^3) + 2(-3^2) = 162 + 18 = 180$

29. **B** Method 1: The easiest way to solve a question like this is to plug in values from the table into the answer choices to see which one is correct for multiple values of x. $6(2) - 1 = 11$. $6(4) - 1 = 23$. $6(6) - 1 = 35$

    Method 2: $g(x)$ is the same as y. Find the slope. $m = \frac{23-11}{4-2} = \frac{12}{2} = 6$. At this point, B has a slope of 6 so it has to be correct. To solve out completely, use point-slope form. $y - 11 = 6(x - 2) \to y - 11 = 6x - 12 \to y = 6x - 1$

30. **D** Method 1: We do not get real numbers when the denominator is equal to 0. The easy way to solve this question is to plug in answer choices and see which answers give values of 0 for the denominator.

    Method 2: Factor denominator to find x-values that make denominator equal to zero and are not part of domain. $x^3 - 16x = 0 \to x(x^2 - 16) = 0 \to x(x - 4)(x + 4) = 0 \to x = 0, 4, -4$

31. **B** Method 1: Plug in numbers starting from 1 and working up until you get to a positive value. 5 is the first value that is positive. 1, 2, 3, and 4 all are negative therefore there are 4 values that are negative.

    Method 2: Algebra. $3z - 13 < 0 \to 3z < 13 \to z < 4.33$. Only 4 possible values (1, 2, 3, and 4) are less than 4.33.

32. **D** $f(g(\frac{1}{4})) = \frac{1}{\frac{1}{4}} + \frac{1}{2(\frac{1}{\frac{1}{4}})} = 4 + \frac{1}{2(4)} = 4 + \frac{1}{8} = 4\frac{1}{8}$

33. **D** Step 1: Find the slope. $m = \frac{19-10}{1-(-2)} = \frac{9}{3} = 3$

Step 2: Use point-slope form to find the equation of the line. We will use point $(-2, 10)$.

$y - 10 = 3\big(x - (-2)\big)$ → $y - 10 = 3x + 6$ → $y = 3x + 16$ → $k(x) = 3x + 16$

Step 3: $k(4) = 3(4) + 16 = 28$

34. **A** Insert 3 for x and 17 for $f(x)$. $17 = 2a(3)^2 - 5(3) - 4$ → $17 = 2a(9) - 15 - 4$ → $17 = 18a - 19$ → $36 = 18a$ → $a = 2$

35. **D** $f(-4) = 1$, $f\left(-\frac{5}{2}\right) = -1$, and $f(4) = -1$. By asking for $f(-4)$, $f\left(-\frac{5}{2}\right)$, and $f(4)$, the question is asking you to look at the graph at the x-value of -4, $-\frac{5}{2}$, and 4 and determine the y-value.

36. **A** $f\big(g(x)\big) = \sqrt{4x + b}$ → $f\big(g(5)\big) = \sqrt{4(5) + b}$ → $4 = \sqrt{4(5) + b}$ → $16 = 4(5) + b$ → $16 = 20 + b$ → $b = -4$

37. **18** $f(x - 2) = 3(x - 2)^2 - 5(x - 2) + 10 = 3(x^2 - 4x + 4) - 5x + 10 + 10 = 3x^2 - 12x + 12 - 5x + 20 = 3x^2 - 17x + 32$ → $3x^2 - 17x + 32 = ax^2 + bx + c$

$a = 3$, $b = -17$, $c = 32$ → $3 + (-17) + 32 = 18$

38. **D** $f(x) = g(x)$ when the two lines intersect. The two points of intersection are when $x = 6, 12$

39. **A** Method 1: The easiest way to solve this question is to plug the numbers from the table into the equations. Make sure to check multiple pairs of values from the table as typically multiple answers will work for a single pair of values. For the point $(1, 3)$: $3 = (1 - 3)^2 - 1$ → $3 = 2^2 - 1$ → $3 = 3$

For the point $(3, -1)$: $-1 = (3 - 3)^2 - 1$ → $-1 = -1$

For the point $(5, 3)$: $3 = (5 - 3)^2 - 1$ → $3 = 2^2 - 1$ → $3 = 3$

Method 2: Spot that the vertex of the parabola is at $(3, -1)$ by noticing that points $(1,3)$ $(5,3)$ are equidistant from $(3, -1)$.

40. **36** Insert 18 for $f(x)$ and 3 for x in the equation. $18 = k - 2(3^2)$ → $18 = k - 18$ → $36 = k$

41. **1** Insert 8 for $f(x)$ and 2 for x in the equation. $8 = 2(2^3) - t(2) - 6$ → $8 = 16 - 2t - 6$

$8 = 10 + 2t$ → $-2 = -2t$ → $t = 1$

42. **6** $3g(4) = g(5(4))$ → $3g(4) = g(20)$ → $3g(4) = 18$ → $g(4) = 6$

43. **5** To solve for the undefined value(s) of an equation, set the denominator equal to zero and solve for x.

$(x - 3)^2 - 4(x - 2) + 8 = 0$ → $x^2 - 6x + 9 - 4x + 8 + 8 = 0$ → $x^2 - 10x + 25 = 0$ → $(x - 5)(x - 5) = 0$ → $x = 5$

Chapter 16 – Mean, Median, Mode, and Range (Pages 101 – 104)

1. **A** $2 = \frac{10+x}{8}$ → $10 + x = 16$ → $x = 6$

2. **D** Increasing the highest value and decreasing the lowest value will never affect the median because those will not change the order of the numbers from smallest to largest. If we decreased e, it could become less than c. The same reasoning applies to increasing the value of a and increasing the value of b except in this case they could both become greater than c.

3. **B** To find the total number of the brownies John produces per day, multiply his hours by the number of brownies he produces per hour $= 7x$

To find the total number of the brownies Karen produces per day, multiply her hours by the number of brownies she produces per hour $= 6y$

To find the average per hour, add the total number of brownies produced by John and Karen and divide by the total number of hours for John and Karen. $\frac{7x+6y}{7+6} = \frac{7x+6y}{13}$

4. **4.5** Step 1: Find x. $62, 68, 68, 70, 76, 79$. To find the median, average the two middle values. $\frac{68+70}{2} = 69$

Step 2: Find y. $58, 61, 63, 66, 67, 68$. To find the median, average the two middle values. $\frac{63+66}{2} = 64.5$

Step 3: Solve for $x - y$. $69 - 64.5 = 4.5$

5. **A** Outliers can either drag the average significantly higher or lower than the median. Since the mean is higher than the median, there are some very expensive cars making the mean higher than the median.

6. **C** The median will be unchanged because only the values higher than the median were increased. This will not change the median. All other answer choice will increase by different amounts.

7. **A** To solve this question we would set up this equation: $\frac{4,500+2,800+2,400+x}{4} \geq 3,000$

The answer choice of A is a different form of the same equation: $4,500 + 2,800 + 2,400 + x \geq 4(3,000)$

8. **D** Increasing the largest number in a set of numbers will never affect the median since it will not affect the order of numbers from smallest to largest.

9. **C** Step 1: Find which student will be the median. $\frac{21+1}{2} = 11$

   Step 2: Add the frequency column until you find where the 11th student will fall. $6 + 3 + 1 = 10$ so at 2 iPhones, we have yet to hit the portion of the table where the 11th student is. $10 + 5 = 15$ This tells us the 11th student will be in the group that has 3 iPhones.

10. **B** $\frac{x+y}{2} \rightarrow \frac{k+8+3k+12}{2} = \frac{4k+20}{2} = 2k + 10$

11. **B** Find where the median will be. $\frac{80+1}{2} = 40.5$ The median would be the average of the 40th and 41st person. Therefore, the median would fall somewhere between 50 and 100. 18 people scored above that median range and there were two outliers scoring significantly higher, which would bring the average up, making the median less than the mean.

12. **C** Step 1: Find the total weight of each production run.

    Production Run A: $\frac{total\ weight}{35} = a \rightarrow total\ weight = 35a$.

    Production Run B: $\frac{total\ weight}{15} = b \rightarrow total\ weight = 15b$

    Step 2: Solve for the average of the production runs. $w = \frac{2(35a)+1(15b)}{2(35)+1(15)} \rightarrow w = \frac{70a+15b}{85}$

13. **A** Increasing the largest number in a set of numbers never affects the median because it does not affect the order of numbers from smallest to largest.

14. **C** $\frac{280+360+240+320}{4} = 300$

15. **A** The median is 8 since it is the middle number. To find the mean: $\frac{4+7+8+9+12}{5} = 8 \rightarrow 8 - 8 = 0$

16. **C** Step 1: Find the amount Ashley has saved. $5(15) + 5(19) + 5(23) = 285$

    Step 2: Find the amount Ashley wanted to save. $20 \times 15 = 300$

    Step 3: Find how much more Ashley should have saved. $300 - 285 = 15$

    Step 4: Find How much more Ashley should have saved per week. $\frac{15}{15} = 1$

17. **D** $\frac{99+86+93+89+92+x}{6} = 93 \rightarrow 99 + 86 + 93 + 89 + 92 + x = 558 \rightarrow 459 + x = 558 \rightarrow x = 99$

18. **B** Step 1: Find the total number of points scored by all 10 students. $10(23.8) = 238$

    Step 2: Find the total number of points scored by the other 9 students. $9(23) = 207$

    Step 3: Find the difference to find how many points the highest scorer had. $238 - 207 = 31$

19. **C** Step 1: Find where the median will be. $\frac{50+1}{2} = 25.5$. This means the median is going to be the average of the 25th and 26th numbers in the list when ordered from smallest to largest.

    Step 2: Find where the 25th and 26th numbers are when ordered from smallest to largest. Both numbers are in the 11-15 range. $4 + 11 + 8 = 23$ and $23 + 9 = 32$ so both are contained in the 11-15 range.

20. **C** $0(3) + 0(10) + 20(1) + 30(2) + 50(3) + 100(1) = 330$

21. **C** Step 1: Find where the median will be. $\frac{10+1}{2} = 5.5$ This means that the median is going to be the average of the 5th and 6th numbers in the list when ordered from smallest to largest.

    Step 2: Find where the 5th and 6th numbers are when ordered from smallest to largest. $3 + 1 = 4$ and $4 + 2 = 6$ so both the 5th and the 6th numbers are in the 30-point range.

22. **3.5** Step 1: Solve for the mean of the masses that Mike obtained. $\frac{8.3+7.8+9.2+7.6+8.1}{5} = 8.2$

    Step 2: Use the mean from Mike to find the mean for Aaron. $\frac{8.2}{2} = 4.1$

    Step 3: Solve for the value of x. $\frac{5.2+3.5+4.4+3.9+x}{5} = 4.1 \rightarrow 17 + x = 20.5 \rightarrow x = 3.5$

23. **70** Step 1: Find the total number of points the entire class must score. $85 \times 20 = 1700$

    Step 2: Figure out how many points have already been scored by the class. $15 \times 82 = 1230$

    Step 3: Find the difference between the two. $1700 - 1230 = 470$

    Step 4: Solve for the lowest possible score the 16th student can receive. $100 + 100 + 100 + 100 + x \geq 470$ In order to find the lowest score the 16th student can receive, use the maximum score (100 points) for the other four students. $400 + x \geq 470 \rightarrow x \geq 70$ so the lowest possible score the 16th student could score is 70.

Chapter 17 – Geometry Part 1 – Angles (Pages 108 – 110)

1. **C** Use the total interior angles of a triangle to solve for x. $2x + x + 45 = 180 \rightarrow 3x = 135 \rightarrow x = 45$
2. **D** Step 1: Recognize that angle x is the same as the adjacent angle to the left of 40°.
   Step 2: $40 + x = 180 \rightarrow x = 140$
3. **C** Use the 90-degree angle to solve for x. $90 = 2x + 20 \rightarrow x = 35$
4. **B** Method 1: Identify that $\angle EAD$ and $\angle BCE$ are alternate interior angles, so $\angle EAD = \angle BCE = 32$
   Method 2: Step 1: Identify that triangle AED is isosceles because $AE = DE$. Therefore, $\angle EAD = \angle EDA = 32$
   and $\angle AED = 116$.
   Step 2: Identify that triangle BEC is isosceles because $BE = CE$ and solve for angle measures.
   $\angle AED = \angle BEC = 116$. Therefore, since $BE = CE$, $\angle BCE = \frac{180-116}{2} = 32$

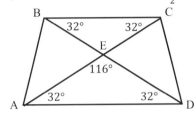

5. **D** Step 1: Use the vertical angle rules to find $\angle JLK = 40°$.
   Step 2: Use the total interior angles of a triangle to solve for $\angle JKL$. $180 - 40 - 45 = 95$
6. **D** Step 1: Using the alternate interior angle theorem, identify the top angle is $54°$.
   Step 2: Using the exterior angle theorem. $x = 30 + 54 \rightarrow x = 84$
   Alternatively, use the total interior angles of a triangle to solve for the adjacent angle to x, which equals $96°$.
   Then, solve for x. $180 - 96 = 84$

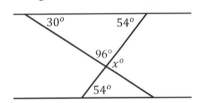

7. **C** Step 1: Using the supplementary angle theorem, identify the angle adjacent to $155°$ is equal to $25°$.
   Step 2: Using the alternate interior angle theorem, identify the top angle is $155°$
   Step 3: Using the sum of the interior angles, solve for b. $360 - 155 - 25 - 43 = 137$

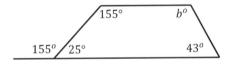

8. **B** This is the exterior angle theorem.
9. **129** Step 1: Solve for the missing angle in the rightmost triangle. $180 - 63 - 90 = 27$
   Step 2: Solve for the left most missing angle. $180 - 102 - 27 = 51$
   Step 3: Use the opposite interior angle theorem to solve for x. $180 - 51 = 129$

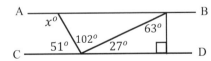

10. **A** Step 1: $\angle EAB = \angle EDB = 125$
   Step 2: Use the opposite interior angle theorem to solve for $\angle ABD$. $180 - 125 = 55$
   Step 3: Using the supplementary angle theorem solve for $\angle CDB$. $180 - 125 = 55$
   Step 4: Use the total interior angles of the triangle to solve for $\angle DBC$. $180 - 55 - 42 = 83$
   Step 5: Add angles $\angle ABD$ and $\angle DBC$ to find $\angle ABC$. $55 + 83 = 138$

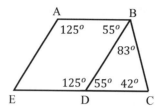

11. **135** Step 1: $\angle ABE = 180 - 130 = 50°$ Therefore, $\angle AEB = 180 - 45 - 50 = 85$
   Step 2: Use the opposite interior angles theorem to solve for $\angle BED = 180 - 130 = 50$.
   Step 3: Add angles $\angle AEB$ and $\angle BED$ to find the measure of $\angle AED$. $85 + 50 = 135$

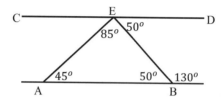

12. **B** Step 1: Plug in the values for x and y.
   Step 2: To find x, use the supplementary angle rule. $180 - 148 = 32$
   Step 3: To find y, use the total interior angles of triangle. $180 - 32 - 70 = 78$
   Step 4: Solve for z. Either identify that these are similar triangles where z is a corresponding angle to the $78°$ or use the corresponding angle theorem since lines k and m are parallel lines intersected by a transversal line.

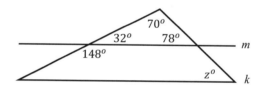

13. **D** Step 1: Use the total interior angles of triangle BAC to solve for angle $\angle BCA$. $180 - 79 - 22 = 79$
   Step 2: Solve for $\angle DCE$ using the supplementary angle theorem. $180 - 79 = 101$
   Step 3: Use the total interior angles of triangle DCE to solve for angle $\angle CDE$. $180 - 101 - 15 = 64$

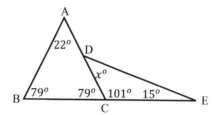

14. **A** Solve for x using the total interior angles of a quadrilateral. $x = \frac{360-54}{3} = 102$
15. **C** Step 1: Use the supplementary angle theorem to solve for x. $6x + 12x = 180 \rightarrow x = 10 \rightarrow \angle MNL = 60$
   Step 2: Use the total interior angles of a triangle to solve for $\angle M$. $180 - 35 - 60 = 85$
16. **D** Use the total interior angles of a pentagon. The total interior angles in a pentagon is $180°(5-2) = 540°$.
   $540 = x + 2.2x + 1.2x + 1.7x + 1.9x \rightarrow x = 67.5$

17. **C** Step 1: Extend a line from AB down further and a line from CD until they intersect at a new point which will refer to as point G, forming a triangle (shown below).
Step 2: Use the triangle to solve for the measure of $\angle BGC$. The adjacent angle next to $129°$ will be equivalent to $180 - 129 = 51$. Therefore, using the total interior angles of a triangle, $\angle BGC = 180 - 53 - 51 = 76$
Step 3: To solve for $\angle CDE$, use the opposite interior triangle theorem. The measure of $\angle BGC$ and $\angle CDE$ must add up to $180°$. $\angle CDE = 180 - 76 = 104$

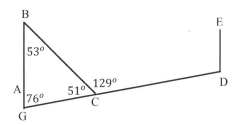

18. **C** Step 1: Use the total interior angles of the hexagon to solve for the remaining two angles.
$180(6 - 2) = 720 \rightarrow 720 - 65 - 70 - 95 - 110 = 380$

19. **C** Step 1: Solve for $\angle DGH$ using the supplementary angle theorem. $180 - 106 = 74$
Step 2: Use the total interior angles of triangle DEF to solve for angle $\angle EDG$. $180 - 35 - 90 = 55$
Step 3: Use the total interior angles of triangle DGH to solve for angle $\angle DHG$. $180 - 74 - 55 = 51$
Step 4: Identify that due to the corresponding angle theorem $\angle DHG = \angle ABC = 51$
Step 5: Use the total interior angles of triangle ACB to solve for angle $\angle ACB$. $180 - 61 - 51 = 68$

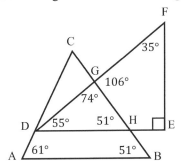

20. **D** The key to working through this question and many tricky angles questions on the SAT is using all of the different triangles. Take a look back with that in mind and see if you can solve it.
Below shows all of the angles that you need to solve for.

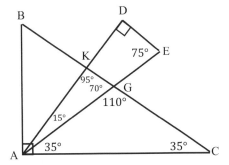

Step 1: Solve for $\angle CAG = 35°$ using the isosceles triangle given that $AG = CG$.
Step 2: Solve for $\angle AGC = 110°$ using the total interior angles of a triangle. $180 - 35 - 35 = 110$
Step 3: Solve for $\angle AGK = 70°$ using the supplementary angle theorem. $180 - 110 = 70$
Step 4: Solve for $\angle EAD = 15°$ using the total interior angles of a triangle. $180 - 90 - 75 = 15$
Step 5: Solve for $\angle AKG = 95°$ using the total interior angles of a triangle. $180 - 15 - 70 = 95$
Step 6: Solve for $\angle AKB = 85°$ using the supplementary angle theorem. $180 - 95 = 85$

Chapter 18 – Geometry Part 2 – Shapes (Pages 118 – 121)

1. **C** Step 1: Use the area of the rectangle to solve for x. $(20x)(2) = 80 \rightarrow 40x = 80 \rightarrow x = 2$
Step 2: Solve for the shaded region. $2 \times 6(2) = 24$

2. **D** Step 1: Use the circumference formula to solve for the radius. $C = 2\pi r \rightarrow 12\pi = 2\pi r \rightarrow r = 6$
Step 2: Use the area formula to solve for the area. $A = \pi r^2 \rightarrow A = \pi(6)^2 \rightarrow A = 36\pi$

3. **D** Without knowing the given angles, it is impossible to solve for the third side of a triangle. Using the third side of the triangle rule of $a + b > c$, the third side length could be defined as x where $2 < x < 14$.

4. **C** Step 1: Find the area of all of the circles using the area formula of $A = \pi r^2$. The largest circle has an area of 100π. The area of each of the two smaller circles is 4π.
Step 2: Solve for the area of the shaded region. $100\pi - 4\pi - 4\pi = 92\pi$

5. **A** Use the third side of the triangle rule of $a + b > c$. $5 + 7 \not> 12$.

6. **B** Step 1: Use circumference formula to find the radius. $16\pi = 2\pi r \rightarrow r = 8$
Step 2: Solve for the area. $A = \pi r^2 = \pi(8 \rightarrow A = 64\pi$
Step 3: Solve for half of the area. $0.5(64\pi) = 32\pi$

7. **B** Step 1: Solve for x using the two equivalent side lengths without k. $6x - 4 = 3x + 2 \rightarrow x = 2$
Step 2: Solve for the length of one side using $x = 2$. $6(2) - 4 = 8$
Step 3: Solve for k by setting the equation equal to the side length of 8. $2x^2 + k = 8 \rightarrow 2(2)^2 + k = 8 \rightarrow 8 + k = 8 \rightarrow k = 0$

8. **C** Step 1: Identify DCE and ACB are similar triangles.
Step 2: Use the proportions to solve for DE. $\frac{DC}{AC} = \frac{DE}{AB} \rightarrow \frac{3}{5} = \frac{x}{8} \rightarrow 5x = 24 \rightarrow x = \frac{24}{5}$

9. **C** Step 1: Identify the $30^\circ - 60^\circ - 90^\circ$ triangle and use the proportions to solve for the base and height of the triangle. $12 = 2x \rightarrow x = 6$ so height $= 6$ and base $= 6\sqrt{3}$
Step 2: Solve for the area. $A = \frac{1}{2}bh \rightarrow A = \frac{1}{2}(6)(6\sqrt{3}) \rightarrow A = 18\sqrt{3}$

10. **D** Step 1: Since the shape is a parallelogram and $\angle ABC = 110^\circ$, $\angle ADC = 110^\circ$
Step 2: Solve for the measure of $\angle ADE$ using the supplementary angle theorem. $180^\circ - 110^\circ = 70^\circ$
Step 3: Recognize that triangle AED is isosceles. Since $AD = AE$, $\angle ADE = \angle AED = 70^\circ$.
Step 4: Solve for the measure of $\angle EAD$ using the total interior angles of a triangle. $180^\circ - 70^\circ - 70^\circ = 40^\circ$

11. **A** Step 1: Use the $45^\circ - 40^\circ - 90^\circ$ triangle side length rules to find $AE = 4\sqrt{2}$ and of $DE = 4$.
Step 2: Solve for the length of EC. $10 - 4 = 6$
Step 3: Solve for the length of BC. $AD = BC = 4$
Step 4: Add up the values to find the perimeter. $AB + BC + EC + AE = 10 + 4 + 6 + 4\sqrt{2} = 20 + 4\sqrt{2}$

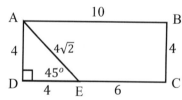

12. **D** Step 1: Use the right circular cylinder equation to solve for the original volume. $Q = \pi r^2 h$
Step 2: Solve for the volume of the new flowerpot based on the changes. $V = \pi(2r)^2(2h) \rightarrow V = 8\pi r^2 h$
The new volume is 8 times as large.

13. **A** Step 1: Draw out a triangle as shown below.

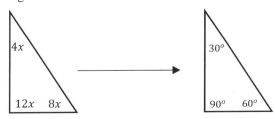

Step 2: Solve for x. $4x + 8x + 12x = 180^o \rightarrow x = 7.5$
Step 3: Solve for the corresponding angles which will result in the triangle on the right above.
Step 4: Use the $30^o - 60^o - 90^o$ ratio to solve for the second longest side given the shortest side is 6. The side opposite of $60°$ will equal $6\sqrt{3}$.

14. **25** Step 1: Solve for the length of AD using Pythagorean theorem. $6^2 + 8^2 = c^2 \rightarrow c = 10$
Step 2: Use the ratio of the similar triangles to solve for the length of AC. $\frac{BC}{ED} = \frac{AC}{AD} \rightarrow \frac{15}{6} = \frac{x}{10} \rightarrow$
$150 = 6x \rightarrow x = 25$

15. **A** Split the shape into two rectangles. Solve for the area of both rectangles and add them together.
$Small\ rectangle = 2.4 \times 4.7 = 11.28$
$Large\ recatngle = 2.3 \times 12.7 = 29.21$
$Total\ Area = 29.21 + 11.28 = 40.49$

16. **A** Use the volume equation to solve for the width. $V = lwh \rightarrow 2880 = (16)(w)(15) \rightarrow w = 12$
17. **A** Parallelograms have two pairs of equivalent sides. $60 = 2(20) + 2x \rightarrow x = 10 \rightarrow$
$20 + 20 + 10 + 10 = 60$
18. **C** Use the Pythagorean theorem to solve for the length of the fence. $12.5^2 + 6^2 = c^2 \rightarrow c = 13.87$
19. **15.4** $V = lwh \rightarrow 7,400 = (24)(20)(h) \rightarrow h = 15.4$
20. **C** Step 1: Express the sides of the rectangular prism in terms of one variable. $length = 3w,\ height = w,$
$width = w$
Step 2: Solve for w by using the rectangular prism volume equation. $V = lwh \rightarrow 81 = (3w)(w)(w) \rightarrow$
$81 = 3w^3 \rightarrow w = 3$
Step 3: Solve for l. $l = 3w \rightarrow l = 3(3) \rightarrow l = 9$
21. **D** Step 1: Solve for the volume of both cubes. $V = s^3$. Small cube: $5^3 = 125$. Large cube: $15^3 = 3375$.
Step 2: Solve for how many of the cubes with the side length of 5 can fit into one cube with a side length of 15.
$\frac{3375}{125} = 27$
22. **B** Step 1: Use the length of the diameter to find the area of the square by splitting up the square into 4 triangles as shown below.

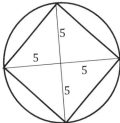

Step 2: Solve for the area of the square by either solving for the area of each of the 4 triangles and then multiplying by 4 or by solving for the two large triangles and multiplying by two.
$A = \frac{(5)(5)}{2}(4)$ or $A = \frac{(10)(5)}{2}(2) \rightarrow A = 50$

23. **C** Step 1: Find the area of both circles. 16-inch diameter circle $= \pi(8)^2 = 64\pi$
8-inch diameter circle $= \pi(4)^2 = 16\pi$

Step 2: Find the area of $\frac{1}{8}$ of the 16-inch diameter pie $= \frac{1}{8}(64\pi) = 8\pi$

Step 3: Find what fraction of the small pie is equal to 8π. $x(16\pi) = 8\pi \rightarrow x = \frac{1}{2}$

24. **C** Step 1: Identify the triangle is a $30^o - 60^o - 90^o$ triangle because a hexagon is made up of 6 equilateral triangles and triangle ABC is an equilateral triangle split down the middle.

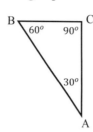

Step 2: Solve for the other side lengths using the $30^o - 60^o - 90^o$ triangle side length ratio. $20 = 2x \rightarrow x = 10 \rightarrow BC = 10$ and $AC = 10\sqrt{3}$.

Step 3: Solve for the area of the triangle. $A = \frac{1}{2}bh \rightarrow A = \frac{1}{2}(10)(10\sqrt{3}) \rightarrow A = 50\sqrt{3}$

25. **325** Step 1: Identify triangles ABC and DEC are similar.

Step 2: Use proportions to solve for x. $\frac{AB}{BC} = \frac{DE}{EC} \rightarrow \frac{x+4}{15} = \frac{x}{9} \rightarrow 9x + 36 = 15x \rightarrow x = 6$

Step 3: Plug in $x = 6$ to solve for AB. $AB = 6 + 4 = 10$

Step 4: Use Pythagorean theorem to solve for AC. $15^2 + 10^2 = c^2 \rightarrow c^2 = 325 \rightarrow c = \sqrt{325}$

Step 5: Since $AC = \sqrt{325} = \sqrt{a}$, $a = 325$.

26. **A** Use volume of a sphere equation to solve. $V = \frac{4}{3}\pi r^3 \rightarrow 950 = \frac{4}{3}\pi r^3 \rightarrow r = 6.1$

27. **C** Step 1: Solve for the diameter of the circle. $A = \pi r^2 \rightarrow 16\pi = \pi r^2 \rightarrow r = 4 \rightarrow d = 2r \rightarrow d = 8$

Step 2: Split the triangle down the middle to create two $30^o - 60^o - 90^o$ triangles

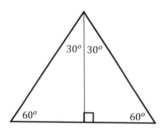

Step 3: Use the $30^o - 60^o - 90^o$ triangle side length ratio to solve. The side length opposite of $60°$ corresponds to the $x\sqrt{3}$. $8 = x\sqrt{3} \rightarrow x = \frac{8\sqrt{3}}{3} \rightarrow$ Base of the triangle $= 2\left(\frac{8\sqrt{3}}{3}\right) = \frac{16\sqrt{3}}{3}$

Step 4: Solve for the area of the triangle. $A = \frac{1}{2}bh \rightarrow A = \frac{1}{2}\left(\frac{16\sqrt{3}}{3}\right)(8) \rightarrow A = \frac{64\sqrt{3}}{3}$

28. **A** Step 1: Identify that since the triangles are all similar, they are all $30^o - 60^o - 90^o$ triangles.

Step 2: Use the ratio of $DF:CG$ and the length of DC to solve for the length of DE.
The ratio between any two corresponding sides of a similar triangle is the same ratio for all other corresponding sides of a similar triangle. $\frac{DE}{CD}$ has a ratio of $\frac{2}{3} \rightarrow \frac{DE}{18} = \frac{2}{3} \rightarrow DE = 12$

Step 3: Use the $30^o - 60^o - 90^o$ triangle side length ratio to solve for the length of DF. $12 = x \rightarrow DF$ corresponds to the side length opposite of $60°$ which is equivalent to $x\sqrt{3} \rightarrow DF = 12\sqrt{3}$

Step 4: Solve for the area of the triangle. $A = \frac{1}{2}bh \rightarrow A = \frac{1}{2}(12)(12\sqrt{3}) \rightarrow A = 72\sqrt{3}$

Chapter 19 – Arcs and Sectors (Pages 126 – 127)

For all of the answer explanations, the step of reducing the fraction is added since many of arcs and sectors questions occur in the no-calculator section. This step makes reaching the final answer significantly easier.

1. **A** Step 1: Set up the proportion: $\frac{x}{30\pi} = \frac{60}{360}$

    Step 2: Reduce the fraction and cross multiply. $\frac{x}{30\pi} = \frac{1}{6} \rightarrow 6x = 30\pi \rightarrow x = 5\pi$

2. **A** Step 1: Recognize that since the diameter is 12, the radius is 6.

    Step 2: Solve for x. $4x + 3x + 5x = 180 \rightarrow x = 15$

    Step 3: Using angle properties, the central angle of minor arc AB is equivalent to $8x$, which equals $120°$.

    Step 4: Set up the proportion and solve for x. $\frac{120}{360} = \frac{x}{12\pi} \rightarrow \frac{1}{3} = \frac{x}{12\pi} \rightarrow 3x = 12\pi \rightarrow x = 4\pi$

3. **B** Step 1: Use the length of AB to solve for the radius. Since AB is the diameter, the radius is 5.

    Step 2: Solve for the length of arc AB. The central angle is $180°$. The circumference of an entire circle with a radius of 5 would be 10π. Therefore, the arc AB, which makes up half of the circle, is 5π.

    Step 3: Add the arc length and the length of line AB to find perimeter. $5\pi + 10$

4. **C** $S = \frac{60}{360}\pi(6)^2 \rightarrow S = 6\pi$

5. **B** Step 1: Solve for the circumference. $2\pi(2) = 4\pi$

    Step 2: Set up the proportion and solve. $\frac{\frac{\pi}{2}}{4\pi} = \frac{x}{360} \rightarrow \frac{1}{8} = \frac{x}{360} \rightarrow 8x = 360 \rightarrow x = 45$

6. **6** $L = \frac{120}{360} \times 2\pi(9) \rightarrow L = 6\pi$ so $a = 6$.

7. **108** Recognize the proportion. Since the length of arc AC is $\frac{3}{10}$ of the circumference, the central angle must be

    $\frac{3}{10}$ of 360. $\frac{3}{10} = \frac{x}{360} \rightarrow x = 108$

8. **90** $\frac{x}{360} = \frac{16\pi}{64\pi} \rightarrow \frac{x}{360} = \frac{1}{4} \rightarrow 4x = 360 \rightarrow x = 90$

9. **B** $\frac{4}{24} = \frac{x}{360} \rightarrow \frac{1}{6} = \frac{x}{360} \rightarrow 6x = 360 \rightarrow x = 60$

10. **40** $\frac{360}{9} = 40$ The information about the calories is not needed.

11. **A** Step 1: Solve for $\angle POM = 30°$. Since PO and PM are both radii, $PO = PM$ and triangle PMO is isosceles.

    Step 2: Solve for $\angle MPO = 120°$ using the total interior angles of a triangle. $180° - 30° - 30° = 120°$

    Step 3: Solve for $\angle OPN = 60°$ using the supplementary angle theorem. $180° - 120° = 60°$

    Step 4: Solve for the length of arc NO. $L = \frac{60}{360} \times 2\pi(6) \rightarrow L = 2\pi$

12. **D** Step 1: The central angle of the sector ABCD is $210°$.

    Step 2: Set up the proportion and simplify the fraction to solve for x. $\frac{x}{36\pi} = \frac{210}{360} \rightarrow \frac{x}{36\pi} = \frac{21}{36} \rightarrow$

    $36x = 756\pi \rightarrow x = 21\pi$

13. **C** Solve using a proportion. $\frac{50}{4\pi} = \frac{310}{x} \rightarrow 50x = 1240\pi \rightarrow x = 24.8$

14. **72** Step 1: Solve for the length of arc ACB. Since the radius of the semicircle is 8, the length is 8π.

    Step 2: Solve for the measure of x using a proportion. $\frac{3.2\pi}{8\pi} = \frac{x}{180} \rightarrow 8\pi x = 576\pi \rightarrow x = 72$

15. **C** $\frac{135}{360} = \frac{3}{8}$

16. **C** $\frac{6}{18} = \frac{x}{360} \rightarrow \frac{1}{3} = \frac{x}{360} \rightarrow 3x = 360 \rightarrow x = 120$

Chapter 20 – Lines (Pages 134 – 137)

1. **A** $m = \frac{5-(-4)}{-7-1} = -\frac{9}{8}$

2. **C** Use the midpoint formula. $\left(\frac{2+6}{2}, \frac{6+10}{2}\right) = (4, 8)$

3. **C** Put into slope-intercept form. $3y - 4x = -6 \rightarrow 3y = 4x - 6 \rightarrow y = \frac{4}{3}x - 2$

4. $\frac{7}{3}$ **or 2.33** Put into slope-intercept form. $7x - 3y = 4 \rightarrow -3y = -7x + 4 \rightarrow y = \frac{7}{3}x - \frac{4}{3}$

5. **D** Use midpoint formula. $(2,4)$ is the midpoint, and the endpoint is $(-2,3)$. Place the points into the midpoint formula and solve for the missing endpoint. $\frac{2+x}{2} = -2$, $\frac{4+y}{2} = 3 \rightarrow 2+x = -4, 4+y = 6 \rightarrow$
$x = -6, y = 2$.

6. **C** The y-intercept is 4. Use 2 points to find the slope. We will use $(2,0)$ and $(0,4)$. $m = \frac{0-4}{2-0} = \frac{-4}{2} = -2$
so the line of the graph is $y = -2x + 4$

7. **A** Step 1: Solve for the slope. $m = \frac{28-10}{4-(-2)} = \frac{18}{6} = 3$
Step 2: Plug a point into point-slope form. Here, we will use $(-2,10)$. $y - 10 = 3(x - (-2)) \rightarrow$
$y - 10 = 3x + 6 \rightarrow y = 3x + 16$
Alternatively, use $y = mx + b$ and plug in a point after finding the slope. $10 = 3(-2) + b \rightarrow 16 = b \rightarrow$
$y = 3x + 16$

8. **B** The rate is the same as the slope. To find the slope, pick two points and solve for the slope. We will use
$(10, 50)$ and $(0,0)$. $m = \frac{50-0}{10-0} = 5$

9. **D** Andrew finishes the 100-meter race in 10 seconds. After 10 seconds, Stan has rowed 50 meters, so he needs a 50-meter head start.

10. **C** Since the line is parallel to the y-axis, it must be vertical. Since we are 4 units to the left of the y-axis, we have to be at $x = -4$.

11. $-\frac{5}{2}$ **or** -2.5 Use points $(0,6)$ and $(3,-1.5)$ to find the slope. $m = \frac{6-(-1,5)}{0-3} = \frac{7.5}{-3} = -\frac{5}{2}$

12. **D** Step 1: Solve for the slope of $f(x)$. You can use any two points, but we will use $(0,2)$ and $(2,1)$.
$m = \frac{2-1}{0-2} = -\frac{1}{2}$
Step 2: Solve for the slope of $g(x)$ by finding the negative reciprocal of the slope of $f(x)$. $-\frac{1}{2} \rightarrow \frac{2}{1} = 2$

13. **A** Step 1: Use point-slope form to find slope-intercept form. $y - (-7) = \frac{1}{3}(x - (-6)) \rightarrow$
$y + 7 = \frac{1}{3}x + 2 \rightarrow y = \frac{1}{3}x - 5$
Step 2: Multiply by 3 to convert slope-intercept form to standard form. $3(y) = 3\left(\frac{1}{3}x - 5\right) \rightarrow 3y = x - 15$
Step 3: Identify which equation is an equivalent form of the one we just found.

14. $\frac{12}{5}$ **or** 2.4 To find the x-intercept, set $y = 0$ and solve for x. $\frac{5}{4}x = 3 \rightarrow x = \frac{12}{5} = 2.4$

15. **C** Step 1: Solve for the slope of line a. You can use any two points. We will use $(0,-3)$ and $(1,-1)$.
$m = \frac{-3-(-1)}{0-1} = \frac{-2}{-1} = 2$
Step 2: Find the line that has the same slope.

16. $\frac{21}{4}$ Step 1: Find the slope of line t by putting it into slope-intercept form. $4x + 3y = 10 \rightarrow 3y = -4x + 10$
$\rightarrow y = -\frac{4}{3}x + \frac{10}{3}$. Since line v is perpendicular, the slope of line v is $\frac{3}{4}$.
Step 2: Use point-slope form to solve for the y-intercept. $y - 3 = \frac{3}{4}(x - (-3)) \rightarrow y - 3 = \frac{3}{4}x + \frac{9}{4} \rightarrow$
$y - \frac{12}{4} = \frac{3}{4}x + \frac{9}{4} \rightarrow y = \frac{3}{4}x + \frac{21}{4}$

17. **10** Step 1: Find the slope. $m = \frac{10-6}{0-4} = \frac{4}{-4} = -1$
Step 2: Use the point-slope form to find slope-intercept form. $y - 10 = -1(x - 0) \rightarrow$
$y - 10 = -x \rightarrow y = -x + 10$
Step 3. Plug in $y = 0$, $x = a$, and solve for a. $0 = -1a + 10 \rightarrow -10 = -a \rightarrow a = 10$

18. **34** Step 1: Put line l into slope-intercept form to find the slope. $x + 4y = -5 \rightarrow 4y = -x - 5 \rightarrow$
$y = -\frac{1}{4}x - \frac{5}{4}$
Step 2: Since lines l and k are parallel, line k also has a slope of $-\frac{1}{4}$. Use point-slope form.
$y - 8 = -\frac{1}{4}(x - 2) \rightarrow y - 8 = -\frac{1}{4}x + \frac{1}{2} \rightarrow y = -\frac{1}{4}x + \frac{17}{2}$
Step 3: Plug in $y = 0$ to solve for the x-intercept. $0 = -\frac{1}{4}x + \frac{17}{2} \rightarrow \frac{1}{4}x = \frac{17}{2} \rightarrow x = 34$

19. **B** (a,b) is the same as (x,y). Plug a in for x and b in for y and solve for k. $b = ka - 2 \rightarrow b + 2 = ka \rightarrow$
$\frac{b+2}{a} = k$

20. **A** $(2a, 6a)$ is the same as (x, y). Therefore, plug $2a$ in for x and $6a$ in for y. Use point-slope form since we have a point and the slope. $y - 6a = 3(x - 2a) \rightarrow y - 6a = 3x - 6a \rightarrow y = 3x + 0a$

21. **D** Use the distance formula. $d = \sqrt{(3 - (-9))^2 + (7 - (-2))^2} = \sqrt{12^2 + 9^2} = \sqrt{225}$

22. **C** Step 1: Use the distance formula. $d = \sqrt{(8 - (-2))^2 + (14 - 6)^2} = \sqrt{10^2 + 8^2} = 12.8$
    Step 2: Multiply by 10 to convert to miles. $12.8(10) = 128$

23. **D** Step 1: Put into slope-intercept form. $6x = 4y + 10 \rightarrow -4y = -6x + 10 \rightarrow y = \frac{3}{2}x - \frac{5}{2}$
    Step 2: The perpendicular slope is the negative reciprocal. $\frac{3}{2} \rightarrow -\frac{2}{3}$

24. **D** First, we want to pick a point on the line that contains two negative integers. An easy point to pick is $(-3, -9)$ since the graph passes through the origin and the positive point $(3, 9)$ is graphed. Since the coordinates are (h, k), $h = -3$ and $k = -9$. The ratio of $k : h$ is $-9 : -3$, which simplifies to $3 : 1$.

25. **D** Step 1: Find the slope-intercept form of line w. New slope $= \frac{1}{2}(6) = 3$ and new y-intercept $= 2(-4) = -8$. The slope-intercept form of line w is $y = 3x - 8$.
    Step 2: The fastest way to find the point of intersection is to set the two lines equal and solve for x.
    $6x - 4 = 3x - 8 \rightarrow 3x = -4 \rightarrow x = -\frac{4}{3}$
    At this point, we can look at the answer choices and know that the correct answer is D. To solve for y, plug $x = -\frac{4}{3}$ into either of the initial equations. $y = 6\left(-\frac{4}{3}x\right) - 4 \rightarrow y = -12$

26. **B** Step 1: Place the original equation into slope-intercept form to find the slope. $4x - 3y = 10 \rightarrow -3y = -4x + 10 \rightarrow y = \frac{4}{3}x - \frac{10}{3}$
    Step 2: Find the perpendicular slope. $\frac{4}{3} \rightarrow -\frac{3}{4}$
    Step 3: Put the answer choices into the slope-intercept form to find the one with a slope of $-\frac{3}{4}$.
    $6x + 8y = -7 \rightarrow 8y = -6x - 7 \rightarrow y = -\frac{6}{8}x - \frac{7}{8} \rightarrow y = -\frac{3}{4}x - \frac{7}{8}$

Chapter 21 – Interpreting Lines (Pages 141 – 144)

1. **C** Plug in what the variables represent in the equation. Hours fishing (x) + hours surfing $(y) = 200$

2. **C** 212.5 is the y-intercept and the y-intercept represents the initial value when $t = 0$.

3. **A** Step 1: The y-intercept is 28 since that is the initial value.
   Step 2: The slope is 2 since each layer (n) is 2 mm.

4. **B** Solve for the number of laps per minute. $\frac{60 \text{ seconds}}{20 \text{ seconds}} = 3$ lap per minute, so slope is equal to 3.

5. **B** 2.2 is the slope, which represents the change in the y value per unit of x. Since x is the number of weeks since Max has begun working at the bakery and y is the number of croissants he makes per day, the 2.2 means that he can make an additional 2.2 croissants per day for every additional week that he is working at his job.

6. **B** m is the slope because it is the rate of change per year. p is the y-intercept because it is the initial value.

7. **D** Identify the slope of the equation is 9, which displays the increase in a boy's weight per year. $9 \times 4 = 36$.
   Alternatively, solve for the weight of a boy at his 3rd and 7th birthdays and find the difference.
   3rd birthday: $w = 9(3) + 19.5 = 46.5$ 7th birthday: $w = 9(7) + 19.5 = 82.5 \rightarrow 82.5 - 46.5 = 36$

8. **A** Since m represents the number of movers and h is the total number of hours the job will take using m movers, the 25 represents how much the company is charging per hour for each mover.

9. **B** Solve for the slope of the line of best fit. The dots represent recorded values. Pick any two points on the line of best fit (do not use the dots unless they are on the line of best fit) and use the slope equation to solve for the slope. $(10, 35), (20, 50) \rightarrow \frac{50-35}{20-10} = 1.5$

10. **C** Use the smallest possible value for y to get the largest possible value for x. $800 = 8x + 6(40) \rightarrow 560 = 8x \rightarrow x = 70$

11. **D** 0.62 is the slope. For each one-inch increase in beak length, the wingspan increases by 0.62 feet. Alternatively, test the answer choices by plugging values into the equation to see if they are true. D works and can be checked by plugging in two values and any two values will work. We will use $b = 0$ and $b = 1$.
    $W(0) = 0.62(0) + 5 = 5 \rightarrow W(1) = .62(1) + 5 = 5.62$ so with a 1-inch increase in beak length, we see a 0.62 foot increase in wingspan.

12. **D** Step 1: The y-intercept is 48 since that is the initial value.
    Step 2: Solve for the slope using any of the points provided. $(0, 48), (2.5, 93)$ and $(4, 120) \rightarrow \frac{93-48}{2.5-0} = 18$

13. **B** Use the answer choices and check the statements in the answer choices by plugging them into the initial equation to see which one is correct. $-19(2) + 290 = 252$.

14. **A** Step 1: The y-intercept is at 21%. This means both C and D are wrong.
    Step 2: Solve for the slope. The slope statement is for every 1000 feet above sea level, the effective oxygen percentage drops by 0.9%. $m = \frac{0.9}{1000} = 0.0009$
    Alternatively, you can find points that must be on the graph and test the answer choices. Here, we know the point $(0, 21)$ must be on the graph. For a second point, we know that at 1000 feet, the effective oxygen level will be 20.1%, so we can also plug in the point $(1000, 20.1)$. Only A works with these points.

15. **A** Step 1: The y-intercept, which is the initial price for signing up, is 65.
    Step 2: Find the slope. Annie pays $200 every 4 weeks for 5 meals per week. Solve for the slope, which is the cost per meal. $m = \frac{200}{(5)(4)} = 10$

16. **A** 5.21 is slope. Since x is the number of years since 2005 and y represents the total number of turtles each year, 5.21 is the estimated increase in the number of turtles that came to the beach each year from 2005 to 2015.

17. **B** Use the demand function, identify the slope, and plug in the increase of 6 to find how the quantity demanded will change. $D(T) = 100 - \frac{3}{2}p. \rightarrow -\frac{3}{2}(6) = -9$. Alternatively, pick two prices 6 dollars apart and see how the demand changes.

18. **C** $2p$ is the slope of the function, so number of shoes supplied will increase by 2 for every additional \$1 increase in the price.

19. **A** The y-intercept represents the initial value when time rented equals zero. Therefore, it is the initial cost of renting a kayak.

20. **B** Step 1: Identify the y-intercept is 20.
    Step 2: Solve for the slope using any two point along the line. Using $(0, 20)$ and $(5, 80)$, $m = \frac{80-20}{5-0} = 12$

21. **C** Test to see which answer choice is correct by using the initial equation. B and D are incorrect because they say years rather than months. C is correct because $-180(6) = -1,080$

22. **A** Step 1: The y-intercept is 46 since that is the initial value when years $= 0$.
    Step 2: Solve for the slope using the two data points on the line. Since the initial height is 46 in, we know the point $(0, 46)$ is on the line. In 2012, the height is 104 in 2012, so $(72, 104)$ is on the line. $m = \frac{104-46}{72-0} = 0.806$

Chapter 22 – Exponential Growth and Decay (Pages 147 – 150)

1. **A** Step 1: The initial value is 5,436.
   Step 2: Add to 1 for a 3% increase. $1 + 0.03 = 1.03$

2. **D** Step 1: The initial value is 20,000.
   Step 2: Subtract from 1 for a 14% decrease. $1 - 0.14 = 0.86$

3. **D** Step 1: The initial value is 995.
   Step 2: Subtract from 1 for a 15% decrease. $1 - 0.15 = 0.85$

4. **C** Add to 1 for the 6% increase. $1 + 0.06 = 1.06$

5. **C** For exponential decrease, subtract from 1 for a 7% decrease. $1 - 0.07 = 0.93$
   After 5 days, the population decreases by 7%. Plug in 5 for t. In the correct answer, the exponent becomes $\frac{1}{5} \times 5 = 1$, so the equation will decrease by 7% every 5 days.

6. **B** The only element changed in the answer choices is the exponent. Solve for the number of 3-month periods in a year. $\frac{12}{3} = 4$. Alternatively, the investment must grow 7% after 3 months. Since 3 months is $\frac{1}{4}$ years, plug in $y = \frac{1}{4}$ to see which answer choice gives a 7% increase after 3 months.

7. **B** 7.86 is the initial value. The function is defined as the number of people who live within 15 miles of San Diego n years after 2017, so the initial value is for 2017.

8. **D** Step 1: The equation has a 2% increase given by the 1.02. Since the equation is giving the desired 2% percent increase, we want to make the exponent equal to 1 so as to not change the increase.
   Step 2: Identify what value of h will make the exponent equal to 1. $\frac{h}{5} \rightarrow \frac{5}{5} \rightarrow h = 5$
   Step 3: Convert 5 hours into minutes. $5 \times 60 = 300$.

9. **C** Subtract from 1 for a 50% decrease. $1 - 0.5 = 0.5$

10. **A** 15% decrease each time period is exponential. All other answer choices are linear.

11. **A** Step 1: Identify the initial value of 150,000.
Step 2: Solve for the number of doubling periods. $\frac{60}{20} = 3$

12. **D** $29,500(0.85)^3 \approx 18,100$

13. **A** Step 1: The initial value is 236.
Step 2: Add to 1 for a 0.8% increase. $1 + 0.008 = 1.008$. Since the rate is 0.8% since 1975, the same rate applies for every year since 1980 as well.

14. **A** Step 1: Solve for the percent increase over one two-month time period. $\frac{18-8}{8} = \frac{10}{8} = 1.25$ This tells us there is a 125% increase. $1 + 1.25 = 2.25$. A or B must be correct.
Step 2: Solve for the exponential portion of the equation. The easiest way is to plug in $m = 2$ to test which equation gives you the correct weight of 18. Exponent of $\frac{m}{2}$ will give the correct increase.

15. **D** Step 1: The initial value is 3.
Step 2: Add to 1 for an 8% increase. $1 + 0.08 = 1.08$
Step 3: Use the exponent to change the 8 percent increase every 16 years to every y years. $\frac{y}{16}$
Alternatively, the city population must increase 8% every 16 years, so plug in $y = 16$ and see which equation gives an 8% increase, which will occur when the initial value of 3 is multiplied by 1.08.

16. **C** Step 1: The initial value is 250.
Step 2: Correctly identify a doubling time of 14 days by checking to see which equation will double after plugging in $d = 14$: $N(14) = 250(2)^{\frac{14}{14}} \rightarrow N(14) = 500$

17. **D** Convert from y years to m months. Since there are 12 months in a year, the exponent must be $\frac{m}{12}$.
$N = 25(1.15)^y \rightarrow N = 25(1.15)^{\frac{m}{12}}$

18. **D** Step 1: The ship is doubling its speed every 73 days, so the value 35,000 will be multiplied by 2 after 73 days.
Step 2: Convert the doubling time of 73 days into years. 73 days is $\frac{1}{5}$th of a year. Plug in $y = \frac{1}{5}$ to the answer choices to see which one doubles the speed. D is correct because $5 \times \frac{1}{5} = 1$ and 2^1 will double the speed. Therefore, the value will double every fifth of a year. A and B are wrong because the exponents are in years but the increase in the speed of 0.096% is per day.

Chapter 23 – Scatter Plots (Pages 153 – 155)

1. **C** Count number of points above the line of best fit.

2. **C** Step 1: Identify the median will be the fifth point when they are ordered from smallest to largest. This is the point at (120,150).
Step 2: Find the difference in price, displayed by the y-coordinates, between the point and the line of best fit at $x = 120$.

3. **A** Find the slope by picking an approximate start and end point. You do not need to be very specific for questions like this, as only one answer choice will be close to the slope. Try to be smart about the points you pick. Here we will use $(0, 5)$ and $(15, 14)$. $\frac{14-5}{15-0} = 0.6$.

4. **A** Brownies are on the y-axis, so find where the y-value is equal to 60 on the line of best fit. When the y-value is 60, the x-value, which represents the number of minutes, is 40.

5. **3** Count the number of points below the line of best fit.

6. **B** Find the difference between the point, the actual value, and the line of best fit, the predicted value, at an x-value of 8. The difference is around 7.

7. **B** Step 1: Identify that the y-intercept cannot be visually identified since the x-value at the bottom left of the scatterplot graph is not 0. Many students mistakenly think the y-intercept is 50.
Step 2: Pick two approximate points of along where the line of best fit should be to find the slope of the line of best fit. Here, we will use the point $(7, 60)$ and $(9, 90)$. $\frac{90-60}{9-7} = 15$. This is closest to 14, so B must be the correct answer since we already know that the y-intercept is not 50. Step 3 below is how to algebraically finish in case you cannot tell from the answer choices.
Step 3: Use a point to solve for the y-intercept. We will use $(7, 60)$
$y = 14x + b \rightarrow 60 = 14(7) + b \rightarrow b = -38$, which is very close to -40, so B must be correct.

8. **A** Step 1: Identify the y-intercept is 13,400 since that is the average number of people crossing when $x = 0$. Step 2: Find the slope using any two points. Here, we will use $(2007, 13,400)$ and $(2011, 17,500)$. $\frac{17,500-13,400}{2011-2007} = 1,025$. Since the question asks for which equation best models, choose the slope that is closest.

9. **D** Step 1: Identify this is an exponential graph and 750 is the initial value. The correct answer must be C or D since A and B are both linear. C gives an 80% exponential decrease while D gives a 20% exponential decrease. Looking at the graph, you can tell D must be correct. You can calculate this decrease by finding the percent decrease from each point to the next point one year later. $\frac{750-600}{750} = 0.2$. Remember for exponential decay, the equation is $(1 - r)^x = (1 - 0.2)^x = 0.8^x$

10. **B** Method 1: Step 1: Pick two points to solve for the slope. Here, we will use $(15, 35)$ and $(17, 40)$. $\frac{40-35}{17-15} = \frac{5}{2}$
Step 2: Look at the y-intercept. Here, we see that the y-intercept is not at 22 since the x-value is 10 not 0. Therefore, B must be correct. You could also use point slope form. $y - 35 = \frac{5}{2}(x - 15) \rightarrow$
$y - 35 = \frac{5}{2}x - 37.5 \rightarrow y = \frac{5}{2}x - 2.5$
Method 2: Step 1: Look for the y-intercept. Here, we cannot find the y-intercept because $x \neq 0$ at the bottom left of the graph.
Step 2: Pick a point on the line to plug into the answer choices to see which choice is correct. An easy point to pick is $(15, 35)$
Step 3: Plug the point into the answer choices. Whichever answer gives a true statement is correct.
$35 = \frac{5}{2}(15) - 2.5 \rightarrow 35 = 35$

Chapter 24 – Statistical Analysis (Pages 164 – 168)

1. **D** Although the students who attended the extra review session scored higher on the driving test than those who did not attend, it does not mean that the extra review class caused the students to score higher. This is a case of cause-effect bias. There are a bunch of other reasons that those students could be scoring higher: they are more motivated, have better study habits, etc.

2. **B** For standard deviation questions, you do not need to calculate the standard deviation. Look at the spread of the numbers. The numbers in Set A are relatively close together compared to those in Set B. Therefore, the standard deviation in Set B is going to be larger than the standard deviation of Set A.

3. **C** Add and subtract the margin of error from the reported mean. Any mass between 442 pounds and 518 pounds is a plausible value for the mean mass of the sea lions in La Jolla. D and A are wrong because they reference the mass rather than the mean mass. B is wrong because the sample was only done in La Jolla, so it can only be applied to sea lions in La Jolla.

4. **B** B is the only random sample. A will be alphabetical, C will be done based on who attends first, and D will be based off of those who volunteer, which results in self-selection bias.

5. **D** By surveying residents at a skate park, the survey is most likely sampling individuals who like skate parks and therefore would support the measure at a higher rate than people in the rest of the community.

6. **A** News websites usually are pro-liberal, pro-republican, or will sit in the middle of the political spectrum, so a single website will not get an accurate sampling of the entire US population. Additionally, only a minority of Americans will read news websites. There could have been some respondents who said they did not know or chose not to respond to the question, so the "Yes" and "No" answers do not need to add to 100%.

7. **A** All of the numbers in set A are closer together compared to those in set B. Therefore, the standard deviation in set B is going to be larger than the standard deviation of set A.

8. **C** The median is displayed by the line inside of the box.

9. **A** Add and subtract the margin of error from the reported mean. It is plausible that between 15% and 21% of oncologists believe cancer will be cured in the next 50 years.

10. **A** Step 1: Find the median value in the table. To find the median value in a table, add 1 to the total and divide by 2. This is covered in chapter 16. $\frac{181}{2} = 90.5$. This means the 90th and 91st values will need to be averaged to find the median. To find where these values are in the table, add the number of employees in the right column until you hit 90 and 91 or initially add past 90 and 91. $12 + 26 + 39 = 77 \rightarrow 77 + 68 = 145$. When adding the 68 people who spend 300-400, we go past 90 and 91, so the column with the 68 will contain the median. The median is somewhere from 300-400.
Step 2: Find the median of the box and whisker plot. The median is the middle bar. The median is a bit below 200.

11. **D** Step 1: Find the median value of the table. We just covered this in step 1 in the answer explanation to question 10. The median is somewhere from 300-400.
Step 2: To find the 25th and 75th percentiles, multiply the total number of people in the survey by 0.25 and 0.75 and find where those values lie in the table. For the 25th percentile: $180(0.25) = 45$. We need to find the 45th term in the table.
$12 + 26 = 38$ $38 + 39 = 77$ When adding the 39 people from 200-299, we go past 45, so 200-300 will contain the 25th percentile.
For the 75th percentile: $180(0.75) = 135$. We need to find the 135th terms in the table.
$12 + 26 + 39 = 77$ $77 + 68 = 145$. When adding the 68 people from 300-400, we got past 135, so 300-400 will contain the 75th percentile.
Step 3: Find the minimum and maximum of the table. < 100 is the minimum and > 400 is the maximum.
D gives the ends of the box and whisker plot as the values where the minimum and maximum lie. The 25th percentile minimum is in the range of 200-300. The median is in the range of 300-400. The 75th percentile is in the range of 300-400. The maximum is greater than 400. All other answer choices do not have the values in the right positions.

12. **A** Add and subtract the margin of error from the reported mean. It is plausible that the true value of seniors who would vote to change the school mascot is between 48.5% and 53.5%. There is not enough evidence to know if over 50% of the seniors would vote to change the school mascot.

13. **D** This is an example of cause-effect bias. There is no way to know if the chocolate is causing the higher standardized test scores or something else that is common among those who eat chocolate. Only men are surveyed, so we can make not assumptions about women from this survey.

14. **62, 63, 64, 65, 66.** The median is displayed by the line in the box for both plots. Acceptable values for Donovan's median are 86, 87, and 88. Acceptable values for Christina's median value are 22, 23, and 24

15. **D** The range is displayed by the difference between whiskers in a box and whisker plot. Exact values cannot be determined, but if we estimate the values, only D can be correct. Here, we will estimate the minimum to be 14 and the maximum to be 38. $38 - 14 = 24$

16. **C** The only option that provides a random selection of Walker High School students. Any survey that includes students outside of Walker High School cannot be generalized to the Walker High School students.

17. **C** The margin of error gives an interval estimate from the reported mean in a random sample. The reported mean was 43% and the estimate is 35% to 51%. To find the margin of error, find the difference between the reported mean and the estimates. $51 - 43 = 8$ $43 - 35 = 8$

18. **D** You can generalize the results of the survey to the same population that was surveyed. Here, we only survey people who like the tri-tip sandwich. Without sampling everyone who likes the local market's tri tip sandwich, you can only get an estimate rather than the exact percentage of people who will like the local market's tri tip sandwich.

Chapter 25 - Probability (Pages 171 – 174)

1. **A** $\frac{Red}{Total} = \frac{25}{70} = \frac{5}{14}$

2. **C** $\frac{Not\ Italian}{Total} = \frac{17}{27}$

3. **B** Step 1: Find probability of a blue bead. $\frac{Blue}{Total} = \frac{3}{10}$
Step 2: Multiply by total trials to find the expected number: $\frac{3}{10} \times 150 = 45$

4. **D** Step 1: To find the total number of marbles in the bowl, use the $\frac{1}{7}$ probability of choosing a blue marble. x is the total number of marbles in the bowl. $\frac{blue}{total} = \frac{1}{7} \rightarrow \frac{6}{x} = \frac{1}{7} \rightarrow x = 42$
Step 2: Solve for the number of black marbles. $42 - 12 - 6 = 24$

5. **C** $\frac{Not\ Lemon}{Total} = \frac{8}{13}$

6. **B** Step 1: Find the area of all three squares. $1^2 = 1$ $2^2 = 4$ $3^2 = 9$
Step 2: Since all squares have the same center, the smallest and second smallest squares are inside of the largest square. Probability is then $\frac{Area\ of\ smallest\ square}{Area\ of\ largest\ square} = \frac{1}{9}$

7. **A** $\left(\frac{1}{5}\right)^4 = \frac{1}{625}$

8. **A** $\frac{Dogs\ that\ lost\ weight\ and\ received\ diet\ B}{Dogs\ that\ lost\ weight} = \frac{75}{175}$

9. **C** $\dfrac{Dogs\ that\ received\ Diet\ A\ and\ gained\ weight}{All\ dogs} = \dfrac{50}{300} = \dfrac{1}{6}$

10. **A** $\dfrac{Chemistry\ Professors\ whose\ primary\ focus\ is\ research}{All\ Professors} = \dfrac{85}{445} = 0.191$

11. **B** $\dfrac{Chemistry\ Professors\ whose\ primary\ focus\ is\ research}{All\ Professors\ whose\ primary\ focus\ is\ research} = \dfrac{85}{217} = 0.392$

12. **A** $\dfrac{All\ Thin\ Crust\ Pizzas}{All\ Pizzas} = \dfrac{12+8}{80} = \dfrac{20}{80} = \dfrac{1}{4}$

13. **D** $\dfrac{All\ Thin\ Crust\ and\ All\ Gluten\ Free\ Pizzas}{All\ Pizzas} = \dfrac{12+8+7+9}{80} = \dfrac{36}{80} = \dfrac{9}{20}$

14. **C** $\dfrac{Gluten\ free\ chesse\ pizzas}{All\ cheese\ pizzas} = \dfrac{7}{38}$

15. **C** $\dfrac{Total\ adults\ who\ had\ an\ increase\ in\ resting\ heart\ rate}{All\ adults} = \dfrac{80}{380} = \dfrac{4}{19}$

16. **D** $\dfrac{Adults\ prescribed\ weight\ training\ who\ had\ a\ decrease\ in\ resting\ heart\ rate}{All\ adults\ prescribed\ weight\ training} = \dfrac{140}{200} = \dfrac{7}{10}$

17. **A** $\dfrac{People\ who\ purchased\ both\ food\ and\ a\ beverage}{All\ People} = \dfrac{100}{250}$

18. **C** $\dfrac{People\ who\ purchased\ food\ and\ did\ not\ purchase\ a\ beverage}{All\ People\ who\ purchased\ food} = \dfrac{45}{45+100} = \dfrac{45}{145}$

Chapter 26 – Trigonometry (Pages 181 – 183)

1. **C** Identify which side is opposite and which side is hypotenuse. $\sin C = \dfrac{6}{12} = \dfrac{1}{2}$

2. **D** To solve for $\cos C$, identify which side is adjacent and which side is hypotenuse. Solve for the adjacent side by using Pythagorean theorem. $3^2 + b^2 = 5^2 \rightarrow b^2 = 16 \rightarrow b = 4$ so $\cos C = \dfrac{4}{5}$

3. $\dfrac{3}{5}$ *or* $\dfrac{6}{10}$ This is a trigonometric identity. When there are two acute angles x and y, $\sin x = \cos y$
   Alternatively, draw out a triangle, label the sides based on where you place x and y, and solve for $\cos y$. To solve for $\cos y$, identify the adjacent side and the hypotenuse. $\cos y = \dfrac{6}{10} = \dfrac{3}{5}$

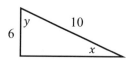

4. **B** Step 1: Draw a triangle and solve for the missing side using Pythagorean theorem. $2^2 + b^2 = 7^2 \rightarrow b^2 = 45 \rightarrow b = \sqrt{45}$

   Step 2: Solve for $\tan C$. $\tan C = \dfrac{\sqrt{45}}{2}$

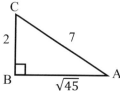

5. $\dfrac{6}{10}, \dfrac{3}{5}, 0.6$ Step 1: Draw out a triangle, label the sides, and solve for the third side using Pythagorean theorem. $6^2 + 8^2 = c^2 \rightarrow 36 + 64 = c^2 \rightarrow 100 = c^2 \rightarrow c = 10$

   Step 2: Solve for $\cos B$. $\cos B = \dfrac{6}{10} = \dfrac{3}{5}$

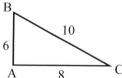

6. **C** To solve for $\tan \theta$, identify the opposite and the adjacent side lengths. From the sine equation, 12 is opposite. From the cosine equation, 5 is adjacent. $\tan \theta = \dfrac{12}{5}$

7. **D** $\cos^{-1}\left(\dfrac{b}{c}\right)$ is the only equation that correctly fills out an equation using the proper corresponding sides.

8. $\frac{5}{17}$ This is a trigonometric identity. When there are two acute angles x and y, $\sin x = \cos y$. Alternatively, fill in the side lengths that give the adjacent and the hypotenuse based on $\cos x$. 5 is the adjacent side and 17 is the hypotenuse. Therefore, the $\sin y = \frac{5}{17}$.

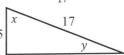

9. **B** Step 1: The height of the wall is opposite the $47°$ and the other side given is 7, which is the hypotenuse. Use sine.
Step 2: Solve for the height. $\sin 47 = \frac{x}{7} \rightarrow 7 \sin 47 = x$

10. **A** Step 1: Label the side lengths based off of the sine value given. The easiest way to do this question is to relabel the sides. Many triangles on the SAT are 3, 4, 5 right triangles. Relabel side AB as 5 because the answer choices are reduced to the lowest terms. 3 will be opposite based off of $\sin A = \frac{3}{5}$
Step 2: Recognize the Pythagorean triple of 3, 4, 5 or use the Pythagorean theorem to find the length of AC which is 4.
Step 3: Solve for $\tan B = \frac{4}{3}$

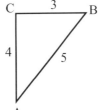

Alternatively, scale to find the true length of the sides of the triangles. Since $\sin \angle A = \frac{3}{5}$ and $AB = 20$, $BC = 12$. From there, you can use steps 2 and 3 above to find $\tan B$.

11. **0.3 or $\frac{3}{10}$** This is a trigonometric identity. When there are two acute angles in a right triangle a and b, $\sin a = \cos b$.
Alternatively, draw out and label a triangle. Solve for the missing side length using Pythagorean theorem and then solve for $\cos b$.

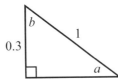

12. **B** $\sin A = \frac{3}{15}$ and $\sin D = \frac{9}{15}$, so $\sin A = \frac{1}{3} \sin D$ because $\frac{3}{15} = \frac{1}{3} \left(\frac{9}{15} \right)$.

13. **A** Angles A, B, and C must add up to $180°$. We know that $\angle B = 90°$, so $\angle A + \angle C = 90°$. Since $\angle C = \frac{1}{2} \angle A$, $\angle C = 30°$ and $\angle A = 60°$. Recognize the 30, 60, 90 triangle and the proportions that come with a 30, 60, 90 triangle. The side opposite 30 is x, the side opposite 60 is $x\sqrt{3}$, and the hypotenuse is $2x$. Therefore, the $\sin C$ is $\frac{x}{2x} = \frac{1}{2}$. The rest of the information in the question is unnecessary.

14. **B** Since $\sin \theta = 0.8 = \frac{x}{18}$, we can set equal and solve. $0.8 = \frac{x}{18} \rightarrow x = 14.4$

15. **B** $\cos x° = \sin (90° - x°)$ This is a trigonometric identity.

16. **C** Step 1: The side length given is opposite $\angle A$, and we must solve for side length AB, which is the hypotenuse. Use sine.
Step 2: Solve for AB. $\sin A = \frac{7}{AB} \rightarrow AB = \frac{7}{\sin A}$

17. $\frac{8}{5}$, **1.6** Step 1: Label the sides using the tangent value given.

Step 2: Solve for AB using the tangent value. $\tan B = \frac{8}{6} = \frac{32}{AB} \rightarrow AB = 24$.

Step 3: Use the Pythagorean theorem to find the length of side length CB, which is 40. Then solve for the $\cos C = \frac{32}{40} = \frac{4}{5}$

Alternatively, re-label the sides. First, reduce the fraction from $\frac{8}{6}$ to $\frac{4}{3}$. Many triangles on the SAT are $3, 4, 5$

right triangles, so keep your eye out for them! Re-label side AC as 4, BA as 3, and BC as 5. $\cos C = \frac{4}{5}$.

$\cos B = \frac{3}{5}$.

Step 4: Add the fractions. $\frac{4}{5} + \frac{3}{5} = \frac{8}{5}$

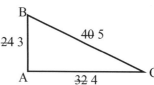

18. **A** Step 1: Correctly label the triangle and solve for the missing side length using Pythagorean theorem.
$3^2 + b^2 = 11^2 \rightarrow b^2 = 112 \rightarrow b = \sqrt{112} = 4\sqrt{7}$

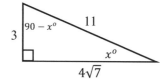

Step 2: Solve for $\cos x$. $\cos x = \frac{4\sqrt{7}}{11}$

19. **24** Step 1: The tangent of $\angle BCA = 0.75 = \frac{3}{4}$. We can relabel this triangle as $AC = 4$, $AB = 3$, and $BC = 5$
after identifying the 3, 4, 5 triangle or using the Pythagorean theorem to solve for BC. Note that these show us
the ratio of the side lengths not the actual side lengths.

Step 2: Solve for the value of AC. $\frac{4}{5} = \frac{AC}{30} \rightarrow 5AC = 120 \rightarrow AC = 24$

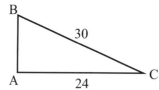

20. **10** Step 1: Identify the ratios of the two triangles. Since there are two triangles and the smaller triangle is
created by a line parallel to the base of the larger triangle, triangles ABC and EDC are similar. This will always
be the case in triangles like this. The cosine of $C = \frac{4}{5}$ means that CB can be labeled 4, AC can be labeled 5, and,
by identifying the 3, 4, 5 right triangle or using the Pythagorean theorem, AB can be labeled 3. This also means
than CD can be labeled 4, CE can be labeled 5, and ED can be labeled 3. These are not the actual lengths but
provide the ratio of the side lengths.

Step 2: Use the ratio and given side length of $ED = 6$ to find the length of EC. $\frac{3}{5} = \frac{6}{EC} \rightarrow 3EC = 30 \rightarrow$
$EC = 10$. The figure below shows the scaled sides (on the left) and the actual side lengths (on the right).

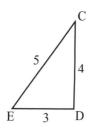 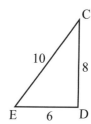

Chapter 27 – Circles (Pages 189 – 191)

1. **C** The center of the circle is $(3, -4)$ because we have $(x - 3)^2$ and $(y + 4)^2$.
2. **D** Using the standard form of a circle, the radius of the circle is the $\sqrt{36} = 6$.
3. **B** Step 1: Move the 5 to the right side and group the x-terms and y-terms together to begin completing the square. $(x^2 + 4x \quad) + (y^2 - 8y \quad) = -5$
    Step 2: Complete the square by dividing the middle term in half and squaring it. Add this value to both sides of the equation. $(x^2 + 4x + 4) + (y^2 - 8y + 16) = -5 + 4 + 16$
    Step 3: Factor both quadratics. $(x + 2)^2 + (y - 4)^2 = 15$
    Step 4: Find the center of the circle. $(-2, 4)$
4. **B** Step 1: Solve for the two unit shift to the left. The x-coordinate of the center is initially at $x = 6$. Shifting two units to the left will move the x-coordinate to $x = 4$.
    Step 2: Solve for the one unit shift down. The y-coordinate of the center is initially at $y = -2$. Shifting one unit down will move the y-coordinate to $y = -3$
    Step 3: Solve for the radius increase of two. To find the current radius take the $\sqrt{9} = 3$. Add two to find new radius. $3 + 2 = 5$. The value in the new circle equation will be $5^2 = 25$
    Step 4: We have a final equation of $(x - 4)^2 + (y + 3)^2 = 25$
5. **A** By moving the circle down 6 units, the new center of the circle has a y-coordinate of -8.
    By moving the circle to the left 3 units, the new center of the circle has a x-coordinate of 3.
    The new equation is $(x - 3)^2 + (y + 8)^2 = 4$
6. **D** Step 1: Find the radius. $\sqrt{144} = 12$
    Step 2: Find the area. $A = \pi(12)^2 = 144\pi$
7. **B** Identify what part of the equation is changing and spot the change. The y-coordinate of the center of the circle B is -9 and the y-coordinate of the center of circle A is -5. Therefore, circle B must be shifted 4 units up to become circle A.
8. **A** Step 1: Identify what shift is being applied. The x-coordinate of the center of the circle is moving from -4 in circle A to 1 in circle B. There is a shift to the right 5 units. The y-coordinate of the center does not change.
    Step 2: Identify how the radius is being changed. The original radius is $\sqrt{16} = 4$. The new radius is $\sqrt{64} = 8$ The radius is multiplied by 2.
9. **B** Plug $(2, b)$ into the equation. $(x + 4)^2 + (y + 3)^2 = 100 \rightarrow (2 + 4)^2 + (b + 3)^2 = 100 \rightarrow 36 + (b + 3)^2 = 100 \rightarrow (b + 3)^2 = 64 \rightarrow b + 3 = 8 \rightarrow b = 5$
10. **5** Step 1: To complete the square, group the x-terms and y-terms. $(x^2 + 4x + \quad) + (y^2 - 6y + \quad) = 12$
    Step 2: Complete the square by dividing the middle term in half and squaring it. Add this value to both sides of the equation. $(x^2 + 4x + 4) + (y^2 - 6y + 9) = 12 + 4 + 9$
    Step 3: Factor both quadratics. $(x + 2)^2 + (y - 3)^2 = 25$
    Step 4: Solve for r. $r^2 = 25 \rightarrow r = 5$
11. **61** Step 1: Plug $(4, 5)$ into the equation. $(x + 2)^2 + (x - 10)^2 = j \rightarrow (4 + 2)^2 + (5 - 10)^2 = j \rightarrow j = 36 + 25 = 61$
12. **A** Step 1: Find the center of the circle. To find the center of the circle when given endpoints of the diameter of the circle, use the midpoint formula. $x = \frac{-4+2}{2} = -1$. $y = \frac{-2+6}{2} = 2$. The center of the circle is at $(-1, 2)$
    Step 2: Solve for the radius of the circle. To solve for the radius of the circle, find the distance between the center of the circle and one of the endpoints of the diameter. Use the distance formula. We will use the points $(-1, 2)$ and $(2, 6)$. $d = \sqrt{(-1 - 2)^2 + (2 - 6)^2} = \sqrt{(-3)^2 + (-4)^2} = \sqrt{25} = 5$. The radius is 5.
    Step 3: The final equation is $(x + 1)^2 + (y - 2)^2 = 25$
    Alternatively, you can plug in one of the given points for the x and y-values to find which equation is correct. A is correct because using the point $(2, 6)$, $(2 + 1)^2 + (6 - 2)^2 = 25 \rightarrow 25 = 25$. No other answer choice will work.

13. **A** Step 1: Move the 16 to the right side and group the x-terms and y-terms together.
$(x^2 + 4x + \quad) + (y^2 + 8y + \quad) = 16$
Step 2: Complete the square by dividing the middle term in half and squaring it. Add this value to both sides of the equation. $(x^2 + 4x + 4) + (y^2 + 8y + 16) = 16 + 4 + 16$
Step 3: Factor both quadratics. $(x + 2)^2 + (y + 4)^2 = 36$
Step 4: Find the center of the circle. $(-2, -4)$ $a = -2$ $b = -4$
Step 5: Find the radius of the circle. $\sqrt{36} = 6$ $c = 6$
Step 6: $a + b + c = -2 + -4 + 6 = 0$

14. **A** Step 1: Find the center of the circle. Use the midpoint formula. $x = \frac{-4+4}{2} = 0$. $y = \frac{3+-3}{2} = 0$. The center of the circle is at $(0, 0)$
Step 2: Solve for the radius of the circle. To solve for the radius of the circle, find the distance between the center of the circle and one of the endpoints of the diameter. Use the distance formula. We will use the points $(0, 0)$ and $(4, -3)$. $\sqrt{(0 - 4)^2 + (0 - (-3))^2} = \sqrt{25} = 5$. The radius is 5.
Step 3: The final equation is $x^2 + y^2 = 25$
Alternatively, you can plug in one of the given points for the x and y values to find which equation is correct. A is correct because using the point $(4, -3)$, $4^2 + (-3)^2 = 25 \rightarrow 25 = 25$

15. **C** Step 1: Eliminate the equations that do not have a center of $(6, 3)$. A and D are wrong.
Step 2: For the circle to be tangent to $y = 6$ it needs to just touch that line. Since the y-coordinate of the center of the circle is 3, there needs to be a radius of 3 so that the circle will just reach $y = 6$.

16. **C** Step 1: Move the 23 to the right side and group the x-terms and y-terms together.
$x^2 + y^2 - 8x + 10y - 23 = 0 \rightarrow (x^2 - 8x + \quad) + (y^2 + 10y + \quad) = 23$
Step 2: Complete the square by dividing the middle term in half and squaring it. Add this value to both sides of the equation. $(x^2 - 8x + 16) + (y^2 + 10y + 25) = 23 + 16 + 25$
Step 3: Factor both quadratics. $(x - 4)^2 + (y + 5)^2 = 64$
Step 4: Find the center of the circle. Center of the circle is $(4, -5)$

17. **B** Step 1: To find the center of the circle when given endpoints of the diameter of the circle, use the midpoint formula. We know the x-coordinates, so we can solve for h. $h = \frac{-2+8}{2} = 3$.
Step 2: Use $h = 3$ to solve for k. $hk = 18 \rightarrow 3k = 18 \rightarrow k = 6$
Step 3: Use the value of k to solve for $a + b$ by using the midpoint equation from step 1 to find the center of the circle given two endpoints. $k = \frac{a+b}{2} \rightarrow 6 = \frac{a+b}{2} \rightarrow 12 = a + b$

18. **C** Step 1: For the circle to be tangent to both the x-axis and y-axis, it has to be just touching both. This means the center of the circle must a distance equal to the radius away from both axes.
Step 2: Find the radius. $\sqrt{25} = 5$
Step 3: Find the equation that places the coordinates of the center of the circle 5 units away from the x-axis and y-axis. The circle could be centered at $(5, 5), (-5, -5), (5, -5),$ or $(-5, 5)$. C is the only answer that has one of these options.

19. **9** Plug $(a, 9)$ into the equation and solve for a. $(a - 4)^2 + (9 - 6)^2 = 34 \rightarrow (a - 4)^2 + 9 = 34 \rightarrow (a - 4)^2 = 25 \rightarrow a - 4 = \pm 5 \rightarrow a = 9$ or $a = -1$. The questions say $a > 0$, so the answer is 9.

20. **7** Step 1: Divide the entire equation by 2. $2x^2 + 2y^2 + 12x + 16y - 48 = 0 \rightarrow x^2 + y^2 + 6x + 8y - 24 = 0$
Step 2: Move the 24 to the right side and group the x-terms and y-terms together.
$(x^2 + 6x + \quad) + (y^2 + 8y + \quad) = 24$
Step 3: Complete the square by dividing the middle term in half and squaring it. Add this value to both sides of the equation. $(x^2 + 6x + 9) + (y^2 + 8y + 16) = 24 + 16 + 9$
Step 4: Factor both quadratics. $(x + 3)^2 + (y + 4)^2 = 49$
Step 5: Solve for the radius. $49 = r^2 \rightarrow r = 7$

21. **C** Step 1: Use the circle equation to find the center of the circle and the radius. The center is $(-4, -2)$ and the radius is 6.
Step 2: Look at the answer choices for a point that is more than 6 units away from the center. Start by looking for any points that are more than 6 units away from the x-coordinate or y-coordinate of the center. The distance from $x = -4$ to $x = 3$ is 7 coordinate units, so C has to be correct.
Alternatively, use the distance formula to find the distance between each answer choice and the center.

22. **B** Step 1: Use the circle equation to find the center of the circle and the radius. The center is at $(3, 4)$ and the radius is 8.
Step 2: Look at the answer choices for a point that is more than 8 units away from the center. Start by looking for any points that are more than 8 units away from the x-coordinate or y-coordinate of the center. No points are more than 8 units away from the center. However, for B the y-coordinate is 8 units away from the center and the x-coordinate is 7 unit away from the center, so B must be outside of the circle. Using the distance formula, you could find that $(-4, -4)$ is 10.63 units from the center.

23. **C** To find which point lies on the circle, plug in the x and y-values to the equation to see which one makes the equation true. $(5 + 3)^2 + (10 - 4)^2 = 100 \rightarrow 8^2 + 6^2 = 100 \rightarrow 100 = 100$
All other answer choices will make the left side of the equation not equal 100 and are therefore incorrect.

Chapter 28 – Complex Numbers (Pages 195 – 197)

1. **B** $(5 + 4i) - (-3 + 2i) = 8 + 2i$
2. **C** $(8 + 2i) + (3 + 3i) = 11 + 5i$
3. **A** $(2 + 7i) + (6 + 5i) = 8 + 12i$
4. **C** $(3 + 6i) - (3i - 5) = 8 + 3i$
5. **B** Step 1: Multiply the complex numbers $(4 + 5i)(-3 + 3i) = -12 + 12i - 15i + 15i^2$
Step 2: Substitute in -1 for i^2 and combine like terms. $12 - 3i + 15(-1) = -12 - 3i - 15 = -27 - 3i$
6. **A** Step 1: Multiply the complex numbers $(3 + 4i)(3 - 4i) = 9 - 12i + 12i - 16i^2$
Step 2: Substitute in -1 for i^2 and combine like terms. $9 - 16(-1) = 16 + 9 = 25$
7. **B** $(-4 + 6i) - (1 + 3i) = -5 + 3i$
8. **D** $\frac{i^7}{i^3} = i^4 = 1$
9. **B** $(6 + 5i) - (2i + 3) = 3 + 3i$
10. **B** $4(3 + 2i) - 0.5(-8 + 6i) = 12 + 8i + 4 - 3i = 16 + 5i$
11. **D** $(i^5)(i^3) = i^8 = 1$
12. **D** Distribute the negative sign and plug in -1 for i^2. $5 + 4i - (8i^2 - 8i) = 5 + 4i - 8i^2 + 8i = 5 + 4i - 8(-1) + 8i = 5 + 4i + 8 + 8i = 13 + 12i$
13. **B** Multiply by the complex conjugate. $\frac{4}{1-3i} \times \frac{1+3i}{1+3i} = \frac{4+12i}{1-9i^2} = \frac{4+12i}{10} = \frac{2}{5} + \frac{6}{5}i$
14. **A** Find where in the repeating powers of i pattern the 37th term falls. The pattern repeats itself every 4 powers of i so find a multiple of 4 near 37. $4 \times 9 = 36$. Therefore, $i^{36} = 1$, so i^{37} will be in the first spot in the 4-part repeating pattern of i. $i^{37} = i^1 = i$
15. **B** Step 1: Multiply the complex numbers. $(6 + 3i)(2 + i) = 12 + 6i + 6i + 3i^2$
Step 2: Substitute in -1 for i^2 and combine like terms. $12 + 12i + 3(-1) = 12 + 12i - 3 = 9 + 12i$
16. **C** $\frac{i^{12}}{i^6} = i^6 = -1$
17. **16** Plug in 1 for i^4 and -1 for i^2 and then simplify. $12(1) + 8(-1) + 12 = 12 - 8 + 12 = 16$
18. **84** Step 1: Reorder the second term to get $(8 + 4i)(-3 + 6i)$
Step 2: Multiply the complex numbers. $(8 + 4i)(-3 + 6i) = -24 + 48i - 12i + 24i^2$
Step 3: Substitute -1 for i^2 and combine like terms. $-24 + 36i + 24(-1) = -48 + 36i$
Step 4: Solve for a and b. $a + bi = -48 + 36i$ so $a = -48$, $b = 36$
Step 5: Solve for $b - a$. $36 - (-48) = 84$
19. **A** Multiply by the complex conjugate and solve. $\frac{5}{2-4i} \times \frac{2+4i}{2+4i} = \frac{10+20i}{4-16i^2} = \frac{10+20i}{20} = \frac{1}{2} + i$
20. **C** Multiply by the complex conjugate and solve. $\frac{3}{3-3i} \times \frac{3+3i}{3+3i} = \frac{9+9i}{9-9i^2} = \frac{9+9i}{18} = \frac{1}{2} + \frac{1}{2}i$
21. **34** Step 1: Plug in 1 for i^4 and -1 for i^2 and then simplify. $8(1) - 20(-1) + 6 = 8 + 20 + 6 = 34$
22. **36** Step 1: Multiply the complex numbers. $(5 + 3i)(4 + 2i) = 20 + 10i + 12i + 6i^2 = 20 + 22i + 6i^2$
Step 2: Substitute -1 for i^2 and combine like terms. $20 + 22i + 6(-1) = 14 + 22i$
Step 3: Solve for a and b. $a + bi = 14 + 22i$ so $a = 14$, $b = 22$
Step 4: Solve for $a + b$. $14 + 22 = 36$

Chapter 29 – Unit Conversion (Pages 200 – 201)

1. **D** $\frac{4\ decagrams}{1} \times \frac{10\ grams}{1\ decagram} \times \frac{100\ centigrams}{1\ gram} = 4,000\ centigrams$

2. **A** $\frac{6\ feet}{1} \times \frac{12\ inches}{1\ foot} = 72\ inches \rightarrow 72 \div 2 = 36 \rightarrow 36 \div 4 = 9$

3. **A** $\frac{1,800\ pounds}{1} \times \frac{1\ kilogram}{2.2046\ pounds} = 816.47\ kilograms$

4. **B** $2 \times 50 = 100\ gallons\ of\ flour \rightarrow \frac{100\ gallon}{1} \times \frac{4\ quarts}{1\ gallon} = 400\ quarts\ of\ flour \rightarrow \frac{400}{3} = 133.33$.
   Round down to 133 since you cannot make a loaf with 0.33 quarts of flour. The information about the water is not important as there is no limit on water presented in the problem.

5. **D** Step 1: Find the number of pieces from the 25-foot plank: $\frac{25\ feet}{1} \times \frac{12\ inches}{1\ foot} = 300\ inches \rightarrow \frac{300}{10} = 30$
   Step 2: Find the number of pieces from the 12-foot plank: $\frac{12\ feet}{1} \times \frac{12\ inches}{1\ foot} = 144\ inches \rightarrow \frac{144}{10} = 14.4$
   Round down to 14 since the last 0.4 will not give a full 10-inch piece.
   Step 3: Add to find total pieces: $30 + 14 = 44$

6. **A** $\frac{3\ inches}{hour} \times \frac{36\ hours}{1} \times \frac{1\ foot}{12\ inches} = 9\ feet$

7. **D** $\frac{5\ miles}{hour} \times \frac{2\ hours}{1} \times \frac{20\ city\ blocks}{1\ mile} = 200\ city\ blocks$

8. **B** $\frac{120\ pounds}{1} \times \frac{1\ kilogram}{2.2046\ pounds} = 54.43\ kilograms = 54\ kilograms$

9. **C** $Circumfrence = \pi d \rightarrow C = \pi(1,447) \rightarrow 4,640.13\ miles$
   $\frac{4,545.88\ miles}{1} \times \frac{1\ kilometer}{0.6214\ miles} = 7,467\ kilometers$

10. **D** $\frac{3\ inches}{hour} \times \frac{7\ hours}{1} \times \frac{127\ millimeters}{5\ inches} = 533\ millimeters$

11. **192** $\frac{9\ gallons}{1} \times \frac{128\ ounces}{1\ gallon} \times \frac{1\ cup}{6\ ounces} = 192\ cups$

12. **34** $6,000\ yards - 4,000\ yards = 2,000\ yards$. This gives the total distance the object will pass through.
   $\frac{2,000\ yards}{1} \times \frac{3\ feet}{1\ yard} \times \frac{1\ mile}{5,280\ feet} \times \frac{1\ hour}{2\ miles} \times \frac{60\ minutes}{1\ hour} = 34\ minutes$

13. **46** $\frac{13\ miles}{17\ minutes} \times \frac{60\ minutes}{1\ hour} = 46\ miles\ per\ hour$

14. **3.02** $Circumference\ of\ tire = 2\pi r \rightarrow c = 2\pi(1) = 6.28\ feet$
   $\frac{6.28\ feet}{1\ tire\ rotation} \times \frac{2,876\ tire\ rotation}{1\ minute} \times \frac{1\ minute}{60\ seconds} \times \frac{53\ seconds}{1\ lap} \times \frac{1\ mile}{5,280\ feet} = \frac{3.02\ miles}{lap}$

Chapter 30 – Word Problems (Pages 203 – 205)

1. **C** Jenny made x cookies per hour for 2 hours so $2x$. Cara made y cookies for 3 hours so $3y$. The total number of cookies can be given by the expression $2x + 3y$.

2. **D** Step 1: Identify the word problem as an interpreting coordinate geometry question.
   Step 2: Identify the 42 as the y-intercept, which is the starting point.

3. **C** John's meal = y Matt's meal = $y + 6$ Price each pays = $\frac{y+y+6}{2} = \frac{2y+6}{2} = y + 3$

4. **B** Multiplying the number of avocados by their price and adding that to the number of bananas multiplied by their price will give the total amount of money spent purchasing avocados and bananas.

5. **C** Red yarn: $\frac{90\ feet}{1} \times \frac{1\ yard}{3\ feet} = 30\ yards\ of\ red\ yarn$
   Blue yarn: $\frac{45\ feet}{1} \times \frac{1\ yard}{3\ feet} = 15\ yards\ of\ blue\ yarn$
   Total Price: $2(30) + 3(15) = 105$

6. **C** Method 1 – Backsolving. Step 1: Write the equations. We will use x to represent the smaller integer and y to represent the larger integer. $xy = 84 \qquad x = \frac{1}{2}y + 1$
   Step 2: Rewrite the 2nd equation. $x = \frac{1}{2}y + 1 \rightarrow y = 2x - 2$
   Step 3: Combine equations by plugging in $2x - 2$ for y. $x(2x - 2) = 84$.
   Step 4: Backsolve. The correct answer is shown. $7(2(7) - 2) = 84 \rightarrow 7(12) = 84 \rightarrow 84 = 84$
   Method 2 – Algebra. Steps 1-3 are the same as above. Step 4 is to solve the equation algebraically.
   $x(2x - 2) = 84 \rightarrow 2x^2 - 2x = 84 \rightarrow 2x^2 - 2x - 84 = 0 \rightarrow x^2 - x - 42 = 0 \rightarrow$
   $(x - 7)(x + 6) = 0 \rightarrow x = 7, -6$

7. **C** $(40 + 28 + 35)7 = 721$

8. **D** $146 = \frac{1}{2}x - 12 \rightarrow 158 = \frac{1}{2}x \rightarrow x = 316$. If you could not write the equation correctly, you can also backsolve.

9. **D** x represents pies and y represents trays of cookies. $\frac{8\ hours}{1} \times \frac{60\ minutes}{1\ hour} = 480\ minutes$

   Step 1: Write the equations. $20x + 30y = 480 \qquad x = \frac{1}{2}y$

   Step 2: Combine equations and solve. $20\left(\frac{1}{2}y\right) + 30y = 480 \rightarrow 10y + 30y = 480 \rightarrow 40y = 480 \rightarrow y = 12$

10. **C** x represents the price of 1 burger. $5x + 0.22 = 30.97 \rightarrow 5x = 30.75 \rightarrow x = 6.15 \rightarrow 6.15(4) = 24.60$

11. **A** Step 1: Solve for overtime wage. $8.5 \times 1.5 = 12.75$
    Step 2: Solve for overtime hours. $8.5(40) + (12.75)(x) = 505.75 \rightarrow 340 + 12.75x = 505.75 \rightarrow$
    $12.75x = 165.75 \rightarrow x = 13$
    Step 3: Solve for the total hours. $40 + 13 = 53$

12. **B** $acceleration = \frac{change\ in\ speed}{time} = \frac{43-8}{3.5} = 10$

13. **A** $\frac{4\ meters}{1} \times \frac{100\ centimeters}{1\ meter} = 400\ centimeters.$ $\frac{400}{20} = 20$

14. **C** $\frac{7\ days}{1} \times \frac{24\ hours}{1\ day} \times \frac{60\ minutes}{1\ hour} \times 0.2 = 2,016$

15. **B** Step 1: Write the equations. Let m represent the number of sticks of dynamite manufactured on Mondays and t represent the number of sticks of dynamite manufactured on Tuesdays. $m = t + 63 \qquad m + t = 873$
    Step 2: Combine equations and solve. $(t + 63) + t = 873 \rightarrow 2t = 810 \rightarrow t = 405$

16. **B** $\frac{934\ kilometers}{1} \times \frac{0.62\ miles}{1\ kilometer} = 579\ miles$

17. **D** $\frac{110\ yards}{1} \times \frac{3\ feet}{1\ yard} = 330\ feet$ $\qquad \frac{70\ yards}{1} \times \frac{3\ feet}{1\ yard} = 210\ feet \rightarrow 330 \times 210 = 69,300$

18. **D** $40\ tbsp + 24\ tbsp + 12\ tbsp = 76\ tbsp \rightarrow \frac{76\ tbsp}{1} \times \frac{1\ cup}{16\ tbsp} = 4.75\ cups = 4\frac{3}{4}\ cups$

19. $5 \leq x \leq 8.75$. **Any number in that range is correct.** To find the highest number of days it would take, use the minimum number of logs both can chuck. To find the lowest number of days it would take, use the maximum number of logs both can chuck. You could use any values in between the two to find a correct answer.
    Maximum number of days: $13x + 7x \leq 175 \rightarrow 20x \leq 175 \rightarrow x \leq 8.75$
    Minimum number of days: $19x + 16x \geq 175 \rightarrow 35x \geq 175 \rightarrow x \geq 5$
    Alternative method is to pick integers and play guess-and-check if you cannot find any other way to do a question like this.

20. **29** $750x + 13,050 \leq 35,000 \rightarrow 750x \leq 21,950 \rightarrow x \leq 29.26 \rightarrow x = 29$

21. **9** To find the initial cost per person, divide 18,000 by the number of people, which we will call x. Initial price is $\frac{18,000}{x}$. The increased cost when 3 fewer people are paying is then $\frac{18,000}{x-3}$. To make these values equal, we must subtract 1,000 from the increased cost. $\frac{18,000}{x} = \frac{18,000}{x-3} - 1000 \rightarrow \frac{18,000(x-3)}{x(x-3)} = \frac{18,000x}{x(x-3)} - \frac{1,000(x)(x-3)}{x(x-3)} \rightarrow$
    Cancel out denominators $\rightarrow 18,000x - 54,000 = 18,000x - 1,000x^2 + 3000x \rightarrow -54,000 =$
    $-1,000x^2 + 3000x$. Divide by 1,000 $\rightarrow -54 = -x^2 + 3x \rightarrow x^2 - 3x - 54 = 0 \rightarrow (x - 9)(x + 6) =$
    $0 \rightarrow x = 9, x = -6$
    $x = 9$ because there cannot be a negative number of people attending the party.

22. **20** To find the initial donation per company, divide 250,000 by the number of companies, which we will call x. The initial donation per company is $\frac{250,000}{x}$. The decreased donation when 5 more companies donate is then $\frac{250,000}{x+5}$. To make these values equal, we must add 2,500 from the decreased donation.
    $\frac{250,000}{x} = \frac{250,000}{x+5} + 2,500 \rightarrow \frac{250,000(x+5)}{x(x+5)} = \frac{250,000(x)}{x(x+5)} + \frac{2,500(x)(x+5)}{x(x+5)} \rightarrow$ Cancel out denominators $\rightarrow$
    $250,000x + 1,250,000 = 250,000x + 2,500x^2 + 12,500x \rightarrow 1,250,000 = 2,500x^2 + 12,500x$
    $2,500x^2 + 12,500x = 1,250,000 = 0$ Divide by 2,500 $\rightarrow x^2 + 5x - 500 = 0 \rightarrow (x + 25)(x - 20) =$
    $0 \rightarrow x = -25, x = 20.$ $x = 20$ because there cannot be a negative number of people initially donating to pay for the field.

Chapter 31 – Absolute Value (Pages 207 – 208)

1. **A** Step 1: Subtract the values inside the absolute value bars. $|8 - 5| - |4 - 8| = |3| - |-4|$
    Step 2: Apply the absolute value bars and solve. $|3| - |-4| = 3 - 4 = -1$
2. **C** Step 1: Simplify terms inside the absolute value bars. $|5(-3) + 4| = |-15 + 4| = |-11|$
    Step 2: Apply the absolute value bars. $|-11| = 11$
3. **D** Step 1: Plug -7 in for x and simplify terms inside the absolute value bars. $|3(-7) - 4| + 5 = |-21 - 4| + 5 = |-25| + 5$
    Step 2: Apply the absolute value bars and add. $|-25| + 5 = 25 + 5 = 30$
4. **6** Set equal to 24 and -24 and solve. $3x + 6 = 24$ and $3x + 6 = -24 \rightarrow 3x = 18$ and $3x = -30 \rightarrow x = 6, -10$. The question says $x > 0$, so the answer is 6.
5. **D** Step 1: Set terms inside absolute value bars equal to 8 and -8. $|x + 4| = 8 \rightarrow x + 4 = 8$ and $x + 4 = -8$
    Step 2: Solve for x. $x = 4, -12$
6. **15** Step 1: Set terms inside absolute value bars equal to 6 and -6. $|9 - x| = 6 \rightarrow 9 - x = 6$ and $9 - x = -6$
    Step 2: Solve for x. $x = 3, 15$
7. **B** Step 1: Plug in $x = 4$ and simplify terms inside the absolute value bars. $|3(4) - 6| + |-4(4) + 8| = |12 - 6| + |-16 + 8| \rightarrow |6| + |-8|$
    Step 2: Apply the absolute value bars and add. $|6| + |-8| = 6 + 8 = 14$
8. **18** Step 1: Set the terms inside the absolute value bars equal to 18 and -18. $|36 - 3x| = 18 \rightarrow 36 - 3x = 18$ and $36 - 3x = -18$
    Step 2: Solve for x. $-3x = -18$ and $-3x = -54 \rightarrow x = 6, 18$
9. **15** Step 1: Move all terms outside of the absolute value bars to the right side of the equation. $|4a + 4| - 4 = 12 \rightarrow |4a + 4| = 16$
    Step 2: Set the terms inside the absolute value bars equal to 16 and -16. $|4a + 4| = 16 \rightarrow 4a + 4 = 16$ and $4a + 4 = -16$
    Step 3: Solve for the two values of a, which are x and y. $4a = 12$ and $4a = -20 \rightarrow a = 3, -5$
    Step 4: Solve for the absolute value. $|xy| = |3(-5)| = |-15| = 15$
10. **B** Step 1: Move all terms outside of the absolute value bars to the right side of the equation. Here, we just need to do this step for the first equation. $|4x - 3| + 2 = 15 \rightarrow |4x - 3| = 13$
    Step 2: Set the terms inside the absolute value bars equal to the positive and negative value and then solve for x and y. For the first equation: $4x - 3 = 13$ and $4x - 3 = -13 \rightarrow 4x = 16$ and $4x = -10 \rightarrow x = 4, -2.5$
    For the second equation: $5y + 3 = 17$ and $5y + 3 = -17 \rightarrow 5y = 14$ and $5y = -20 \rightarrow y = \frac{14}{5}, -4$
    Step 3: Check all combinations to find the combination of x and y that creates the smallest possible value. $(4)(-4) = -16$

Chapter 32 – Ratios and Proportions (Pages 211 – 213)

1. **A** $11\, total - 6\, girls = 5\, boys \qquad boys: girls = 5: 6$
2. **B** $35: 42 = 5: 6$
3. **C** $\frac{\frac{1}{2}}{15} = \frac{3\frac{1}{2}}{x} \rightarrow \frac{1}{2}x = 52.5 \rightarrow x = 105$
4. **C** $38\, total - 16\, boys = 22\, girls \qquad girls: boys = 22: 16$
5. **7** $\frac{\frac{1}{5}}{10} = \frac{x}{350} \rightarrow 10x = 70 \rightarrow x = 7$
6. **D** $\frac{17}{2,000} = \frac{x}{30,000} \rightarrow 510,000 = 2,000x \rightarrow x = 255$
7. **D** $\frac{8}{6} = \frac{x}{42} \rightarrow 336 = 6x \rightarrow x = 56$
8. **C** Step 1: Convert hectares to acres. $\frac{4\, hectares}{1} \times \frac{2.5\, acres}{1\, hectare} = 10\, acres$, so 1 L of Atrazine can spray 10 acres.
    Step 2: Set up proportion and solve. $\frac{1\, L\, Atrazine}{10\, acres} = \frac{25\, L}{x\, acres} \rightarrow x = 250$
9. **C** Step 1: Convert minutes to seconds. $\frac{2\, minutes}{1} \times \frac{60\, seconds}{1\, minute} = 120\, seconds$
    Step 2: Set up proportion and solve. $\frac{30}{6.8} = \frac{x}{120} \rightarrow 3,600 = 6.8x \rightarrow x = 529.4$
10. **D** Make y-values the same to compare across ratios. $x: y \quad y: z = 7: 2 \quad 3: 2 \rightarrow 3(7: 2): 2(3: 2) \rightarrow 21: 6 \quad 6: 4 \rightarrow x: z = 21: 4$

11. **D** Fun : Charity $= 1x: 4x \rightarrow 1x + 4x = 25{,}000 \rightarrow 5x = 25{,}000 \rightarrow x = 5{,}000$
Fun : Charity $= 1(5{,}000): 4(5{,}000) = 5{,}000: 20{,}000 \rightarrow$ Charity $= 20{,}000$

12. **75** $\frac{36\ inches}{1} \times \frac{1\ foot}{12\ inches} = 3\ feet \rightarrow 3 \times 25 = 75$

13. **D** $\frac{\frac{3}{4}}{3.5} = \frac{3}{x} \rightarrow \frac{3}{4}x = 10.5 \rightarrow x = 14$

14. **B** $2x + 3x + 4x = 9x$. 27 is the only answer choice divisible by 9. The correct answer choice must be divisible by 9 because you cannot have a fraction of a button.

15. **D** $\frac{30}{44} = \frac{70}{x} \rightarrow 30x = 3{,}080 \rightarrow x = 102.66$

16. **D** Saturn weight: $150\ kg \left(\frac{21}{10}\right) = 315\ kg$ Mars weight: $150kg \left(\frac{6}{10}\right) = 90kg \rightarrow 315 - 90 = 225$

17. **A** Step 1: Solve for x. $7x: 4x \rightarrow A = lw \rightarrow 252 = (7x)(4x) \rightarrow 252 = 28x^2 \rightarrow x^2 = 9 \rightarrow x = 3$
Step 2: Plug in $x = 3$ to solve for side lengths. $7x: 4x \rightarrow 7(3): 4(3) \rightarrow 21: 12$ Shorter side is 12.

18. **C** Step 1: Solve for what fraction must be blue. $\frac{1}{4}\ black + \frac{1}{8}\ red + \frac{1}{2}\ yellow + x\ blue = 1 \rightarrow$
$\frac{2}{8} + \frac{1}{8} + \frac{4}{8} + x = 1 \rightarrow x = \frac{1}{8}$
Step 2: Use the number of blue balls to solve for black. $\frac{1}{8} = blue = 20 \rightarrow black = \frac{2}{8} \rightarrow 20 \times 2 = 40 \rightarrow$
$black = 40$

19. **C** This question is an average question that incorporates ratios. If the set up does not make sense, look through the mean, median, mode, and range chapter 16. In the numerator, we are multiplying to find the total amount raised by the sophomores, juniors, and seniors and then dividing by the total number of sophomores, juniors, and seniors in the denominator.
$\frac{2(40)+4(55)+5(72)}{11} = x \rightarrow \frac{660}{11} = x \rightarrow x = 60$

Chapter 33 – Shifting and Transforming Functions (Pages 217 – 219)

1. **B** The shift from x^2 to $(x - 2)^2$ is shifting two units to the right. The shift from -5 to -1 is shifting up 4 units.

2. **D** To shift up 4 units, add 4 to the value outside of the parentheses. To shift left by 1 unit, add 1 to the value in the parentheses.

3. **D** To change from $f(x + 2) + 1$ to $f(x)$, shift the graph to the right two units and then down one unit. This means that the point that was $(-2, -6)$ is now at $(0, -7)$ on $f(x)$. Therefore, the y-intercept is at -7.

4. **A** Shift the graph down 3 coordinates and keep the same slope.

5. **B** $f(x) = -3(x + 2)^2 - 1$ will be a downward facing parabola with a vertex at $(-2, -1)$. After shifting the function up 4 units. The function will be $f(x) = -3(x + 2)^2 + 3$ with a vertex at $(-2, 3)$.

6. **B** The constants in front of each equation stretch or compress the graph vertically, causing the vertex to move farther from or closer to the x-axis. The constant with the greatest absolute value will move the graph the farthest from the x-axis. Therefore, B is correct.
Alternatively, to solve for the vertex, find the midpoint of the two x-intercepts. $x = \frac{-1+5}{2} = 2$. Then, plug in $x = 2$ for both x-values in the equation and solve each answer choice. The answer choice that will result in the y-value farther from the x-axis will be based upon the value outside of the parenthesis as it will be multiplying the same value for each answer choice

7. **C** Shift the graph 3 units to the right to delay the pass 3 seconds.

8. **B** To solve, set all of the equations equal to y. A and C are wrong because they do not have a negative sign for the leading coefficient for the x^2 term, so they will be facing upwards. B is rewritten as $y = -2x^2 + 5$. B is downwards facing and the positive 5 shifts the graph up 5 units, so the vertex is at $(0,5)$, which is above the x-axis. D is downward facing but is below the x-axis because the -4 shift the graph 4 units down. The -3 shifts the graph 3 units right, so the vertex is below the x-axis at $(3, -4)$.

9. **D** To shift from $(x + 2)$ to $(x - 2)$, shift 4 units to the right. To shift from $+11$ to $+9$, shift down two units.

10. **A** The graph displayed is after $f(x)$ been shifted by 4 units to the right and 1 unit up. Therefore, to find $f(x)$, shift four units left and one unit down. The vertex of $f(x)$ will be at $(-2, 3)$. Only answer choice A has the correct vertex.

11. **B** The graph displayed in the question has been shifted two units to the left and 3 units down. Therefore, to find $f(x)$, shift two units right and 3 units up.

Chapter 34 – Interpreting Constants in Linear and Polynomial Functions (Pages 225 – 226)

1. **D** To find x-intercept, set $y = 0$ and solve for x. $0 = 2x + 6 \rightarrow x = -3$. D is the only answer with -3 as a constant.

2. **A** Shortcut method: A is the only answer choice written in vertex form and correctly displays $(4, -4)$ as the vertex. A is the only answer with 4 as a constant.
   Math method: To find the x-coordinate of the vertex, find the two x-intercepts by factoring out the quadratic and then find the midpoint of the two x-intercepts. $(x - 6)(x - 2) \rightarrow x = 6, 2 \rightarrow$ vertex at $x = \frac{6+2}{2} = 4$
   Alternatively, remember to find the x-coordinate of the vertex use $x = -\frac{b}{2a} = -\frac{-8}{2(1)} = 4$

3. **D** To find y-intercept, set $x = 0$. $2(0) + 3y = 12 \rightarrow 3y = 12 \rightarrow y = 4$. D is the only answer with 4 as a constant.

4. **C** To solve for x-intercepts, set each factor equal to 0 and solve for x. $x - b = 0 \rightarrow x = b$
   $x + c = 0 \rightarrow x = -c$

5. **C** To find the x-intercept, set $y = 0$ and solve for x. $6x + 4(0) = 24 \rightarrow 6x = 24 \rightarrow x = 4$. C is the only answer choice with 4 as a constant.

6. **A** Shortcut method: A is the only answer choice written in factored form.
   Math method: To find the x-intercepts, factor the quadratic and then set factors equal to 0. Here we only need to factor the quadratic to find the answer. $y = (x - 9)(x - 4)$. x-intercepts at $x = 9$ and $x = 4$.

7. **C** Shortcut method: C is the only answer choice written in factored form.
   Math method: Step 1: Rewrite the equation in terms of x. $x - y^2 + 8y + 5 = 2y + 13. \rightarrow x = y^2 - 6y + 8$
   Step 2: Factor to find the y-intercepts. $x = y^2 - 6y + 8 \rightarrow x = (y - 4)(y - 2)$. y-intercepts at $y = 4$ and $y = 2$.

8. **A** To find the y-intercept of a parabola, set $x = 0$ and solve for y. $y = -3(0 + 2)(0 + 3) \rightarrow y = -18$
   A is correct because it is the only choice that displays -18 as a constant.

9. **C** Shortcut method: C is the only answer choice written in factored form.
   Math method: To find the x-intercepts of a parabola, factor the quadratic and set your factors equal to 0. Here we only need to factor the quadratic to find our answer. $y = x^2 - 6x + 8 \rightarrow y = (x - 4)(x - 2)$.
   x-intercepts at $x = 4$ and $x = 2$.

10. **D** To find the x-intercept(s), set $y = 0$ and solve for x. $y = x^2 - z \rightarrow 0 = x^2 - z \rightarrow 0 = x^2 - z \rightarrow$
    $0 = (x - \sqrt{z})(x + \sqrt{z}) \rightarrow x = -\sqrt{z}, \sqrt{z}$.

11. **B** Step 1: To solve for x-intercept(s) set $y = 0$ and solve for x. $x - 3(0^2) - 18(0) + 13 = 0 \rightarrow$
    $x + 13 = 0 \rightarrow x = -13$ B is the only answer choice that displays -13 as a constant or coefficient.

12. **B** The y-intercept is displayed as a constant because when you set $x = 0$, $y = 3$. Alternatively, the parabola is written in standard form, so the 3 is the y-intercept.

13. **B** Step 1: Put the equation into vertex form. To solve this question, you must know vertex form of a parabola, which is $y = a(x - h)^2 + k$. Since $f(x) = y$, we can set it up as $y - d = a(x - b)^2 + c \rightarrow$
    $y = a(x - b)^2 + c + d$
    Step 2: Recognize what part displays the y-coordinate of the vertex. $c + d$ gives the y-coordinate of the vertex.

14. **D** The y-coordinate of the vertex is displayed as a constant. This is a horizontal parabola and can be put into vertex form. $(y - 3)^2 + 8 - 2x = 0 \rightarrow 2x = (y - 3)^2 + 8 \rightarrow x = \frac{1}{2}(y - 3)^2 + 4$. Vertex at $(4, 3)$

15. **A** Step 1: Factor and then solve for the x-intercepts. $y = x^2 - x(a + b) + ab \rightarrow y = (x - a)(x - b) \rightarrow$
    $x = a, b$
    Step 2: Find the midpoint of the x-intercepts to find the x-coordinate of the vertex. $\frac{a+b}{2}$
    Shortcut method: The equation to find x-coordinate of the vertex is $x = -\frac{b}{2a} \rightarrow -\frac{-a-b}{2} = \frac{a+b}{2}$

Chapter 35 – Special Quadratics (Pages 230 – 231)

1. **C** Step 1: Spot the perfect squares addition pattern. $a - b = 3$ is not needed to solve.
   $(a + b)^2 = a^2 + 2ab + b^2$
   Step 2: Plug in the values and solve. $(7)^2 = a^2 + 2ab + b^2 \rightarrow 49 = a^2 + 2ab + b^2$

2. **A** Step 1: Spot the perfect squares subtraction pattern. $l + k = 9$ is not needed to solve.
$(l - k)^2 = l^2 - 2lk + k^2$
Step 2: Plug in the values and solve. $(3)^2 = l^2 - 2lk + k^2 \rightarrow 9 = l^2 - 2lk + k^2$

3. **B** Step 1: Spot the difference of squares pattern. $(x + y)(x - y) = x^2 - y^2$
Step 2: Plug in the values and solve. $(11)(5) = x^2 - y^2 \rightarrow 55 = x^2 - y^2$

4. **C** Step 1: Spot the perfect squares of addition pattern. $a - b = 9$ is not needed to solve.
$(a + b)^2 = a^2 + 2ab + b^2$
Step 2: Plug in the values and solve. $(a + b)^2 = 36 \rightarrow a + b = 6$

5. **B** Step 1: Spot the difference of squares pattern. $(a + b)(a - b) = a^2 - b^2$
Step 2: Plug in the values and solve. $(12)(4) = a^2 - b^2 \rightarrow 48 = a^2 - b^2$

6. **C** Step 1: Spot the difference of squares pattern. $(x + y)(x - y) = x^2 - y^2$
Step 2: Plug in the values and solve. $(x + y)(5) = 75 \rightarrow x + y = 15$

7. **2** Step 1: Simplify the exponents by subtracting them. $\frac{3^{x^2}}{3^{y^2}} = 3^{12} \rightarrow 3^{x^2 - y^2} = 3^{12}$
Step 2: Since the bases are the same, set the exponents equal to each other. $x^2 - y^2 = 12$
Step 3: Spot the difference of squares pattern. $(x + y)(x - y) = x^2 - y^2$
Step 4: Plug in the values and solve. $(6)(x - y) = 12 \rightarrow x - y = 2$

8. **400** Step 1: Spot the difference of squares pattern. $(m + l)(m - l) = m^2 - l^2$
Step 2: Plug in the values and solve for $m^2 - l^2$. $(10)(4) = m^2 - l^2 \rightarrow 40 = m^2 - l^2$
Step 3: Plug in values and solve entire equation. $(m + l)(m^2 - l^2) = (10)(40) = 400$

9. **C** Step 1: Spot the perfect squares of subtraction pattern. $(a - b)(a - b) = a^2 - 2ab + b^2$
Step 2: Reorganize the terms and plug in the values. $(a - b)^2 = (a^2 + b^2) - 2ab \rightarrow$
$(a - b)^2 = (12) - 2(-6) \rightarrow (a - b)^2 = 24$
Step 3: Take the square root and simplify the radical. $a - b = \sqrt{24} = 2\sqrt{6}$

10. **B** Step 1: Spot the difference of squares pattern. $(a^2 - b^2)(a^2 + b^2) = a^4 - b^4$
Step 2: Plug in the values and solve. $(6)(12) = a^4 - b^4 \rightarrow 72 = a^4 - b^4$

11. **9** Step 1: Reduce the bases so all terms have a base of 2. $(2^{x^2})(2^{-y^2}) = 4^9 \rightarrow (2^{x^2})(2^{-y^2}) = (2^2)^9 \rightarrow$
$(2^{x^2})(2^{-y^2}) = 2^{18}$
Step 2: Simplify the exponents by adding them. $(2^{x^2})(2^{-y^2}) = 2^{18} \rightarrow 2^{x^2 - y^2} = 2^{18}$
Step 3: Since the bases are the same, set the exponents equal to each other. $x^2 - y^2 = 18$
Step 4: Spot the difference of squares pattern. $(x + y)(x - y) = x^2 - y^2$
Step 5: Plug in the values and solve. $(x + y)(2) = 18 \rightarrow x + y = 9$

12. **B** Step 1: Spot the difference of squares pattern. $(\sqrt{x} - \sqrt{y})(\sqrt{x} + \sqrt{y}) = x - y$
Step 2: Plug in the values and solve. $(9)(\sqrt{x} + \sqrt{y}) = 45 \rightarrow \sqrt{x} + \sqrt{y} = 5$
Step 3: Solve for the solution. $3\sqrt{x} + 3\sqrt{y} = 3(\sqrt{x} + \sqrt{y}) \rightarrow 3(5) = 15$

13. **4** Step 1: Reduce the bases so the terms have a base of 3. $\frac{3^{a^2}}{3^{b^2}} = 9^4 \rightarrow \frac{3^{a^2}}{3^{b^2}} = (3^2)^4 \rightarrow \frac{3^{a^2}}{3^{b^2}} = 3^8$
Step 2: Simplify the exponents by subtracting them. $\frac{3^{a^2}}{3^{b^2}} = 3^8 \rightarrow 3^{a^2 - b^2} = 3^8$
Step 3: Since the bases are the same, set the exponents equal to each other. $a^2 - b^2 = 8$
Step 4: Spot the difference of squares pattern. $(a + b)(a - b) = a^2 - b^2$
Step 5: Plug in the values and solve. $(2)(a - b) = 8 \rightarrow a - b = 4$

14. **4** Step 1: Simplify the exponents by subtracting them. $\frac{x^{a^2 - ab}}{x^{ab - b^2}} \rightarrow x^{a^2 - 2ab + b^2} = x^{16}$
Step 2: Since the bases are the same, set the exponents equal to each other. $a^2 - 2ab + b^2 = 16$
Step 3: Spot the perfect squares of subtraction pattern. $(a - b)^2 = a^2 - 2ab + b^2$
Step 4: Plug in values and solve. $(a - b)^2 = 16 \rightarrow (a - b) = 4$

Made in the USA
Columbia, SC
14 October 2023

24436111R10161